THE CHILDREN OF ABRAHAM

Also by Marek Halter
The Book of Abraham
The Jester and the Kings

THE
CHILDREN OF
ABRAHAM

MAREK HALTER

TRANSLATED FROM THE FRENCH BY LOWELL BAIR

ARCADE PUBLISHING · NEW YORK

LITTLE, BROWN AND COMPANY

First English-language Edition

This is a work of fiction. It is based on the real-life experiences
of the author, Marek Halter, and his search for the explanation of his
cousin Hugo Halter's assassination in Jerusalem in 1961. This search
takes him all over the world, and many of the events, historical figures,
and family members are real, but they have been fictionalized for the purposes
of this novel. Except for known figures and events, the characters
and incidents in this book are the product of the author's imagination.

Library of Congress Cataloging-in-Publication Data

Halter, Marek.
    [Fils d'Abraham.   English]
    The children of Abraham / Marek Halter; translated from the
French by Lowell Bair.
        p.   cm.
    Translation of: Les fils d'Abraham.
    ISBN 1-55970-076-9
    I. Title.
PQ2668.A434F5513   1990
843'.914 — dc20   90-36640

Published in the United States by Arcade Publishing, Inc., New
York, a Little, Brown company

10   9   8   7   6   5   4   3   2   1

HC

*Published simultaneously in Canada
by Little, Brown & Company (Canada) Limited*

Printed in the United States of America

To my mother,
Perl Halter, a Yiddish poet
whose work is written in the language
of a murdered people,
for having passed on to me
her love of words.

CONTENTS

viii

THE CHILDREN OF ABRAHAM

1

ISRAEL

Rendezvous in Jerusalem

MARCH 29, 1961

With gentle little shoves on the steering wheel, Hugo Halter nudged his car around the turns in the road clinging to the hillside. Each turn made one of Jerusalem's many apparitions sway against the sky. He was making this trip for the fourth time in a week, yet he still had the same thrill in his heart while he waited for the moment when the city would finally unfold before him, standing out sharply and precisely at the end of the last straight line.

He glanced at his wife; Sigrid seemed overwhelmed by the heat and rather indifferent to the landscape. He drove on awhile longer and passed a deserted crossroads. Then, as though not wanting to lose anything of that blessed moment, he slowly came to a stop on the roadside overlooking the Arab village of Abu Gosh, whose slopes were covered with a fuzz of young shrubs. He turned off the engine, opened the car door on to the vista of faraway crenelated walls made of white and gray stones that gleamed in the sunlight, and took a few steps.

"Come and look, Sigrid. It's like a watercolor."

Sigrid didn't move. Hugo turned toward her, raised his hands and repeated, "Come and look. I don't think I'll ever get tired of this."

"It's cooler here in the car," she said mockingly, and closed the door.

Disappointed, he sat down on a stone marker and pressed his thin arms against his body, as if to protect himself. He went on sitting there for long moments, motionless and enraptured, trying once again to locate the Kidron Valley, the Gihon Spring and the dark source of the bright light that always dazzled and delighted him — and also frightened him a little — each time he came here.

Long before Jerusalem was built in this place, he thought, there had been Salem, where King Melchizedek received Abraham one day. And Mount Moriah, with its big flat rock intended for sacrifices, where David had the idea of erecting a temple to the Almighty. There had been Solomon's Temple, destroyed by Nebuchadnezzar, rebuilt by Ezra, torn down by Antiochus Epiphanes, rebuilt again by the Hasmoneans, demolished again by Pompey, rebuilt yet again by Herod, until Titus, closer to our time . . .

So many words, so many names. . . . He never tired of thinking about the heroes of all that legendary, mythical history. Actually, Sigrid was right. How could she share his excitement? How could she take as much pleasure as he did in the fragrance of that dust whose every particle was heavily charged with spirit and memory?

At this point in his reflections, Hugo squinted at the glaring sunlight, inching his gray eyebrows closer together. He looked like an ordinary tourist silently and secretly enjoying that panorama unlike any other in the world. And that was when a military truck appeared at a bend in the road below him, raising a cloud of dust that seemed about to veil the sun for a moment. *That's odd,* he thought, *on this deserted road . . .*

Before he could wonder about it any longer, the truck reached his level and the roar of its engine was drowned out by a noise he knew well.

"My God!" he exclaimed, throwing himself facedown on the ground and unthinkingly reaching for a pistol that he didn't have.

That deafening noise was the sound of a submachine gun firing from the covered back of the truck. Bullets sprayed his car, then the stone marker he had been sitting on, then the car again. When he raised his head and stood up, he saw that the car was riddled with bullet holes. Sigrid was still in it, but she was now slumped across the seat with her head against the steering wheel.

"My God!" he repeated. "My God . . ."

He ran toward the car. Another burst of gunfire, then still another, followed by an explosion just as he was trying with all his strength to pull open the jammed door, drunk with pain and gasping for breath. The force of the explosion threw him back to the stone marker he had left only a few moments before.

Everything had happened very quickly. He had just had time to see Sigrid's open mouth and bulging eyes. Then came an image of some old Jews in long black coats, with prayer shawls on their heads, whom he had seen in the darkness of a synagogue on a day as sunny as this one. Then the burning of the family print shop in Berlin, and the face of his uncle Abraham in Warsaw. . . . He scarcely heard the wail of sirens, the screech of tires beside him, the exclamations in Hebrew above him.

"When the dead man rests," he murmured almost without moving his lips, "let the memory of him rest."

With his eyes closed, his mouth full of blood, and pain in his belly, thighs and head, he saw a patch of darkness in the pale sky.

Someone leaned over him. He tried to struggle, and maybe to say a word or a vague name, but his body had forsaken him.

PARIS, MARCH 1961

What did I know about my cousin on that spring day when I learned of his death from a telegram sent by another cousin, Mordecai, who lived on Kibbutz Dafneh in Israel? I knew what we all knew in the family: that he was the most secretive, the one whose life — and death, now — was full of deep mystery. For all of us, he had always had that matchless aura of heroes and men who lived in shadow.

The first image that came to me (but was it already a memory, a legend, rather than an image?) went back to Warsaw, in the years of violent upheaval. I was three. It was my birthday — the last one, though I didn't yet know it, that would be celebrated by my whole family. Fleeing from Germany, Hugo came into our apartment unexpectedly. Thin, unshaven, with a bulky knapsack on his back, he made the festivities stop abruptly. He looked like one of the Three Wise Men, or an exhausted, vaguely disquieting Santa Claus with the anxious eyes of a hunted animal. But there were no gifts or delicacies in his knapsack. He gave us only these grave words:

"The Germans," he said in a breathy voice, with an expression of infinite weariness, "will soon be in Warsaw. The Jews have to leave Poland. There's no time to lose."

My father protested. My mother exclaimed that a family couldn't just run away like that, leaving everything behind. My uncle David tried to take things lightly and make fun of what Hugo had said. I can still see him, with his look of great wisdom and his reassuring beard, explaining that Hitler couldn't break the Munich Pact so quickly, that the cruelty of the Nazi persecutions shouldn't be exaggerated, that they were no worse than the czarist pogroms, and that we Jews, unfortunately, knew pogroms all too well. I began crying — yes, crying bitterly for my ruined birthday, the cake that no one wanted to eat now, the terrible dangers that my childish soul felt coming toward us. And while my father gave me a scolding look, cousin Hugo took me in his arms. His beard scratched my cheek. On the lapel of his jacket I saw a streak of dust that suddenly made me think, *Cousin Hugo has come a long way and I'm in his arms.* That was when he raised his forefinger and said these words that are forever engraved in my memory:

"You see these Jews, Marek? If they don't change, they'll die."

He slept in our apartment that night and the two following nights. Then he left as he had come, with his knapsack on his back. I later heard that grandfather Abraham had given him his savings so he could take a ship to America.

Years later, on the evening of the first Yom Kippur after the war, Hugo's shade returned. My parents and I were among the survivors of the slaughter, orphans of a people that had nearly been annihilated. Now we were in Lodz, with a few friends in a little room that served as a synagogue, where the smell of death still hung in the air. For several months my father had been spending all his time trying to locate what was left of the family. Every evening he wrote advertisements that he sent to Yiddish newspapers all over the world. He sorted out and classified the answers, and wrote to people without knowing whether or not they were still alive. And now this evening, in the summer of 1946, he received a letter that Hugo had sent from New York.

We learned from it that after the famous night of my birthday in Warsaw, our mysterious cousin had made his way across Poland on roads clogged with military traffic and tens of thousands of refugees, escaped a dozen times from policemen looking for German spies, invented all sorts of stratagems for traveling in trucks and trains requisitioned by the army, and finally reached Gdynia. There, with grandfather Abraham's savings, he bought a ticket that allowed him to travel in the hold, near the engines, of the *Stefan Batory,* one of the last passenger ships to go to America. What became of him then? How did he spend all the days and years that followed? I have his letter here before me; it is both garrulous and enigmatic, as he himself always was. I think it best simply to quote from it.

I arrived in New York early in March 1939. The Joint Distribution Committee, a humanitarian organization, helped me find a place to live, and Jacob Kastoff, a friend of uncle Abraham's, got me a job as a makeup man in the print shop of the Yiddish newspaper *Forward* at 175 East Broadway in Brooklyn. In those days it was still a Jewish neighborhood.

In spite of their power, which many of them didn't know they had, American Jews paid no more attention to what I reported than Polish Jews had done. Poland was already occupied. The news that came to us from there was distressing. *Forward* even published an article on the existence of a concentration camp near Lublin. But the newspaper itself didn't believe there was any great threat. No one, absolutely no one, thought that the destruction of Europe's Jews was a real possibility. And it wasn't till 1943 that a magazine published a cover story of our martyrdom. Yes, 1943 — a few days after the destruction of the Warsaw ghetto.

I was overwhelmed with despair. I even wondered if I shouldn't have stayed in Berlin and died at home, with my family, since I was going to die anyway. But despair is the concern of the heart and I decided to save my soul. I withdrew to a *shtibl,* a little synagogue, in Brooklyn, and for long weeks I prayed and prayed, imploring the Almighty, the God of Israel, not to abandon His people, to open their eyes to the danger, to make the blind, unconcerned world realize that it was sleeping under a volcano whose lava would soon take the form of millions of human beings.

Yes, for four weeks I constantly thought of you back in Warsaw, dreaming under a sky covered with the scales of dead fish. I knew that sky was going to fall onto the earth, covering it with filth and plunging it into darkness. Don't smile, my friends. Don't make fun of my pathetic literary efforts. I'm a man of the shadows, not a writer, and I'm only trying to tell what I know.

Misery, isolation, a feeling of being alone, terribly alone, and preaching in a desert, pleading with a void. I spent my free time writing to newspapers and trying to put pressure on politicians. In September 1941 I even succeeded in meeting Rabbi Stephen Wise, one of the most famous leaders of American Judaism, and his associate, Nahum Goldmann. I told them what was happening in Europe, what I had seen in Germany, what I knew about the deportation of Polish Jews. I explained to them that this wasn't a pogrom, a manifestation of ordinary hatred, but that those people were carrying out a definite plan to wipe us off the face of the earth. They both listened to me with great attention, but you can imagine my sadness and anger a few days later when I heard Nahum Goldmann say on the radio that the problem of the European Jewish communities was more a matter of aid than of politics.

Meanwhile, there were continuing demonstrations against American involvement. The famous Charles Lindbergh, the first pilot to make a solo flight across the Atlantic, publicly accused the Jews of trying to push America into the war. Several newspapers, including some of the most honorable ones, reproached the Jews for their unwillingness to assimilate — in America, the land of minorities! I sank further and further into despair and even thought of killing myself.

Luckily for all of us, Japan attacked America. Yes, I maintain that on December 7, 1941, at Pearl Harbor, the Japanese saved the world. Take it from someone who was living in the United States at that time: if it hadn't been for that military humiliation, America would not have gone to war. I was elated, and relieved. At the end of 1941 I was among the first who volunteered to go and fight the Nazis. I was sent to Morocco, then to Tunisia to be a German interpreter for General Omar Bradley, and there I took part in the liberation of Hammam Lif.

Do you think you know war? You don't know what it's

like for those who kill. At Hammam Lif, for the first time in my life, I had to kill. I had to kill Nazis, it's true, but they were still human beings. And I was greatly afraid of dying. I remember advancing along the beach with the Second Corps, under fire from enemy artillery on the heights of Bou Kournine. I fired my rifle and shouted. I think I shouted very loudly. And I think my shouting saved me — from my fear. I felt as never before that I was a living creature in a world teeming with life, and that my only duty, my only purpose, was to live, at any cost. Guilt, innocence — nothing counted anymore, except life. At the end of the day the city and, of course, the palace of the Bey of Tunis were liberated. Several hundred German soldiers from the Afrika Korps, looking dazed, waited in the main public square to be questioned. Strange as it may seem, I felt no hatred of them. To me, they belonged to a dead world, and I was eager to be back among the living.

That evening, when I was surrounded by a crowd of people who had come to look at the German tanks stranded on the beach, a man blessed me. I couldn't tell if he was a Muslim, a Christian, or a Jew. But I suddenly remembered that it was Saturday, Shabbat, and that Hammam Lif had a large Jewish community. I chose an old man at random and asked him the way to the synagogue. Surprised by my uniform, he said in English, "Jew?" I nodded, pointed to him and asked him the same question: "Jew?" His answer was to tell me to follow him.

In Africa, night comes all at once, without transition. It was dark by the time my guide and I went into a little courtyard where I heard a melody that I remembered from my childhood. He opened a door and I saw a family gathered around a table in a square, low-ceilinged room. They were obviously an Arab family, and my guide, whose name was Salem, spoke in Arabic. The master of the house received me with the incomparable Middle Eastern hospitality that I later had many occasions to appreciate. And do you know what happened then? The children came up to me. The women began clearing the table. I was given a glass of wine. Neighbors came in and soon the room was full. Someone began singing and the others joined in. And what do you think they sang, those Arabs in Hammam Lif? *Al Ira Avdi Jakob* — "Fear Not, My Servant Jacob."

A man with a white beard as sparse as the ones I had seen on Chinese in New York's Chinatown, but whose face was surprisingly young, spoke to me in Hebrew. His name was Taieb. He was my host's father. He pointed to a radio on a little pedestal table inlaid with ivory and mother-of-pearl and asked me if I wanted to listen to the news. At first we heard only static, then faint, uncertain voices, then a loud hubbub of different languages all being spoken at once, and finally a voice clearly and slowly announcing in English that the Warsaw ghetto had been destroyed.

"What's wrong?" asked the grandfather, seeing my consternation, my grief and my tears. I was staring into space and at first I could only stammer, "Warsaw . . . ghetto . . . my family . . ." Then I murmured the names of my relatives — *your* names, dear Salomon and Perl — and I repeated, in a disorderly way, what I told you that night when I came to your apartment. The old man understood. He said a few words in Arabic. And while big tears ran down his cheeks too, one of the women began wailing, another covered her face, and a third clawed at her bosom. I was in Hammam Lif. Facing those immoderate Jews who seemed exactly like Arabs and were weeping for my relatives in Warsaw, I was struck by an unexpected feeling. It was like a sudden shift inside me, or a revelation. It was as if an invisible spring had been abruptly released. I had just realized that Judaism didn't stop at the walls of the Warsaw ghetto. And in spite of the deaths, and the disappearance of the world I belonged to, I felt a kind of savage joy, cruel, unique, miraculous. For the first time since I ran away from Berlin, I was sure, yes, sure that Hitler had lost the war. At least his war against the Jews.

"Man carries his destiny tied to his neck," the Arabs say. I, my dear cousins, carried my old leather satchel, which you may remember. In it I had the few pages of the family book that uncle Abraham had given me — unknown to all of you, but with great ceremony — that night in your apartment. I was determined never to part with that satchel and its precious contents. I had been given what I regarded as a sacred mission: preserving memories. I knew I was the witness, the torch bearer, the prophet of the whole lineage. All through those years I never lost the conviction that I would go back to Berlin and Warsaw.

Meanwhile, however, I had a year to spend in Tunis. I met a few women with whom I made love hastily, furtively, as though to kill time, allay anxiety or ward off death. I also made friends, because, as the Bible says, "A friend loveth at all times." One of them, Marwan Assadi, had a son named Hidar, who was then fifteen. Hidar's intelligence, and maybe also his charm and grace, sometimes made me think, "He's like the son I don't have and maybe never will have." He was an Arab. We didn't agree on anything. We spent whole nights discussing Palestine, which, I told him, had never existed except in the absurd dreams of Hadrian and, much later, the British, and which I never tired of recognizing as the land that had been waiting two thousand years for Abraham's return. But I still liked him. And he was, as I've already said, like a son or a younger brother.

In July 1944 I went to Palermo. A month later I landed on the French coast, near a small town named Saint-Raphaël, and began racing across France. In the Ardennes, I was a liaison officer for a distinguished-looking marshal. I was in Strasbourg while bombs were falling and machine guns were chattering, but I was still able to visit the cathedral, walk through the old Jewish quarter and stroll along the Quai Finckwiller. In my heart and my head were the pages that uncle Abraham had entrusted to me. I reread them many times during lulls in the fighting. They told me the story of our family, including the adventure of Gabriel, son of Aaron, and the beginning of our first print shop. In Strasbourg, wanting to verify and relive everything, and see that "Green Mountain" where our Gabriel learned the printing trade from Gutenberg himself more than five centuries ago, I requisitioned a jeep.

And I got lost in the maze of war, just as I sometimes got lost in my memories. A detachment of German soldiers spotted me in my jeep about twenty kilometers from the city and opened fire. Wounded in the shoulder and belly, I had to abandon my jeep and begin running cross-country to rejoin the Allied lines. I was bleeding like a stuck pig, and before long I felt as if I were going to faint at any moment. Then, as I was crossing a road, I was sideswiped by a car going in the direction of the Rhine. The driver was Sigrid, Sigrid Furchmuller. The advance of the French forces had taken her by surprise while she was visiting a friend in Strasbourg, and she was desperately trying to get home. I don't remember very well what happened next. Sigrid, it seems, had very little interest in me personally, but she couldn't get her car started again, war had sharpened her survival reflexes, and she thought, with good reason, that taking care of an American officer might be useful to her. If the Allies arrived first, she was saving one of their men; if it was the Germans . . . It was the Allies, of course. Sigrid saved my life. In return, I testified in favor of her and her family. The following year she went to the United States with me, converted to Judaism — and I found myself married to a German woman, the daughter of a Nazi general.

I forgot to tell you that the blood from my wound had blotted out the ink on the pages I was carrying in my satchel. My life had been saved, but at the price of memory. I had come back to the world of the living, but I had broken off with the world of the dead. Should I see that as symbolic? It was Sigrid, the beautiful young wife I felt so guilty about, who persuaded me to begin trying to regain that lost history.

"Publish requests for information in newspapers," she said, "write to international organizations, the Refugee Office, the Red Cross, the Joint Distribution Committee, UNRWA. . . . Each answer you get will be like a miracle, and you'll feel a little calmer."

Sigrid was right. She even became a kind of custodian of that tattered memory. She wrote to some people, badgered others, gave me ideas for letters to send, suggested answers for letters I received. The war was over. Nazism had been defeated. I — we — still had to fear another source of misfortune: forgetting. It's strange that the duty of tying the threads together should have fallen on me, Hugo, the least pious of the Halters, perhaps the least Jewish. Everything is there again, in my heart and in a little notebook that packs centuries of history into a few pages.

The third and last part of the sequence came fifteen years later, in 1961. Officially, at least, our cousin was still living in America and had resumed his work in the print shop of the Yiddish newspaper *Forward*, which was a curiously modest position for a man of his culture. At distant intervals, from the postcards he sometimes sent us, we had learned about his strange trips to faraway places: Beirut, for example, and Cairo, Prague, Yemen. One of my parents' friends even claimed to have met him one day in Frankfurt. He had a mustache, he wore horn-rimmed glasses, his hair was dyed black and he looked like a banker, but there could be no doubt of who he was. He was sitting at a table in the backroom of a café, absorbed in conversation with Israel Beer, who at that time was considered to be a close adviser of Ben-Gurion. Why that deviousness and that disguise? Why all that mystery? And why didn't Hugo ever find time to pass through Paris and visit us?

Those questions exasperated my parents, and I finally became almost obsessed with them. Then, in 1961, our enigmatic cousin came to visit us at last. It was a week before Passover. My mother was busy cleaning up the apartment for the holidays. He rang our doorbell unexpectedly and came in with his wife Sigrid, whom we had never met. He looked hardly any older, except that his cheeks were a little hollow now and his blond hair was slightly thinner. He seemed perfectly at ease, and glad to be able to exchange a few words in Yiddish with us. And it turned out that he and my father were rivals in reconstructing the family memory; they had both decided to do it at the same time, independently of each other.

What was really in his mind that day? Who was he really, that intellectual-looking man I can still see leaning against the windowsill with his long legs elegantly crossed in front of him? What was hidden by his strange bass voice, which gave such modern accents to the language of the ghetto and irresistibly took me back to the blond, determined young man who had taken me in his arms one evening in January 1939 in the heart of the ghetto? Hugo was there, talking to us. He introduced Sigrid, the wife who had intrigued us so much from a distance.

"This is Sigrid," he said, "my wife . . . the daughter of a general in the former German army."

And I can still see her, too: blond, willowy, wearing a gray skirt with a matching suit jacket, a white silk blouse and low-cut lizard-skin shoes that enhanced the slenderness of her ankles. She smiled, spoke to my mother, joked.

We had suspected Hugo and his wife of snubbing the family, but now they were with us, close to us, relaxed and natural, sharing our modest dinner. Yet I felt that they were further away than they had ever been before. Maybe that was why their death a few days later, on the heights of Abu Gosh in Israel, seemed to me both appalling and "in the order of things." There was something in their faces, their bodies and their lives that exempted them from the common fate.

Perhaps I should add, for the sake of completeness, that it was to us, the Halters in Paris, that Mordecai sent Hugo's personal belongings immediately after his telegram. Why to us? I don't know. But the fact is that one morning we received Hugo's passport, wallet, checkbook and keys — as well as the little notebook in which he had undertaken to reconstruct and record our common family memory. My father was deeply moved by its unexpected arrival at a time when he was engaged in that same attempt at reconstruction. I remember him that evening, poring over the thin notebook with a shiny black cover in which he found some names he knew, others he had forgotten, and still others that were like the missing pieces of a jigsaw puzzle that he had lost hope of ever being able to complete.

"It's odd, what's happened to our family book," he said to me one night after dinner. "It grew thicker and thicker through the centuries, then it took less than five years to shrink to the size of a little address book."

And then, another night, in a determined, almost brutal tone that we had never heard him use before:

"Together, thanks to Hugo's notebook, we'll finally reunite all the children of Abraham."

My father was a good and simple man. He was a printer, the son and grandson of printers, and so on back for many generations. He passionately loved that role of intercessor between the world of signs and the world of reading. When he composed the text of an article or a book on his Linotype machine, he sometimes changed a word or the structure of a sentence. And that, I think, was the worst "transgression" of principles and virtue ever committed by that old Jew, whose whole life seemed destined to flow along at the leisurely pace of those minor corrections and revisions. That explains why I was so surprised by his sudden determination and the sight of that modest scribe abruptly turning into a zealous, relentless archaeologist of memory. I was astounded to see my father as an explorer of the past, dedicated to a glorious mission, a fervent architect of the invisible house that is Jewish memory. My mother and I discovered a new man. And I will never forget my amazement one night when I went into the little attic room where he liked to go when he couldn't sleep and saw him working in front of a big panel covered with names, some crossed out and others underlined, like an accountant for a bankrupt company trying to find what was left of its former wealth. I saw the disconcerting face of a man who was impassioned, possessed, goaded by contradictory feelings. I didn't understand those feelings, but they made me say, with the expression of an obedient son, which wasn't at all common with me:

"Yes, Father, we'll work together on this. Together we'll carry on the legacy cousin Hugo has left us."

2

NEW YORK – TEL AVIV

Sidney and Mordecai

APRIL 1961

Sidney, our American cousin and Mordecai's brother, was a highly regarded doctor. He learned of Hugo's death while he was visiting his father in Winnipeg, Canada. That trip to Winnipeg was important to him. His family had never really accepted his marriage to Marjory. She was fascinated with Judaism, she observed all the Jewish rites and ceremonies better than a real Jew, but she wasn't Jewish. She was an Irish Catholic. And the introduction of a goy into the family was resented as a betrayal, a kind of scandal.

"But Ruth the Moabite was the origin of King David's lineage," Sidney often pointed out.

"History doesn't repeat itself," his father invariably replied.

"Why is it," Sidney would ask, "that you appeal to the Law to condemn me, but reject Tradition as a basis for absolving me?"

It was like a conversation between two deaf men; the misunderstanding between them was insurmountable. On one side, there was old Samuel, Abraham's younger brother, steeped in the old ghetto morality, who, even though he had been in the New World for a quarter of a century, had never really left Warsaw. On the other side, a young Jew of forty, red-haired like a Scotsman, husky as a football player, for whom Judaism went very well with modernism, and tradition with adaptation. An American to his fingertips, he believed in happiness and progress. He had come to Winnipeg, having left his patients and his hospital in New York, because Marjory was expecting another child and he wanted this one to be born in a renewed atmosphere of family harmony. Things had gone so badly with little Richard, seven years earlier. Sidney had been so unhappy when his father refused to come to the circumcision! And this time he wanted so much for things to be different!

The child was born: a beautiful little girl whom they decided to name Marilyn. Old Samuel was pleased. His relations with Marjory had become almost courteous. And everything was going well when Mordecai's telegram arrived.

Of all the Halters, Sidney was probably the one who, at that time, felt closest to Hugo. He had known him in New York during the war. Sidney was only nineteen then, and interested only in his medical studies, but he was immediately fascinated by that cousin from far away who was regarded by most of his fellow Jews as both a troublemaker and a bird of ill omen. But Sidney believed him. He knew that coolheaded preacher was the only one who saw clearly when he painted an apocalyptic picture of Nazified Europe. And the two of them, the conspirator and his young disciple, could often be seen wandering after dark between Washington Square and Ninth Street.

After the war they lost sight of each other. Hugo resumed his life as a nomad and a Cassandra, while Sidney gradually became an exemplification of the American Way of Life. Then came the day in October 1960, a few months before his trip to Canada, when his enigmatic cousin again turned up in his life. They met, as in the old days, at the White Horse Tavern. Hugo still had the look of an outlaw, or a hunted animal, but in his eyes there was a new anxiety that made a strong impression on the young doctor.

He said he needed three hundred thousand dollars. A bank had agreed to lend it to him, provided he had a cosigner. Would Sidney be that cosigner? Would he do him that favor in the name of the sacred bonds that united them? Moved but apprehensive, Sidney refused. He often worked for humanitarian causes, but he liked clear causes and transparent business affairs, and he was wary of the mysteries his cousin seemed to delight in. Why did he want that loan? What did he intend to do with the money? How and when would he pay it back? Sidney wasn't very proud of his response and his mental reservations, but there was Marjory, the future baby, the ideal American life he had tried so hard to achieve. . . . He sensed too many unavowed implications in Hugo's request to take the risk of following him along that path.

Oddly enough, Hugo seemed neither surprised nor angered by his unwillingness. He seemed to expect it, and maybe understand it.

"You're the only representative of our family here in New York," he said, lowering his voice as if he were telling him a secret. "If something happens to me, can you see to it that I'm buried in the cemetery in Jerusalem?"

Was this humor? Provocation? A presentiment, perhaps? Sidney pretended to find the idea absurd. He answered with a little laugh that seemed to say, "Come, come, my dear cousin, don't play that kind of game with me! But if you insist . . ."

And it wasn't until he had Mordecai's telegram before his eyes, in Winnipeg, that he realized the meaning of all that — and how blind he had been.

A few words with Marjory, a private discussion with his father, a melancholy night beside his baby . . . He had made his decision: even though the funeral had already taken place, he still had to go to Israel; he owed Hugo the homage of his vigilance, as he had promised, especially since there was something strange about . . . He couldn't help thinking all night and all through the next day about that conversation, which now seemed so terribly premonitory to him. What was he going to do in Tel Aviv? He didn't know. But he would go there.

It was a warm, beautiful morning when he landed at Lod airport, where Mordecai was waiting for him. The two brothers liked each other. They saw each other now and then, in Tel Aviv or New York, and they shared the same passion for history, though they didn't always draw the same conclusions from it. Strangely, however, they couldn't have been more different. The American was tall. He had red hair combed straight back from a high forehead, the precise movements of an athlete, dark eyes sparkling with mischievous humor, a charming smile and a short, carefully groomed beard. The Israeli was rather short. He had mobile features. His eyes squinted from nearsightedness and were magnified by his thick glasses. He constantly talked about "his" kibbutz and often affected the tone and mannerisms of a peasant. Seeing them sitting together in the lobby of the Dan Hotel, in the midst of tourists and Israeli army officers, it would have been impossible to guess that they were both nephews of Abraham Halter and equally entitled to call themselves his heirs.

In the car, Mordecai had told Sidney everything: the murder, the bodies riddled with bullets, the police investigation that had led nowhere, the burial in a small tomb in the Mount of Rest cemetery in Jerusalem, the sad ceremony attended by only a few people: he, his wife, one or two old Jews who had come from nobody knew where, an Arab writer from Nazareth, two men he had never seen before, who looked like cops or informers. . . . Yes, everything had taken place normally. No, he hadn't noticed anything unusual. Yes, of course he would drive him to the cemetery. It was so nice of him to come! Poor cousin Hugo had actually been all alone. . . .

Sidney had listened attentively, saying only that he didn't want to see the scene of the crime, but would like to visit Hugo's grave. Now, in the hotel lobby, without yet revealing any details, he said he knew something that might or might not turn out to be important. A conversation, just a conversation, but maybe it would interest the police. Could Mordecai arrange for him to report it? Did he know someone he could tell his story to?

Mordecai, intrigued, told him that he did know someone. Not very well, but he knew him. He was a man in the defense ministry who had been following Hugo's case and had come to question him, Mordecai, two or three times. The defense ministry seemed greatly interested in Hugo's past: his Arab friends, that puzzling murder just outside Jerusalem. . . . Did Sidney want Mordecai to contact that man? It would be very simple; most things were simple in Israel.

Without waiting for an answer, Mordecai stood up, went to the phone, came back a minute later and said almost casually, "His name is Benjamin Ben-Eliezer and he'll be here in an hour. Shall we wait for him?"

Yes, they would wait for him. They passed the time with the affectionate, sometimes bantering talk of two brothers reunited after a long separation.

"You have a son too," Sidney began. "Tell me about him."

"Arieh is the soul of my soul, the flesh of my flesh. Just think how lucky he is: he was born here, in this land, whereas we, or at least I . . ."

"And what about your kibbutz? How's it going? They say in the States that morale on the kibbutzim isn't what it used to be, that the heroism of the early days is gone and —"

"That's ridiculous! Stop talking nonsense and worrying about us! *Our* only worries are military: terrorists from Syria and Lebanon are making incursions more and more often."

"When are you going back to the kibbutz?"

"Tomorrow, after our visit to the cemetery."

The conversation then took on a falsely playful tone that was actually quite heavy, weighed down by the shadow of death and Hugo's ghost. Sidney, Mordecai thought, had said either too much or not enough. What was it that he wanted to tell the authorities investigating Hugo's death? Why was he being so mysterious about it, and why did he seem so ill at ease?

When Mordecai had launched into a lyrical description of Kibbutz Dafneh's achievements, Sidney interrupted him:

"What happened to Hugo's personal belongings?"

"I sent them to Salomon, in Paris."

"Salomon?" Sidney said thoughtfully. "He once wrote to me, a long time ago. I don't remember if I answered. Do you know him?"

"Yes, of course. We sometimes write to each other, and he's come to the kibbutz."

After another silence, Sidney asked with increased uneasiness, "Do we also have relatives in Moscow?"

"Yes."

"Do you know them?"

"No."

"That Khrushchev interests me. He seems determined to change things in Russia. He acknowledges Stalin's crimes. But they say he doesn't like Jews any more than Stalin did."

Mordecai leaned forward a little, squinting his eyes. He hadn't heard the end of Sidney's last sentence because a group of tourists were noisily going down the flight of steps, flanked by fountains, that led to the salon.

Sidney repeated, "They say that Khrushchev doesn't like Jews any more than Stalin did." He raised his voice: "Why do Jews stay in the Soviet Union?"

"Because they like the KGB!" Mordecai answered, laughing. "But here's Benjamin. I told you he'd be here in an hour! You see how punctual Israelis are?"

The man coming toward them was young, younger than they were, no more than thirty. He had a shy smile, he was dressed all in gray, and he really didn't look like a fighter or a secret agent. He spoke softly, in a neutral tone, but his subject — terrorism — was chilling.

"Terrorism will soon be the main means of access to the media, an unmatched possibility of action in parts of the world protected by nuclear weapons, a perverse effect of technical prog-ress, one of the things at stake in the confrontation between super-powers." Satisfied with the effect he had produced and obviously glad to be holding forth on a subject he knew well, he went on: "And terrorism will benefit especially from conventional warfare's poor yield in relation to cost. Basically, it's nothing but a new diplomatic language; what counts is being able to decipher it correctly, prefer-ably in time."

Sidney was surprised by this young man. He had expected an American-style cop, an incorruptible crime fighter. He found himself facing a scholar, an expert in his field who talked about all that as if it were the rules of a new science of warfare.

"In your opinion," he asked in a voice that had lost some of its self-assurance, "what were the terrorists trying to tell us by killing our cousin Hugo?"

"The police haven't yet found anything specific. They're inclined to think that his murder was simply a blind act of terrorism, like all the others that have been committed in Israel. But it might also be explained by his complex personality, his links with certain Arab nationalist leaders, and especially his friendship with Hidar Assadi, a Tunisian who has recently lived in Moscow and acted as a liaison agent between the Soviets and the ANM, the Arab Nationalist

Movement." He leaned toward Sidney. "But your brother tells me that you know some things, too. About Hugo's past, his Arab friends. . . . Any additional information may greatly facilitate the investigation."

"Yes . . . no," Sidney said, a little embarrassed.

"Is it something about his life during the war? After the war?"

"After. Yes, after the war. Hugo married a German woman."

"Yes, we know that."

"The daughter of a Nazi general, no less."

"We know that," the Israeli repeated with a touch of impatience in his voice. "That's surely not why you came to Israel to visit his grave."

"Let's say it was because I had a guilty conscience."

"Repentance and good deeds are the shields that protect us from heaven's anger," Benjamin said. "But tell me more. Why did you have a guilty conscience?"

"In October, last year," Sidney began, looking even more embarrassed, while his brother stared at him in bewilderment, "Hugo asked me to cosign a loan for three hundred thousand dollars."

"Three hundred thousand!" Benjamin exclaimed. "That's a lot of money! And you refused?"

"Yes. But that's not all."

"Oh?"

"He asked me to see to it, if he died, that he would be buried in Israel, in Jerusalem."

"He didn't tell you anything else?"

"No."

"Did you know he was in danger?"

"No, of course not. I thought he was joking."

"What did you say?"

"Nothing. I just laughed."

Benjamin took off his glasses and thought for a few seconds before asking, "Did he tell you which bank was willing to lend him that money?"

"No."

"Did he actually say, 'if I die'?"

"No. His exact words were 'if something happens to me.'"

Benjamin seemed more and more thoughtful.

"There's nothing else?" he asked after a silence, apparently disappointed at not having learned more. "Are you sure you've told me everything?"

"Yes, I'm sure."

Benjamin stood up to leave. Mordecai, who had said nothing since the beginning of the conversation, finally intervened.

"The notebook. . . . Do you know about the notebook?"

"What notebook?" Benjamin asked, sitting down again.

"A little address book that Hugo had on him when he was killed. I sent it, along with his other personal belongings, to a cousin of ours in Paris."

It would have been an understatement to say that Benjamin was interested. He questioned Mordecai closely. About the size and shape of the notebook. The number of names in it. If he had looked through it, out of curiosity, before sending it to Paris. If he remembered this, that or the other name. If it was possible to get the notebook back and examine it. Where and how he could get in touch with Salomon Halter. If he would be willing to cooperate with the Israeli secret services.

"It was inexcusable for the police to let that evidence get away from them!" he concluded. "But now, thanks to you, thanks to this meeting . . ."

Life was so strange! Mordecai had thought his brother Sidney would be a source of valuable information, and now he himself was the focus of the formidable Ben-Eliezer's curiosity.

The cemetery. Shining between the tall cypress trees pointing at the sky, the uncertain morning light enveloped the Mount of Rest. Infinite calm. Peace. The air was marvelously clear and Sidney could admire the landscape that stretched out below him: Kibbutz Qiryat Anavim in the Valley of Ajalon, and a succession of green patches extending forty miles westward, to the sea.

The Ashkenazi section of the cemetery was squeezed in between two other sections, one for Jews from Bukhara, the other for Jews from Yemen. Hugo's and Sigrid's gravestones, side by side, were almost dazzlingly white and bore carved inscriptions in Hebrew. Sidney couldn't help running his fingertip along the letters. His cousin's name, his own name. All that mystery around his death.

Gravestones as far as the eye could see. Maybe those stones were about to move aside, maybe all those dead people were about to be resurrected. . . . Foolishness, of course; indecent imaginings. No, he didn't like cemeteries very much, and eternity didn't suit him.

Standing in front of Hugo's grave, he wondered what he should do. Pray? Recite the Hashkabah or the Kaddish?

"You don't have to pray if you don't want to," Mordecai said, seeing his hesitation. "Just being here is what matters. Here, no one ever dies."

"What do you mean?"

"During the war I was with the Jewish Brigade in Italy. When we were going through Capo di Bove, with bombs falling around us, and the bodies of dead American soldiers everywhere, I saw a café called *Qui non si muore mai,* 'Here, no one ever dies.' Since then, whenever I feel anxiety, I remember that café in Capo di Bove and it reassures me."

"I didn't know you were in Italy during the war. You might have met Hugo there."

"He didn't stay there long enough. He was sent to France right away."

"Did you belong to that famous group, the Avengers?"

"No. Killing Nazis after the war couldn't bring back the dead. But putting Nazis on trial could help to educate the living."

"I'm in favor of an eye for an eye," Sidney said ardently. "That's all Nazis can understand. The same is true of terrorists, nowadays. . . . I've been told that uncle Abraham tried to talk to the Nazis in the Warsaw ghetto."

"Like you, I admire him. But there's no use talking to people who don't consider human life sacred."

Sidney let his eyes wander over the gravestones and the cypresses. Then, after one last look at Hugo's grave, he turned to Mordecai.

"You don't believe in taking revenge?"

Mordecai hesitated, then quoted a Greek proverb to the effect that the gods of revenge act in silence.

When the two brothers had left the cemetery, Sidney glanced back at it, wondering if he was abandoning Hugo or if he was about to track him down and rejoin him.

3

MOSCOW

The Soviet Cousins

SEPTEMBER 1961

Cousin Rachel learned of Hugo's death several months afterward.

On that day of Rosh Hashana 5722, she was listening to music on the radio. Half attentive and half distracted, she opened closets and drawers and began laying out things that would be needed for the celebration. While she was doing this, her daughter Olga burst into the modest kitchen, holding up a letter whose mere existence was a little unbelievable for a Jewish family in Moscow.

"Mama! Mama! This came from Paris!"

"From Paris?" Rachel said in astonishment, wiping her hands on her apron. She looked feverishly, but in vain, for her glasses. "Open it," she ordered.

"I've already opened it, but I can't make head or tail of it! It looks like Hebrew, or maybe Yiddish."

"Yiddish?"

Rachel stared at Olga, who didn't know whether to laugh or be alarmed, and took the envelope from her hand. Still without her glasses, she asked her daughter to read the address to her. Yes, it was really for her, though it was addressed to her under her maiden name, Rachel Halter. Was that why the letter had taken nearly six months to reach her, judging from the postmark?

More and more excited, the mother and daughter hurried to the end of the hall, where Aron, the husband and father, was working. They found him surrounded by the books that lined the walls of his windowless study. As always at this time of day, he was preparing for the course on ancient Greek and Roman civilization that he had been teaching for the last ten years in the history department of Moscow University.

Rachel handed him the letter.

"It's in Yiddish," she said. "It came from Paris."

Aron took it out of its envelope.

"It's from your cousin Salomon Halter," he said.

In a quiet voice, almost choked by emotion, he began reading aloud. Rachel listened in silence, avidly, then waited while he summarized the letter for Olga, who didn't know Yiddish.

"So many years," Rachel said with a sigh, "so many years . . ."

The truth was that all at once she felt old, from countless sufferings and wounds. She remembered Salomon as a boy. The family, the ghetto . . . those flames — she hadn't seen them, but they still haunted her. Then Salomon again.

"Yes, Salomon," she went on with a faraway look in her eyes, "little Salomon, uncle Abraham's son. . . . He must have been about twenty when I left Poland, in 1930. I clearly remember uncle Abraham and his print shop on Nowolipje Street." She put her hand on Olga's arm. "In his print shop, they sometimes printed revolutionary leaflets in Yiddish. You and your father have never been in Warsaw, so you can't know. . . . Uncle Abraham was the only one who didn't try to make me change my mind when I decided to go to the Soviet Union. He just said to me as he watched me packing, 'Happiness is like an echo: you hear it, but you never see it.'"

The chimes of the Tower of the Savior, in the Kremlin, struck eight. Aron picked up his papers, put them into his briefcase and closed it.

"I have to go," he said. "Goodbye."

"Don't come home late," his wife replied. "The children are coming to dinner tonight."

He stopped in the doorway.

"Yes, of course."

The Lerners lived in an apartment reserved for academics, on the fifth floor of a turn-of-the-century building at the corner of

Kazakov Street and Chkalov Street, near the home of the physicist Andrei Sakharov. Aron Lerner, a man in his fifties, had a bony face and wrinkles at the corners of his lips. His family had come to Moscow from Lithuania more than a century ago. And it was here he had met and married Rachel Halter, a young Jewish woman from Warsaw who had come, with many others, to live in the socialist homeland, take part in the Revolution and help to build socialism. Actually, however, she soon became disillusioned and would have gone back to Poland if she had not suddenly discovered the traditions her parents had always observed, and if her love for Aron hadn't replaced her revolutionary fervor.

Aron had never belonged to the Party. That had enabled him to survive a series of purges, but it was harmful to his academic career. Every week the *Literaturnaya gazeta* praised historians whose lack of rigorous standards was obvious, while he, the author of such excellent books as *The Athenian Republic in the Time of Pericles* and *Greek Art and Karl Marx,* went on vegetating in the midst of almost total indifference. He protected himself from bitterness with a kind of irony about himself, and he presented the strange picture of a man who was both disillusioned and impassioned, cynical and childlike.

It would be an exaggeration to say that he was strongly attached to Judaism. He had spoken Yiddish in his long-ago childhood, but, since then, Athens had become dearer to him than Jerusalem. And although Stalin's persecution of Jewish writers had naturally shocked him, and had made him better understand his wife's attachment to that martyrized culture and tradition, he knew that he had been distressed and appalled more as a humanist than as a Jew.

His children — Sasha, twenty-nine, and Olga, twenty-four — were essentially the same as other young people in Moscow. Sasha was a bright student in the department of foreign languages and Olga was studying medicine. Like most Soviet citizens, they sometimes criticized the Soviet state. And they were fond enough of their mother to put up good-naturedly with what they called her "superstitions." But basically they liked the Soviet Union. They firmly believed that life was better here than anywhere else. While Olga was an easygoing, openhearted young woman who gave her father no problems, Sasha was secretive and ambitious. He was obviously gifted, full of talents, but there was something about him that worried his father. Aron wished he could be sure that Sasha would behave honorably in a world where wolves set the example.

Aron was walking toward the subway. Suddenly feeling cold, he quickened his pace and pulled up his scarf. That letter from Paris had troubled him. It was, he realized now that he thought about it again, their first contact with anyone outside the country since the war. Was it possible that things had changed under Khrushchev? Ten years ago, a message from the West would have been confiscated immediately.

He had reached this point in his thoughts when he heard a voice call out behind him:

"Aron Lazarevich Lerner! Aron Lazarevich!"

He looked back and saw Vasily Slepakov, one of his university colleagues, trotting to catch up with him.

"Aron Lazarevich!" Slepakov repeated, out of breath. "I've been following you and calling you, but you didn't hear me. What's wrong? Bad news?"

"What makes you think I've had bad news, Vasily Petrovich?"

"I hear Rachel got a letter from Paris."

"Well! . . . News travels fast, doesn't it?"

"Nothing goes unnoticed here, my friend — especially when you have the same mailman!"

For a time the two men walked in silence, side by side, carefully avoiding the ruts left by recent work on the pavement. Aron had no desire to tell Vasily about the letter from Paris. He knew how dangerous it could be to confide in anyone, to be the least bit indiscreet. But Vasily stuck with him, and when they reached the Lermontov-skaya subway station he took hold of his sleeve and asked slyly:

"Have you seen your son lately?"

"Sasha? Yes, of course. He was asleep when I left home just now. Why do you ask, Vasily Petrovich?"

Slepakov pretended to think for a moment, then said dramatically, "Because I saw your son last night, and do you know who he was with? Two KGB men, my friend. They were on Gorky Street. He was getting into a big black Chaika."

"Are you sure, Vasily Petrovich? KGB men?"

"Come, come, Aron Lazarevich, you and I have lived in the Soviet Union too long not to be able to recognize them at first sight: the tan trench coats, the shifty look, and that arrogance. . . ." Vasily paused; getting no reply from Aron, he coughed and went on in a falsely casual tone, "But if Sasha didn't tell you about it, it means there's nothing to tell. Just forget what I've said."

Forgetting it was, of course, the last thing Aron was likely to do. The image of his son flanked by KGB men stayed with him all day. Maybe Vasily was wrong, maybe there had been a misunderstanding, a case of mistaken identity.

By the time he went home that evening and found the table set and the candles lighted, he had almost forgotten that it was Rosh Hashana. It scarcely occurred to him that simply having those lighted candles on a white tablecloth was a real danger in Moscow: for less than that, one could be denounced as an adherent of a hidden religion or, even worse, as a Zionist agent. He had passed one of the neighbors on his way up the stairs without taking the precaution of saying that this was his wedding anniversary, as he had done every year till now.

When the time came for Rachel to call the children to the table, he didn't even glance at Olga, despite the fact that she had braided her hair in the way she reserved for great occasions, and he hardly heard Sasha exuberantly praising, as he did each year, the *zakuskis* that his mother had somehow turned up by standing in line in front of all the shops in the neighborhood. And at the end of the ceremony, when the family had abundantly enjoyed those beautiful sacred stories that can really be told only by candlelight, he couldn't restrain himself any longer: he pushed back his plate and questioned his son.

"Tell me, Sasha, what were you doing with two KGB men last night on Gorky Street?"

Far from being flustered, Sasha looked him straight in the eyes and, as though to defy him, slowly and deliberately emptied his glass before answering with a question of his own.

"How do you know that?"

Aron returned his gaze without flinching.

"Everything becomes known here."

Stunned silence around the table. Then Rachel, on the verge of tears, begged her son to explain.

"Don't be angry. I intended to tell you about it calmly on Sunday."

"Let's talk about it now!"

"All right, we will. I'll tell you everything."

The KGB, he said, had made inquiries in the department of foreign languages at the university because they wanted experts for the Committee for Solidarity with the Peoples of Africa and Asia, and they had been told about his thorough knowledge of Persian and Arabic. They had then come to see him and offered him the position of section leader.

"It was something I couldn't turn down," he said. "Travel, an exciting life, working for an ideal. . . . Don't worry: I'm not a stool pigeon. It's wonderful to be helping underdeveloped countries."

His tone had changed. He was touching, with his enthusiasm. And almost believable.

His explanation had relaxed the atmosphere when Olga, half serious and half teasing, said to him, "So what you'll be doing is helping the Arabs to fight Israel!"

Sasha gave her a withering look and said harshly, as though wanting to make her pay for her impudence, "*You* should talk: you go out with an Arab!"

This was too much for Rachel and Aron. They turned to their daughter and demanded an explanation.

"Yes, it's . . . it's true," she stammered, twisting on her chair. "But he's a Tunisian. He's at the medical school. And he's brilliant, believe me. His name is Hidar, Hidar Assadi. It's true that he doesn't like Israel. He says it's an Arab land. But I swear he's not an anti-Semite." She paused to catch her breath, then announced triumphantly, as if she were presenting a decisive argument that would exonerate her and reassure her parents, "In Tunis he was a close friend of one of Mama's cousins!"

"One of my cousins?" Rachel exclaimed.

"Yes, Mama. His name was Hugo Halter and he was an American army officer stationed in Tunis. It was in 1943, in the middle of the war. I never dared to tell you about it till now, but it's true."

"Hugo Halter," Rachel repeated. "Hugo Halter . . ." She turned to her husband. "Aron! Where's that letter from Paris? Let me have it, please. . . . Yes, of course! I didn't make the connection at first!"

Olga gave her a puzzled look. Sasha frowned.

"What letter?" he asked. "What letter are you talking about?"

As for Aron, who had the letter from Salomon in his pocket, he had immediately realized the incredible coincidence. Olga and that Arab, the Arab and Hugo — life was so strange! And that coincidence was so wild!

Rachel burst into tears. Olga seemed dazed. Sasha moved his chair close to his mother's and, with a kind, understanding smile, tried to reassure her.

Aron was lost in his memories, seeing images from the past. Then he observed his children one after the other, for a long time. *My name is Aron Lerner,* he thought. *Centuries and centuries of memory, all the memories in the Book of Abraham. . . . And here are my children, flesh of my flesh and blood of my blood, both in the hands of the most relentless adversaries of what I dare to call my people. Both of them, yes, with their guilelessness, their inexperience and their youth, renouncing the holy memory.*

He had great difficulty going to sleep that night. And great difficulty driving away the ghosts that assailed him. In one day, his two children. In one night, those two omens.

4

BUENOS AIRES

Doña Regina

DECEMBER 1961

The last member of the family to learn of Hugo's death was Doña
Regina, in Buenos Aires. The news came to her, too, in a letter from
her brother Salomon. She saw it as one more proof that Israel was
not, as the Zionists claimed, a miraculous country that guaranteed
every Jew's life and safety.

Doña Regina had come to Argentina in 1918, fleeing from the
czarist police. And despite the forty-three years she had spent on the
banks of the Río de la Plata, she had remained faithful to the ideal
of her youth: she was a Communist, and the Soviet Union was still
her model. Buenos Aires? She had learned to like Buenos Aires. She
had watched the development of that metropolis with a population
of five million, crisscrossed, like New York, by a grid of streets and
avenues, the difference being that here they petered out in the dust
of the pampas, whereas in New York they were bounded by water.
But her heart beat in unison with those of her Soviet comrades.

Hugo's death affected her more than she would have thought.
After all, he was her uncle Joseph's son, her father's nephew. And it
was scandalous that such things should still be happening — in
Jerusalem itself!

"The victory at Stalingrad was in vain," she said to Don Israel, her husband, "if Jews are still being killed all over the world."

She knew that in saying this she was flirting with blasphemy, but she said it anyway. She wasn't afraid of contradictions. She had an expansive nature and liked to say what she thought. Let logic be damned.

She was now past sixty and she had a gruffness that made it impossible to imagine her as a charming young woman. In winter she wielded her knitting needles with a ferocity worthy of the struggle against class enemies. There was nothing she didn't feel capable of doing without anyone's help. She never went to a hairdresser, for example. In front of her mirror, she was both the hairdresser and the customer. She would comb her hair down over her forehead, just above her round, dark eyes, and make conversation with herself. Always in motion, always busy, she took pains to maintain an outer sternness that hid her inner tenderness.

Ever since they came from Poland, Doña Regina and her husband, a shoemaker by trade, had lived in the same modest house with a patio, on San Martín Avenue, in a working-class neighborhood where everyone knew everything about everyone else. During the hot, humid nights between September and March, people sat on their doorsteps with their hands on their knees, exchanging small talk with their neighbors or reverently listening to Carlos Gardel's tangos.

Don Israel was a lively, fun-loving little man who lived in baggy trousers pulled up almost to his armpits by colored suspenders. He had two passions: Stalin and dominoes. Now that Stalin was dead, he concentrated on dominoes, although a cell meeting sometimes made him miss one of the relentless games that began most evenings and went on past midnight. He played with friends who, like him, were Argentinian by adoption. They all spoke Yiddish. And, with their three daily newspapers, their magazines, cafés and theaters, they lived in Buenos Aires as they had long ago lived in Warsaw.

Doña Regina seldom saw her husband, and now that her two sons were married, she felt forsaken. Only her granddaughter Anna Maria, a pretty dark-haired girl of thirteen, came to visit her and relieve her loneliness. Anna Maria was just in high school but, like her grandmother, she already wanted to change the world, build socialism, and so on. She was not, strictly speaking, a Communist, but she was a militant in the Perónist youth movement and said she was convinced that only a "justicial" revolution could make anti-Semitism disappear. Anti-Semitism was the result of social inequality; it was the anger of the poor, diverted to Jewish scapegoats by the rich.

That day, Anna Maria arrived at just the right time. Doña Regina led her into the kitchen, sat her down at the table, poured soup into a soup bowl decorated with blue flowers and ordered, "Eat."

Then she sat down facing her and, without further preliminaries, told her about the death of her distant cousin.

"Did you know him?" Anna Maria asked.

Doña Regina sighed.

"I knew *about* him. Before the war, we wrote to each other often, in the family. We knew about everything: every marriage, every death, every move to a different place. We were never alone, even if we were thousands of kilometers away from the rest of the family. When we were happy, we shared our happiness with the others. If we needed help, we asked for it. But Hugo . . . yes, I knew who he was. He was one of us, you understand? And maybe that was what he was made to pay for, who knows?" Seeing that her granddaughter's bowl was empty, she asked, "Don't you want any more?"

"I've eaten a whole bowlful, as you can see."

"That's all you want? You don't like my soup? While you're still growing, you have to eat!"

Forced to recognize that Anna Maria was no longer hungry, she shrugged and put away her pot.

"And now?" Anna Maria asked.

"Now?" Doña Regina looked at her blankly for a moment, then understood. "Well, now we have almost no family left. Only a few members scattered here and there across the world. Survivors. A peach without a pit falls apart. . . ."

"What about your brother?"

"Salomon? He still writes to me. And he tries to keep a record of all the survivors. But what's the use? Our close relatives can be counted on the fingers of one hand, and as for the others . . ." And, abruptly, "Have you heard the news? It seems a bomb has damaged the building of the newspaper *La Prensa*."

"Oh," Anna Maria said with a skeptical and vaguely disgusted expression. "How do you know?"

"I heard it on the radio."

"More provocation! The army will blame the Perónists. Ever since Perón was overthrown and forced into exile, the army has been trying to eliminate us militants, and the leaders of the people's organizations." Anna Maria said this in the blustering tone she attributed to the great professional revolutionaries of her dreams, then she looked at her watch. "Oh, no! I'm late! We're having a meeting at La Bocca, near the Old Port."

"Well, try to be careful," Doña Regina said with a look of complicity.

A few moments later Anna Maria was outside, hurrying toward her meeting and thinking one last time, before plunging into the night, about that murdered cousin who had already taken a place in her reveries. *What a shame I didn't know him!* she thought.

PARIS, JANUARY 1967

It was at the end of 1961 that Benjamin Ben-Eliezer visited us in Paris. The Israeli embassy had called and told my mother that an Israeli diplomat staying briefly in the city would like to meet my father. Why? The voice at the other end of the line was evasive. We were simply being asked to receive the diplomat in our home and answer his questions as well as we could. When he heard that, my father didn't seem particularly surprised. And, to my own great surprise, he told us he had been expecting that man and would be glad to see him.

When Benjamin Ben-Eliezer came, the next day or the day after, he was given a courteous reception. But, still more surprising, my father refused to let him have the famous notebook he had come to get.

"We need it," Ben-Eliezer said. "The names in it may help the investigation into Hugo's death."

But, with a strangely wary reaction — because, he told us, he didn't want our name to be involved in something that didn't seem quite "open and aboveboard," and probably also for more obscure reasons that didn't appear to me till later — my father shook his head, said that the notebook was unimportant, that it was a family keepsake, and that anyway he had mislaid it. My father was not a decisive man. The only decision he had ever really made was to ask my mother to marry him. So I was deeply impressed by his determination to preserve Hugo's memory, and perhaps his secret, even to the detriment of the murder investigation and the vitally important search for the truth.

Benjamin Ben-Eliezer came back to try again, several days in a row. My father was adamant. Ben-Eliezer finally went away for good, disheartened and rather angry.

His persistence intrigued me as much as my father's refusal. What was in that notebook? Why were they both so determined? Why did my father cling to that little black object so stubbornly? To me, it now had an aura of heady mystery, but I failed in all my efforts to find out more about it. Then, as the years passed and that shadowy episode gradually receded into the past, I finally lost interest in it altogether.

Does that mean I stopped thinking about Hugo? No, because that was also the time when I began carrying on my struggle for peace. I went to the United States, the Soviet Union, Israel and the Arab countries. Wherever I went, I spoke in the same terms, I upheld the ancient prophetic values of the Word and the Law against new waves of violence and hatred. And, to my amazement, people talked to me about Hugo wherever I went. "You remind me of Hugo," I was told in several different languages. "You talk like Hugo." "You're as unrealistic as your cousin Hugo." Wherever I went, he seemed to have been there before me, and I kept meeting his memory or his ghost. He was like a father or a brother whose shadow was always there, no matter what I did or said. And so, instead of moving me further away from him, the passing of time and the course of my life brought me closer to him, though I didn't yet fully realize what it all meant.

During that same time I also kept encountering the shadow of another man, this one quite alive: Hidar Assadi. He too gave me the strange impression that I could scarcely take a step without running into him. Not that he was politically active in the same direction as I was, or shared my pressing concern for peace, but he seemed to be carrying on a kind of investigation into my cousin's death. What was he looking for, exactly? Was he working for the Soviets? The Palestinians? In any case, he was obviously trying to find out something. Arab leaders talked to me about him; so did Israeli doves, and my Soviet cousins, including Olga, of course. Whenever I went to Moscow, he was in the Middle East, and whenever I went to Beirut, he had just gone back to Moscow. That game of hide-and-seek exasperated me, but also greatly intrigued me.

While I was briefly staying in Buenos Aires in 1964, Doña Regina, my Argentinian aunt, told me something that had a strong effect on me. In his youth, she said, Hugo had been a very handsome man. He caught the attention of every woman who saw him, and there was no woman he couldn't seduce if he put his mind to it. Even my mother, my own mother, had been engaged to him. It was he, according to my aunt, who introduced my mother to his cousin Salomon. And Salomon took advantage of Hugo's frequent trips to Berlin to court her and ask her to marry him. It was a commonplace story, actually, yet it troubled me deeply. So Hugo might have been my father, I thought. Really my father. . . . That idea gradually took root in my mind and became an obsession. And so, even though his death, his last days and his whole life were steadily fading into the misty distance, I came to see Hugo as a prodigious being who accompanied me nearly everywhere.

The police investigation had come to a standstill. Some obscure bureaucrat in Tel Aviv had probably filed the case under one of those administrative classifications that are like second gravestones. But in my mind Hugo was still alive. And although I hadn't yet bothered to look for or try to guess the reason, he was becoming my most familiar companion.

5

BEIRUT

Hidar Assadi

FEBRUARY 1967

It was a year when winter had ended especially early in Beirut. Hidar was glad to be there again, happy to be back in the Middle East, with its light blue and saffron-yellow tints, its white sun, its thick smells spread out like tablecloths, and the sound of muezzins calling the faithful to prayer. His happiness, however, was darkened by his separation from Olga, whom he had had to leave in Moscow.

It was 1967: they had been together for more than six years. That exquisite woman was both his joy and his guilty conscience. What could be more exciting than contemplating himself in a pair of amorous eyes? What could compare to the satisfaction of having free access to a milky-white body, modest and wanton at the same time, that often even seemed to take pleasure in the gentle tortures he inflicted on it? Where was she? What was she thinking about? What did their relationship mean to her? She seemed to accept the situation cheerfully, but in her gray eyes he sometimes saw a tinge of bitterness that was close to reproach. Olga was not a *kulturnyi chelovek*, a "person of culture." She was natural, spontaneous, almost guileless, and she wasn't very good at hiding her disappointment or melancholy.

Each time he came back to Moscow, Hidar hurried to her parents' apartment on Kazakov Street, and she always seemed to be expecting him. He didn't doubt that she had other lovers, but at least he was sure she cared more for him than for anyone else. During his last stay, they had seldom been alone together. In his apartment, at the hospital or at his political meetings, there had always been a crowd around them. And just before he left, when he was looking forward so much to spending the night with her, an argument had wrecked that plan. Once again it was an argument about Israel. Israel and Judaism had become their main topic of conversation, and the main stumbling block in their relationship. That evening, he reproached her for her sudden interest in her Jewish background and said he didn't understand why she was paying so much attention to it when she had always ignored it before. They began exchanging heated words and the evening was ruined.

The truth was that Hidar had always been fascinated by the Jews. As he watched them going about their everyday lives, he had the feeling that they formed a people of brothers and sisters, all fathered by the same man and sharing the same flesh. Even the Muslims called themselves children of Abraham. Yes, but that single line of descent seemed to foster among the Jews a strange solidarity and extraordinary networks of mutual aid. And then there was their continued existence. Instead of disappearing like the peoples of Greece and Italy, of Sparta, Athens and Rome, who came long after them, they still survived. The Law to which they were attached, their sacred texts and the rites they practiced, had kept them alive as a people. Their durability was irritating to others. And disconcerting. To Hidar, the Jews were both more transparent and more opaque than anyone else. Anyone could know their history, their ways, their dreams and desires, but without understanding the mystery of their endurance. Maybe it was their perpetuity, even more than their supposed love of money, that aroused the hostility of others.

Was Hidar an anti-Semite? He had read Shakespeare and Balzac, Dostoyevsky and Dickens, the Roman historians, the Koran and Marx. He knew all those writings that ranted about the sordid, hooknosed old Jew who sought his gold in the filthy refuse of humanity. And, to tell the truth, he wasn't always unresponsive to such ideas. Jews produced feelings in him that fed on each other even though he knew they were contradictory: admiration and envy, desire and hatred. . . . Nevertheless, he resisted being influenced by an ideology that he knew to be pernicious. It was responsible for Zionism and, worse, anti-Semitism was its alibi, its daily nourishment. He was privately inclined to believe that Olga's interest in Israel had begun when that letter came from Paris. It had been foolish of him to tell her about Hugo, but how could he have guessed that Hugo would be killed one day on a road in Israel? His father, Marwan, used to say, "When something happens to you and you didn't make it happen, it's destiny." But destiny didn't explain everything.

Hidar tried once again to understand what had really happened. He had sincerely liked Hugo. And even when he didn't approve of what he wanted to do, his friend's enthusiasm was so contagious that he always ended up helping him. When, in 1960, Hidar gave in once more to Hugo's request, he knew, he sensed, that he was putting himself in danger. Then why did he give in? Had he again succumbed to Hugo's charm? Did he believe that the danger he foresaw would be averted? Or did he secretly want his friend to die? Hugo had been dead for six years now, and that question still tormented Hidar.

In those days, Hugo had been trying to find someone who could act as his contact with the ANM, the Arab Nationalist Movement. With the backing of Israel Beer, David Ben-Gurion's personal adviser, he wanted to persuade the Palestinians to agree to a dialogue with their adversaries. When he introduced Hugo to his friends during a meeting in Beirut, Hidar had known that he was making him take too great a risk. The danger came first from the Soviets, who considered that the ANM should be supported not as a means of promoting a dialogue with Israel, but as a tool for applying pressure in the Middle East, and then from the Palestinians, who regarded any form of dialogue with Israel as a betrayal of the Arab cause. And both the Soviets and the Palestinians felt that killing was justified in the case of a pro-Israeli Jew who might meet with ANM leaders and talk about it publicly.

Hidar had always known that a mistake was especially dangerous if you didn't know it was a mistake, but even more dangerous if you considered it an act of virtue. He now realized that he didn't really know about Hugo's activities. Why had he wanted that meeting so much? What had been said, exactly, in that mysterious house in Beirut, near the airport, and later, in the days and weeks that followed? His only certainty was that the Israeli secret services were investigating Hugo's death and that, apparently without knowing about those secret meetings, they vaguely attributed it to his friendship with Hidar. That idea worried Hidar because, if it was true, it meant that he had also been a target of the attack against Hugo.

He suddenly remembered his car being blown up in Beirut a few months earlier. The explosion might have killed him if he hadn't decided at the last moment to walk to the hotel. He still didn't know who had planted the bomb, or why. Had they wanted to kill him, or only threaten him? It didn't matter. The people who killed Hugo had their eyes on him. If only he knew their nationality! Soviet? Palestinian? It was in the hope of finding it out that this morning, for the hundredth time, he had decided to take advantage of a meeting of ANM leaders to talk bluntly and openly with his friends.

But, like a man who, on the way to a first amorous rendezvous with the woman he loves, trembles, becomes frightened and tries to think of a diversion, a reason for delay, or maybe an excuse, Hidar became more and more inclined to see his plan as stupid and dangerous as he approached the Hotel Alcazar, where the meeting was to take place. What if one of the men present was involved in Hugo's death? If he spoke to his friends as he had decided to do, maybe he would expose himself to a danger he could otherwise have avoided. He was gripped by agitation and uncertainty.

By the time he had arrived at the Alcazar and embraced George Habash, Wadi Hadad, Abdel Karim Hamad and Akhmed Yamani, who were gathered in a windowless oval room full of ottomans and thick Persian rugs, he had changed his mind: he would say nothing. So much the worse for honor! Stavrogin, his favorite fictional character, had claimed "the right to dishonor" for himself and his distant descendants.

Hidar Assadi was a refined man. He still had a thorough grounding in bourgeois culture from his studies at the Sorbonne and later at the American University in Beirut (where he had met George Habash and Wadi Hadad). But he was also a formidable "fighter in the shadows," a secret agent whose intuition had been sharpened by long years of undercover activity, and he had known as soon as he stepped into the room that he was in danger and that saying one word too many could be disastrous for him. His friends? Yes, his friends. But they could become his most ferocious adversaries at any moment. Not a word, no. He mustn't let down his guard for one second. He automatically felt to make sure his pistol was in its usual place in the inside pocket of his jacket. If it hadn't been for his rather stiff walk, caused by a childhood polio attack that had left one leg somewhat withered, he might almost have made an impressive entrance.

The meeting would last two hours, he was told at the outset. That was a little short, of course, considering the status of the participants, but Habash was about to leave for Damascus and had asked that matters be handled quickly. Wadi Hadad, who had arrived the day before from Aden, where he had set up a camp for training future fedayeen in urban guerrilla warfare, began by congratulating Hidar: the weapons he had just obtained from Czechoslovakia and Bulgaria, on orders from Moscow, were perfect. Then he described the activities of the three guerrilla groups affiliated with the ANM: the Heroes of the Return, Youth for Revenge and the Palestine Liberation Front. And finally, with an innocent expression, he made a barbed remark about Hidar's Jewish acquaintances.

Hidar shuddered. He knew Wadi's tendency to think like a policeman, his efficiency, and his unscrupulousness. He chose to defend himself, and do it with his head held high.

"We need to know the Jews, we need to know their history, their community organizations and the means they've used to create a state. During the war, Stalin advised the Soviets to learn the Germans' language, history, and culture. You can't win a war against someone you don't know."

Habash nodded in agreement.

"Hidar is right," he said, running his thumb over his mustache, as he often did. "It would be good for our militants to know Hebrew. Reading the Israeli newspapers is the best way to find out what's going on in Tel Aviv."

"We should go farther than that," Hidar said. "We should copy the organization of the Zionist movement before the war, with its conferences, collections, parliament, leadership, army, and shock troops. What was good for them may be good for us. I think it's time for you to leave the ANM and create a purely Palestinian movement."

Habash thought this was a good idea. Abdel Karim Hamad thought it was premature but interesting. After a few minutes of debate, they agreed on a middle course: to create, very quickly, a special group for "the Palestine region." That was all Hidar wanted. Filled with the feeling of power that came from a successful manipulation, a feeling he knew well, he couldn't hold back a faint smile of triumph.

"Are you thinking of something?" asked Wadi Hadad, suddenly wary.

Hidar had never before felt such mistrust and tension in one of their meetings. All at once he had the idea that these men were his enemies, and that his assassin — who could say? — might even be among them. He dismissed that idea and decided to exclude Hugo's bothersome ghost from his thoughts. And the discussion resumed as if nothing had happened, this time on the question of what attitude should be taken toward using non-Arab fighters in the struggle against Zionism. Since it was a question that seemed unlikely to be given a unanimous answer, further consideration of it was postponed.

At nightfall, Hidar went to his usual table at a café called La Grotte aux Pigeons, from where he could contemplate the sea. Did the sea look the same when it was seen from Tel Aviv? Would he know Tel Aviv someday, and Jaffa, and Haifa? He sighed and ordered an arrack. He had a little time to kill before his contact at the Soviet embassy was supposed to meet him at the café. Wadi Hadad had said that war between the Arabs and Israel was imminent. What did he mean? Where did he get his information? Hidar knew that the Soviet Union was preparing Nasser's army for war, but he also knew that Soviet specialists judged Egypt to be incapable of successfully fighting against a perfectly trained army that had mastered the most sophisticated methods of warfare.

He was startled by a muezzin's sudden call to El Leil, the last prayer of the day. A glance at his watch told him that his contact was late. And while the waves fell back into the sea, one by one, as though tired of climbing up the shore, he thought of Olga again. Doubt and desire. Worry and nostalgia. Yes, he loved Olga. When would he see her again?

6

ISRAEL

War

MAY 5, 1967

Mordecai was driving cautiously. The road from Dafneh to Hagesharim was uneven. It threaded its way between boulders, climbed a slope studded with centuries-old oaks, then came back to head for artificial lakes in a straight line.

"Faster, Papa, faster!" Arieh said impatiently.

"Haste makes waste, my son," Mordecai replied, smiling.

"But what about the game, Papa? The game!"

Arieh had brown hair and a matte complexion, and although he was only fourteen he was already built like a man. He belonged to the soccer team of his kibbutz, which was going to play the Hagesharim team today. Having missed the bus that his teammates had taken, he had persuaded his father to drive him to the stadium in his old Ford pickup. Arieh was always late, and yet always so impatient!

Mordecai turned on the radio, hoping it would calm his son. They heard the Beatles and the Rolling Stones singing popular songs from the year before. Then suddenly there was silence. Mordecai was cursing the kibbutz's electrician for having done a bad job of repairing the radio when a quietly dramatic voice, obviously not the voice

of the charming disk jockey who had been talking a short time earlier, announced, "Esther is sick and is waiting at the kibbutz. David
is waiting for his father. David is waiting for his father."

"What kind of crap is that?" the boy exclaimed. "It sounds like
they've gone crazy!"

"We're at war, Arieh."

"At war?"

Arieh looked at his father and saw that his face had changed
color.

"Yes. Those are coded messages. Everyone's being mobilized."

"Including you?"

"Including me."

"And the game. . . . Will it still be played?"

"After the war, Arieh, after the war."

Mordecai turned the truck around at the next crossroads.

"Are you going to fight, Papa?" Arieh asked gravely.

"Of course. Like everyone else."

"But . . ."

Mordecai sensed the great confusion of his son's feelings. But,
with his eyes fixed on the road, his mind already elsewhere and his
heart pounding, he had neither the desire nor the strength to talk
about the war. He simply said, "Don't be afraid. *Qui non si muore
mai.*"

"What does that mean?"

"It's Italian and it means, 'Here, no one ever dies.'"

"Where's 'here'?"

"In Israel."

"What are you talking about?" Arieh said, and tears came into
his eyes.

Mordecai had to drive along the road between Qiryat Shemona
and Mount Hermon. It was already clogged with traffic. In milk
trucks, laundry and butchers' vans, open trucks and private cars,
including some ancient rattletraps barely able to move, members of
the kibbutzim on the Golan Plateau, having been alerted in their
workplaces — fields, forests, fishponds — were answering the call
for mobilization.

For several weeks there had been bellicose outcries from Israel's
borders, constant imprecations against the Jewish state, that "enemy

of the human race." To the surprise of the Egyptians themselves, President Nasser had massed his troops at the edge of the Negev, expelled the United Nations troops from the Gaza Strip and Sharm al-Sheikh, and closed the Strait of Tiran to Israeli ships. Syria had put its troops on the alert, and the Palestinians' representative, Akhmed Shukeiry, speaking to a wildly cheering crowd in the main public square of the city of Gaza, had promised to throw the Jews into the sea.

This wasn't, of course, the first time the Arabs had been stirred up. And while Mordecai and Arieh were listening to the mysterious radio message, contradictory reports were still circulating about the real reasons for that Arab activity. But Jews in the Diaspora were worried, perhaps more worried than the Jews in Israel. Maybe because they knew from experience that when there were two versions of a danger, the worse one nearly always won out. Maybe also because for weeks the Western media had been presenting highly alarming assessments of the situation: apocalyptic television commentaries, whole pages in newspapers where it was emphatically demonstrated that the ratio of forces was strongly unfavorable to Israel, maps of the Middle East in which Israel's tragic encirclement was vividly shown. . . .

Sidney was apprehensive that morning. Sitting on the unmade bed and reading one of the many articles in the *New York Times* showing that the Israeli army could never withstand a combined attack by all Arab forces, he felt terribly powerless.

"Isn't it true that America won't let Israel die?" asked his son Richard, who had just come into the room and already knew the news.

"I don't know," Sidney answered. "Remember what I told you one day? During the war, America didn't do much for the Jews in Poland."

"But *we're* Americans, and we won't let Israel lose the war!"

"I'm counting much more on the Israeli army than on us, Dick."

Richard was about to answer when the phone rang.

As in all Jewish homes during the last two weeks, the phone had been constantly ringing in Sidney's apartment. Brothers, uncles and cousins in Canada and California had been calling to encourage each other or, more often, to share and discuss a piece of news reported on television or in a newspaper. Even the most indifferent, the most assimilated, were beginning to be afraid. This time it was Larry, Sidney's brother in Los Angeles: he had just learned that two Soviet submarines had gone through the Bosporus, heading into the Mediterranean. Sidney answered him as he did the others. Ludicrous rumors were mingled with serious news reports; they discussed them all, sometimes on the verge of panic.

When he came back home later that day, he had two surprises. First, apparently gripped by such strong emotion that she couldn't say anything, Marjory led him to Marilyn's room. It was a simple, attractive room with drawn curtains, furnished with a little table, a bed, a chest for toys and a pink lamp that illuminated the childish drawings thumbtacked to the walls. Marilyn was asleep. Her lips were pale and there were beads of sweat on her face, and when Sidney leaned down to kiss her on the forehead he felt that it was hot.

"Richard went out to collect money for the Israeli army," Marjory said, lowering her voice, "and Marilyn wanted to go to Israel. She was crushed when I told her it was impossible, that a six-year-old girl couldn't be a real soldier. She cried for two hours and fell asleep just a little while ago."

Then came the second surprise: when he turned on the television, he saw Marshal Grechko, the Soviet chief of staff, threatening Israel with military intervention. Marilyn . . . Israel . . . it was all mixed up together in Sidney's poor head. For the first time in a long time he found himself pondering the question his ancestors had tirelessly asked each other for centuries: What does it mean, exactly, to be a Jew?

7

MOSCOW

War in the Family

MAY 1967

Rebroadcast on Soviet television, Grechko's speech infuriated Rachel Lerner.

"How can he lie like that? Who can believe that three million Jews are threatening a hundred million Arabs? It's like hearing Hitler all over again, when he proclaimed that half a million German Jews were threatening sixty million Aryans! Won't we ever be finished with this? Does history have to repeat itself?"

It was Sunday. The whole family had gathered in Rachel and Aron's apartment on Kazakov Street. Olga was there, of course, and so were Sasha, his wife Sonia and their two children. Like the good grandmother she was, Rachel had made tea and put cookies on a tray. But she was so angry and nervous that she filled the cups till they overflowed.

"Calm down, Rachel," Aron said. "You know it's not good for you to get all worked up like that."

"How can you keep from getting worked up? How can you be so unexcitable? You saw, you heard what he said!"

Sasha laughed sarcastically.

"Mama is incredible. To her, everything the Jews do is sacred.

If the Israelis start building concentration camps for Arabs tomorrow, she'll tell us they're nursery schools. It's laughable."

Aron leaped to his feet. His eyes had darkened, a sign of great anger, and the wrinkles at the corners of his lips had deepened a little more.

"How can you say such things about your mother? And where did you learn to talk like that? Listening to people like you is almost enough to make me become a Zionist!"

"Go ahead, do it," his son said with growing insolence. "Become a Zionist, since it's what you dream of doing. The Soviet Union doesn't need citizens like you."

Aron turned pale and trembled from head to foot. His eyes were blurred by tears.

"My poor boy," he said in a softer voice. "What have you turned into? Do you realize what you're saying? You talk like a kapo in a concentration camp. . . . Don't you know that your mother came here to take part in the Revolution? That's right, the *Revolution!* She hoped to see happiness for everyone, a classless society. She wanted to see you and your sister living someday in the society of our dreams. And what happened? You know what happened."

Sasha made no reply.

"Do you want us to go to Israel?" Aron continued. "Why? Because we embarrass you? Because you're now ashamed of what we've done and what we've dreamed of? Oh, my son . . . it makes me feel like crying to see you this way, mixed up with those people, consumed with personal ambition, like them. And soon you'll be corrupt. . . ."

Rachel seemed to have aged ten years in a few minutes. She vainly tried to intervene between the two men, to make them stop talking. Without really believing it would do any good, she warned them about the neighbors, and the danger of informers, and how risky it could be to talk about such things.

"Let them go on," Olga said, almost as upset as her mother. "Maybe we'll finally find out what's really in Sasha's head."

"You and the Arabs . . . ," Sasha said in a dangerously calm voice. "Would you like me to tell our parents everything I know?" Then he shrugged and turned to his children, Natasha and Boris, who were beginning to cry. "Come, my little pigeons, it's time to go home."

Sonia took a step toward Aron and stopped. The children made a move to go over and kiss him goodbye, then turned to their father and also stopped. Aron looked at them sadly. He knew that a break had just occurred in the tacit understanding that till now had governed the life of the family.

That night Rachel couldn't sleep. At three in the morning, exhausted, her nerves on edge, she got up, tiptoed into the living room, and took out a book, then another. What book could soothe the frightful anguish her son had aroused in her?

At dawn she remembered that Vasily Slepakov, one of her husband's colleagues, would soon go to Argentina for a conference on pre-Columbian culture. Maybe he would be willing to deliver a message to the family there. For some reason, the thought reassured and excited her. She took paper and pen and began writing a long letter to Doña Regina in the Yiddish she used so well. She didn't know Regina and her husband — or, for that matter, any of her cousins in the United States, Israel, and France. Six years had gone by since Hugo's death, but suddenly she thought of him and told herself that all of them, scattered over the world, were his cousins. This idea amused her, then calmed her. And all at once it gave her a feeling of power and joy that she hadn't savored for years.

8

MOSCOW

Rachel Lerner's Letter

MAY 6, 1967

Dear Family,

I do not know you, but you are my cousins and you are also the only Jews whose specific existence I know of outside Europe and the Soviet Union. Our brothers and sisters in Israel are in danger and I need to share my anxiety with people who feel it as I do, for the same reasons. My husband Aron, who teaches ancient Greek and Roman civilization at the university here, likes to quote something Sophocles said: that relatives are the only witnesses capable of sharing a relative's suffering. I am sure that at this time we too can count only on our relatives.

Here the newspapers, television, and radio constantly turn out anti-Israeli propaganda. I and a few of my friends have formed a group to study Hebrew. Aron does not know about it. I think he would be opposed to it if he did. The friend in whose apartment we meet once a week created an uproar where he works when he announced that he was in favor of Israel. Most people he knew immediately began to treat him like an outcast. They turned away from him as people used to turn away from lepers. A few brave and loyal friends, Russians as well as Jews, still go to visit him at his home nearly every evening. But that is very rash. KGB spies are always watching his door. There are surely microphones that record everything said in his apartment. So his guests have nothing to do but drink, and they drink to Israel's health. I am, of course, one of those guests.

Anti-Semitism has never disappeared in the Soviet Union, but it has taken different forms. In Stalin's time, for example, there were Jews among the police, and the government had the nerve to use that fact to hold us responsible for the reign of terror. We now know how insane that man was. His insanity wiped out a whole culture: Yiddish culture. How often I have wondered what gave us the strength to fight, to risk everything! I can find no answer to that question. I do not even look for one. After the disappointment of my youth, I tried to hold fast to Jewish tradition, as if I were clinging to a life raft. I was immediately pushed into the rapids, driven by the force of the current, crashing into stones, but overjoyed at the feeling I was experiencing for the first time: the feeling of real freedom!

Shall I tell you more, my dear cousins? That Jewish awakening first manifested itself as a form of protest. National feeling also played an important part, because the government's anti-Semitism became more active when the State of Israel was born in 1948. We were offended and outraged by its propaganda attacks against Israel, which were crude and monstrous in their hatred and hypocrisy. That is why there was a kind of divorce between us and the country in which we lived. One example: when I saw that the Soviet Union was threatening Israel more and more seriously, I imagined the possibility of a war and how terrible it would be for Aron, who was a reserve officer, if in spite of himself he had to fight against Israel and kill Jews who had miraculously escaped the Nazis' efforts to exterminate them. To me, that was a horrifying prospect. I wanted us to have the choice of being among the defenders of Israel, rather than involuntary accomplices of her enemies.

For my son Sasha, that question does not arise: he is a Soviet and a Communist. My daughter Olga is changing. Since the death of our cousin Hugo, who was killed by a group of Palestinians on a road in Israel (I assume you learned of it at the time), her interest in Israel and Jewish history has steadily increased. She is on close terms with an Arab. His name is Hidar. I do not know what he does, but he is often in the Middle East. He knew Hugo in Tunisia. From a few remarks that Hidar has made, I gather that they were involved in political activities together. Always politics. . . . Was Hugo working for peace? Did he arrange meetings between Arabs and Jews? Such behavior deserves respect but, in this world of corruption, violence and evil, it is as dangerous as war.

If only we were allowed to go and help our brothers and sisters in Israel!

It is true that the creation of the State of Israel has made problems for us, but, after the massacres that killed so many of us, it has also given us back our self-esteem.

One of Aron's colleagues is going to a conference in Buenos Aires. I will ask him to take this letter. Will he do it? I think so. His name is Vasily Slepakov. He is not Jewish. He is an honorable man. I know that Regina and her husband are Communists and that they fled Poland at the time of the counterrevolution. I will tell Vasily Slepakov that, and I hope it will put his mind at ease.

I will be grateful to you if you can tell our Israeli cousin, Mordecai, of our solidarity with Israel.

I hope that we will see each other someday. In Jerusalem.

Rachel Lerner (Halter)

9

BUENOS AIRES

An Aborted Visit

MAY 1967

As soon as she was told that Vasily Slepakov would come to visit, Doña Regina showed signs of intense excitement. A professor! And a *Soviet* professor to boot! There could be no better proof that there were scholars and scientists in the Soviet Union, that they were free to travel as they pleased, and that, here too, imperialist propaganda was nothing but a pack of lies! Those who talked about the land of the Soviets as if it were a vast prison — and there were such people even in her family — would have to eat their words. She was jubilant, and at least as excited as she was on the day before Passover. And when Doña Regina was excited, God knows it showed!

She was now busy as a bee, making preparations for the visit: cleaning the house thoroughly, dusting the big portrait of Stalin prominently displayed in the entrance hall, hastily rereading a few classics from which it would be good to quote at the right time. Not even Don Israel escaped the preparations. He was told to change his trousers, clean his suspenders and learn a few words of Russian. The most important activity, however, was in the kitchen, where Doña Regina spent two days making her best cookies.

"Who's going to eat all the cookies you're making, Grandmother?" Anna Maria asked affectionately. "The Russian is just coming to bring you a letter from Moscow."

"It doesn't matter," Doña Regina answered imperturbably. "I'll give him a package for cousin Rachel."

"So you think the Russians have nothing to eat?" Anna Maria said with a falsely innocent expression, knowing perfectly well that she would cut her to the quick.

"No, of course I don't! That's anti-Soviet propaganda! I forbid you to say such things!"

The great day came. The whole family gathered to greet the visitor. Don Israel had put on a new pair of suspenders. Doña Regina wore a lace-trimmed red taffeta dress that rustled when she moved; this was the first time she had worn it in years, and it was so tight she could hardly breathe. Her cookies were heaped up on plates. Her whole house smelled of delicacies and furniture polish. And the absurd fact was that Slepakov never arrived; instead, a lowly messenger from the Soviet embassy came to deliver the famous letter. Shame and despair! Doña Regina scarcely dared to look at her children. Don Israel took refuge in his room, convinced that he was going to be blamed for everything. And the cookies went back to the kitchen.

"It's all right," Doña Regina said. "Since he's not going to eat them, we'll eat them ourselves. We're good enough for that, don't you think?"

To preserve her honor, if not to save face, she sent for her husband, handed him the letter and asked him to translate it aloud. Then, finding herself on familiar ground, she began commenting on the Soviet cousins' "political line."

"I really don't understand our cousin Rachel. Why isn't it possible to be pro-Soviet and pro-Israeli at the same time? We, for example . . ."

"But you're not in the Soviet Union!" Anna Maria said, smiling and spoiling the effect of what her grandmother was about to say.

"You're a leftist and you're anti-Soviet," said her father, Martín, who never missed a chance to catch her in a mistake or an inconsistency, in the hope that she would give up her revolutionary commitments. "With your friends, you're anti-Zionist and you're not worried about Israel."

"Don't strain your brain, Papa. You don't understand anything about dialectical contradiction. As for Israel, that's more complicated. . . . It's a fact that Israel has a powerful proletariat that maintains the class struggle, while the countries threatening it are really reactionary, but —"

Doña Regina had left the room; she now came back with a teapot and cups.

"The Soviet Union is reactionary? You don't know what you're saying, my child. I was there during the Revolution. Before, the people lived in wretched poverty, and I saw, with my own eyes, the revolutionary transformations that were made in their lives."

As always, Martín was both amused and irritated to see that no one in the family really listened to anyone. To change the subject, he announced a piece of news that meant a great deal to him:

"Cousin Mordecai, from Kibbutz Dafneh, will probably come next year to teach Hebrew at the Sholem Aleichem school."

"If he survives the war," remarked Miguel, his younger brother.

"Don't talk nonsense," Doña Regina said, and spat on the floor three times to ward off bad luck.

There was a silence.

"All right," Miguel finally said, "who will volunteer to make copies of Rachel's letter and send them to the rest of the family?"

PARIS, JUNE 1967

It was the end of the day. I was in my car, stuck in a traffic jam. A radio news broadcast announced a sharp rise in the tension of the already tense Middle Eastern situation. President Lyndon Johnson had ordered an aircraft carrier into the Red Sea, and two more Soviet submarines had gone through the Bosporus and into the Mediterranean. War seemed imminent. Egyptian divisions were advancing in the Sinai. Israel was mobilizing. Arab heads of state were making bellicose declarations, and Akhmed Shukeiry, the Palestinians' leader, was promising to drive the Jews into the sea — or at least those who survived the Arab offensive.

War! Explosions, flames, screams, corpses — I had the feeling that my nightmare would never end, and that my generation still hadn't paid the strange tribute it owed to tragedy and horror. If that war broke out, what would my position be? I had nothing against the Arabs, of course, no hostility at all, and I felt that the muezzins' calls in Kokand, in Soviet Central Asia, where my parents and I had taken refuge after escaping from Warsaw, had made them close to me forever. But I couldn't accept the idea of Israel's destruction. It was inconceivable to me that so much effort and hope, and such a rebirth after so many ordeals, could be annihilated.

I had had no experience of the Spanish Civil War. I was born too late for that. I was always stirred by stories of it, partly because of the arid mountains of Ronda, the scorched browns of Toledo, the Jewish quarter of Córdoba and the poems of Antonio Machado, but especially because of the solidarity that the Spanish Republic aroused all over the world. Tens of thousands of men and women who had never been to Spain went there to die for her. More than twenty years after the Holocaust, Israel's survival deserved that kind of fraternal devotion.

For the moment, I still had my faith in the power of words and discussion. It seemed to me that we could ward off the impending disaster by putting pressure on both sides to stop fighting and recognize each other. Full of fervor and impatience, I got in touch with friends and acquaintances who shared my concern. That evening there were about seventy of us in my studio. We talked endlessly about ways to prevent the outbreak of war that was being predicted everywhere. It happened that only a few hours earlier I had received a photocopy of Rachel's letter from Moscow via Buenos Aires. I read it to the gathering at the end of our discussion. We were all politically minded and we had just had a truly political debate, but the fear we felt was the deep fear of family members belonging to the same culture and attached to the same memory.

The next day, I went to my parents to see what their feelings were.

"I understand Rachel," my father said after reading the letter. "If I were younger, I'd go off and fight for Israel."

"They don't need us there," I told him. "Israel has a powerful, well-organized army. All we'd do would be to put some disorder into it."

"Even so . . . you can't understand. . . . When Hugo warned us about the Nazi danger in 1939, we didn't believe him. When he advised us either to leave or get organized for fighting, we did neither. And you know what happened. . . ."

"But the Jews in Israel are organized and the Arabs aren't Nazis."

"They talk like Nazis," my father said. "Have you heard Shukiery and Nasser? You don't talk about fire in front of a man who's just escaped from a burning house." He took out Hugo's little notebook, which he had carried in his pocket for the last six years. "I'm beginning to put the story together again." Then, when I reached out to take the notebook from his hand: "No, no, you know very well . . . this notebook is my affair. . . . I have to go now. They're expecting me at the print shop. But listen to the news."

He turned on the radio. And exactly at that moment, as if the timing were deliberate, an announcer said in a strikingly grave tone, "War has just broken out between Israel and the Arab countries."

10

LEBANON

The Shuf Mountains

JUNE 5, 1967

The old Mercedes bounced along narrow, pothole-infested roads in the violent, desolate, terribly austere landscape of the purple Shuf Mountains. It was June 5, at dawn. For the first time in his long and tumultuous life, Hidar was going into the domain of the Druzes, where he had an appointment with their leader, Kamal Jumblatt — that prodigious patriarch who was said to collect secrets and ruses.

Six miles from Mukhtara, where the Jumblatt family lived, he was stopped by five heavily armed Druzes who demanded to see his papers. Then he was stopped by others, and still others. At the fourth roadblock he had to explain that Kamal Jumblatt was expecting him and that these delays were making him late. It was only after a long discussion and an equally long inspection that they finally let him pass and go on to the Holy of Holies.

There, Kamal Jumblatt reigned. He lorded it over his realm, in the midst of his people. A king whose subjects were his crown, he knew the countless dangers that arise from glory, and the jealousies that fester when a man is obeyed, feared, or even loved. He gleefully watched the helpless fury of his enemies. He had always chosen the right time and place to change adversaries or allies. With his haughty bearing, his air of a great lord defying the centuries and their tumult in that vast pink stone residence, which was like a lair, a palace, an eagle's nest and a glittering labyrinth all at once, he made a powerful impression on Hidar. *This man has nothing in common with Habash or Wadi Hadad,* Hidar thought when the old chief with the manner of both a scholar and a soldier offered him arrack, which he accepted, and hashish, which he declined.

"How do things look in Moscow?" Jumblatt asked bluntly.

"They're looking good. Very good, in fact."

"Brezhnev is consolidating his power?"

"Yes," Hidar said cautiously.

"He's put Grechko at the head of the army and Andropov in command of the KGB. I understand that. But I don't understand why he's pushing Nasser into war. In Nicosia the other day I met Chubakin, the Soviet ambassador to Israel, who tried to convince me that if there's war, Israel will be beaten within twenty-four hours."

"He's exaggerating."

"He's manipulating!"

Jumblatt laughed. A harsh laugh, like the cry of a bird of prey. Then he gestured with his right hand and a water pipe was brought to him. Soon the smell of hashish pleasantly enveloped the two men. Jumblatt took a few puffs before pointing to the valley.

"It's an incredible landscape, isn't it? That was Gustav Flaubert's opinion. Have you read Flaubert? Do you know he visited Lebanon in 1850? He was a good judge of landscapes, believe me."

A little surprised by the turn the conversation had taken, Hidar glanced at his host and saw a hard yet amused look in his eyes. He felt it was time to bring up the reason for his visit.

"If you received an invitation from the Committee for Solidarity with the Peoples of Africa and Asia, would you be willing to go to Moscow?"

"Have you been instructed to invite me?"

"I've been instructed to ask you the question."

They heard the call of a muezzin in the distance. Without answering, Jumblatt stood up.

"I'd like to introduce you to someone."

While he waited, Hidar again admired the sunrise behind the

mountains and the subtle play of colors over the crags. He didn't hear Jumblatt come back.

"This is Samirah," Jumblatt said. "She's a young Palestinian who's ready for anything. She'll be perfect for your political actions. Introduce her to your friends."

Hidar looked at the young woman. Her khaki uniform revealed the shape of an attractive body. Her dark eyes shone with surprising intensity.

"She's going to Beirut," Jumblatt went on. "Can you take her with you?" And he continued without waiting for an answer, "I've asked to have food brought to us. Mountain air whets the appetite and you haven't had breakfast."

Samirah left them without having said a word.

"She's a strange woman," Hidar remarked.

"A strong woman," Jumblatt replied. He turned his chair so that he could see Hidar better. "And what about you? Are you doing all right?"

"Yes, of course. Why?"

"Have you found out who killed your friend in Israel?"

Hidar was so startled by the question that he was momentarily speechless.

"When a man can't protect a friend," Jumblatt said quietly, "he loses some of his influence; when he can't avenge him, he loses his friends. I'm afraid your friend may have died for nothing."

"Oh?" Hidar said. Then, deciding that the old man was treating him too condescendingly and that it would be good to make him a little unsettled too, he asked, "And how is your son Walid?"

Two servants brought in a low table and put it down between Hidar and Jumblatt. Three others began serving. Jumblatt tore off a piece of pita bread and dipped it into a dish of mashed chickpeas. Only then did he answer, taking his time, "My son Walid is quite well, thank you. He chases after women and he drinks. He lacks culture. An eagle should be able to fly over the valley."

"Doesn't he know that?"

"Maybe. But he can't appreciate the beauty of the valley." Jumblatt leaned toward Hidar. "You catch birds with birds. There's a man who knows Hugo Halter's activities well. In a way, he was Halter's confidential Arab. His name is Jemil al-Okby. He's a doctor, and head of the Gaza hospital. I'd be willing to bet a gold water pipe that he has some very specific ideas about your Jewish friend's death."

An armed man burst into the room. Jumblatt remained perfectly placid. The man went up to him, kissed his hand and whispered a few words in his ear. The patriarch stood up.

"Come and listen to the radio," he said to Hidar while other armed men came in.

A few moments later they all went into a big room with a gray marble floor. On the radio, Oum Kalsoum was singing, "Slaughter the Jews! Slaughter!" Then suddenly Nasser's voice rang out: "The eyes of the world are on us in our glorious war against Israel's imperialistic aggression on the soul of our country. . . . Our holy war to preserve the rights of the Arab nation . . . reconquer the stolen land of Palestine. . . . Victory will soon be ours."

And Hidar thought, *What a fool!*

PARIS, JULY 1967

As everyone knows, Israel won the war in six days. And I lost my father just a week later. Did he succumb to too much emotion, to an unbearable anxiety that was suddenly added to a whole lifetime of anxiety? Probably. In any case, his heart failed and he did not live very long after the great fear of the Jewish people.

How many times have I tried to describe his death? How many times have I tried, in dreams or in thought, to remember and imagine it? I have never succeeded. Each time, I only described death in general, as it has been described countless times by others. I succeeded only in adding my note, my version, to the great abstract, collective story that is generic human death, when I was dealing with this man's death, the death of this specific, unique man, and the man who had died was my father. My father's death? A very simple and very complex event, commonplace yet indescribable. At this stage of my narrative, I can do no better than simply give a factual account of that death.

It was at the end of one of those Paris summer days that are so warm in sunlight and so cold in shade. All week long my father had been saying that such days were bad for him. In the streets, traffic was slower than usual, and people less pleasant. The block where we lived, near one of the gates of Paris, seemed more deserted than ever. And when I climbed the stairs, opened the door and briskly called out lighthearted words, as I did every day, thinking they would cheer up my parents, I naturally didn't suspect that anything was wrong. The shadowy entrance hall opened into a strangely illuminated room. My mother was standing in the hall, with the light behind her. Her face was impassive. Without a word, she led me into the bedroom. As I followed her, also without a word, as if I were stubbornly refusing to understand, I straightened a picture on the wall.

My father was lying on his back, motionless. He showed no reaction to my arrival.

"Heart attack," whispered a man beside him, who had been closing a leather case when I came in.

I realized that he was a doctor and that it was serious. I said nothing and didn't even look at his face, but I knew that death was there. Though I was scarcely acquainted with it, I had recognized it immediately. It filled the room, distorting its perspective, infesting and denaturing even the air we breathed there.

My father was pale. He was staring at the ceiling. I looked up too and noticed, I don't know why, some spots caused by dampness.

"The whole apartment needs to be painted," I said unthinkingly.

My father looked at me and smiled. His lips moved silently, then two words came from them:

"What now?"

How can you answer a dying father who asks you, "What now?" I didn't want to answer. I thought I *shouldn't* answer, because I knew he wouldn't die as long as he didn't have an answer. And yet I said, "You'll see, everything will be all right."

I immediately regretted that trite, useless sentence. Unfortunately it was too late. The words had been said, and because I said them I already felt responsible for my father's death.

For the moment, nothing happened. The man who was evidently a doctor was standing behind me and to my right, holding his leather case. I wondered why he was still there. My mother was beside me, to my left. She was looking at my father, smiling. He looked at us and also smiled. He raised his hand, slowly at first, with difficulty, then he pointed imperiously. I turned my head and saw that he was pointing to the dresser facing the bed. Hugo's notebook was on it.

"The notebook?" I asked.

He nodded and let his hand fall. I looked around that room which for a long time had been my bedroom. Part of the wall above the dresser was occupied by a gray picture I had painted soon after we arrived in Paris. Beside it was a photograph of me, the only one that remained from before the war. On the dresser were other photographs: my mother, young and beautiful; my parents and I, skeletonlike, at the end of the war. But beside the photographs was the notebook. I picked it up and took it to my father.

He thanked me with his eyes. Then, putting his pale fingers on the notebook as if he wanted to protect or sanctify it, he began:

"Search, my son. Go on searching. We Halters have always been record-keepers."

Since I could hardly understand him, I leaned closer to him.

"There are so few of us," he continued. "We must never abandon a Jew. Not even when he's dead." He gasped for breath and his voice became fainter. "Six years since Hugo's death. . . . In life, six years is a long time. For memory, it's less than a second." All at once his intonation became normal, his voice stopped quavering and I thought I even saw a little color return to his hollow cheeks. "Go on searching, my son. And when you've found what you're looking for, make it into a book. Remember that history should be written to set down an account, not to prove anything."

Seeing him looking better, I suddenly wanted to know more about Hugo's notebook. I questioned him about his refusal to work with Benjamin Ben-Eliezer and his determination to keep the notebook for himself alone.

"Your secret is your slave," he answered, "but if you let it escape it will become your master."

"Your master?" I asked, disconcerted.

But, strangely, he said no more. His voice died in his throat. His eyes took on a fixed stare. His hand became heavy in mine. I gently put it down on his other arm. And for a long time I again observed the dead room around me.

My mother and I spent the night sitting up with the body. At dawn she dozed off. And that was when I took out the little notebook I had put in my pocket without thinking very much about it. I had just realized that between the Six-Day War and that brief decline into death, I had lost my adolescence.

If I had to generalize, I would say that the days before and after the six days of that war marked the recent history of the Jewish people more deeply than anything else.

The fear that Jews felt then was their first great fear since the Holocaust. Despite the death camps, and their defeat, and the memory of them, it was still possible to threaten us with extermination. Suddenly and without preparation, in the din of battle and a jumble of televised images, the postwar generation, who had believed in normalcy, discovered the unbearable precariousness of their lives. The new Jewish consciousness would be marked by that discovery.

For us Halters, that new awareness, that feeling of the Jews' fragility in the present-day world, dated from Hugo's murder. But our family experience became something like a sign, an omen of a more general experience. Hugo's death and the Six-Day War were mingled in our minds. The quest for peace, to which I was devoting more and more of my time, was combined with my investigation into the causes, mysteries and circumstances of a cousin's death. Everything became interwoven, confused, connected, to the point where I sometimes didn't know which path I was following, within the framework of which search.

In any case, I again found myself on Hugo's trail six years after his death. But this time I had a notebook, my father's last will, and a fierce determination to succeed, along with the lessons I had learned from a war. I could not believe that those lessons were fortuitous.

11

NEW YORK

Sidney's Adventure

JULY 20, 1969

As far as their marriage was concerned, Marjory and Sidney were having smooth sailing. Though she had sometimes shown a few reservations about his Judaism, that was over now. She knew the dates, meanings and rites of the Jewish holidays. She was one of those women who, out of love, yield wholeheartedly to what they assume to be their husbands' secret desires, so much so that it was now her family — her father James, her brother George, her aunts and uncles — who worried. They reproached her for her "Judaization."

"Jesus was a Jew," she persistently pointed out to them, "and so were the Apostles."

But nothing did any good. Each of their meetings turned into an impassioned debate. One side put forward the Jews' forsaking of Jesus; the other countered with the attitude of Pontius Pilate. One side made use of every available argument, but especially the occupied territories; the other, with a mixture of ingenuousness and militant guile, objected, "Occupied? Occupied by whom, exactly?" And, not without concern, Sidney saw his wife, and therefore his children, gradually moving away from one of the sources of their lives. Was he grateful to Marjory for that homage she paid him? Yes and no. He sometimes found himself thinking that it might be making her lose some of her mystery and attraction. Worse, he sometimes wondered if that strangeness, that obscure rebellion, wasn't what attracted him most in her. But all that remained below the surface, scarcely expressed and admitted even to himself. And he remained a model husband, strongly attached to his home. Though he sometimes laughed heartily at his colleagues' coarse jokes, he had always refused to imitate their extramarital affairs.

"Only dead men have no affairs," his brother Larry had once said to him.

"Maybe so," he had answered, "but in that case I must have died of love."

In the summer of 1969, Marjory and the children went to stay with her parents in Vermont. Sidney stayed in New York, leading the life of a peaceful bachelor.

One afternoon in July he left the hospital at about five o'clock. It was a beautiful day. He went down Madison to Fifty-ninth Street, turned right and walked to the Plaza Hotel, then headed down Fifth Avenue, nonchalantly drifting with the crowd. At Fifty-third Street the huge banner in front of the Museum of Modern Art made him suddenly regret that he hadn't gone there in at least two years.

Without knowing exactly why, except that he felt as if he were floating along in the carefree atmosphere of that summer day, he found himself in the lobby of the museum. He bought a ticket and followed the stream of visitors into that world of colors and lines that always made him so happy. A painting. Another. Still another. A swirl of forms that he liked to see all together, without differentiating them very much, like a gigantic bath of beauty made up of dreamlike, indistinct units. It went on until, having gone to one of the upper floors almost without realizing it, he heard a voice murmur close to him:

"*Guernica* . . . don't you recognize *Guernica*?"

No, of course, he didn't "recognize" *Guernica*. But in its place he saw deformed faces, the horse, the lamp — and, as in Hugo's stories, the bombing of Warsaw, shrieking Jews running out of blazing synagogues, weeping mothers searching in the rubble, by the light of kerosene lamps, for the bodies of their buried children. Then that horse again, killed on a street corner by a bomb blast and torn to pieces by a starving crowd.

"It's strong as death," the voice continued, with a slight foreign accent — or rather intonation — that he hadn't noticed at first.

"Yes, I suppose it's strong as death, although that kind of death . . ."

When he turned his head he saw a tall, slender figure in a matching gray skirt and jacket, then a pair of eyes and a smile, smiling eyes. . . .

"Are you a tourist?" he asked, since he had to say something.

"Not quite. I grew up in Detroit, but I've been living in Beirut for many years."

"Oh?" he said, a little surprised by the directness of her tone.

"And you? You like paintings?"

"Yes, I think so."

"I love art. When I come to New York, I never miss an art show. My husband has a collection of old icons, but he also has paintings by Klee and Kandinsky. Do you know their work?"

He nodded.

"Do you like them?"

"Yes, of course. But I prefer Rothko, Sol Lewitt. . . ."

"Are you a collector?"

"Only on a very small scale. It takes a lot of money."

The woman gave him an amused look, then launched into a monologue on art, money and collections. But Sidney didn't follow what she said. Fascinated, he was watching those full, shapely lips opening and closing, and listening to a voice whose sound excited him.

She stopped abruptly, as if she were offended.

"I must be boring you," she said. "Excuse me. I like to talk about those things so much that —"

"No, not at all," Sidney said, coming out of his trance. "You weren't boring me. I was just thinking. . . . I'm really glad to be talking with you." And, to show his interest in her, he asked, "Where are you staying in New York?"

"At the Westbury, at Madison and Sixty-ninth."

"That's not far from where I live," he remarked, becoming dreamy again. "Do you like to walk?"

"Yes, very much."

She said "very much" with a throaty, roguish, openly seductive laugh that made him regret his boldness for a moment. On Madison, near Sixty-second Street, he saw some sidewalk café tables, told himself that Providence must have put them there, and asked her if she would like to have a drink.

"What's your name?" he asked as soon as they had sat down.

"Leila. Leila Chehab."

"You're Arab?"

"Yes. Lebanese. Christian. My grandfather was born in Haifa — you know, in Palestine. He met my grandmother in Beirut. In 1947 my parents emigrated to the United States. I was seven. They settled in Detroit. My father worked for Ford."

Sidney was taken aback by Leila's introduction of herself. Maybe it was completely innocent, but one of her sentences, "My grandfather was born in Haifa — you know, in Palestine," sounded to him like a declaration of war.

"I'm Jewish," he said defiantly. "My grandparents left Poland in 1932, because of the persecutions there. They settled in Winnipeg, Canada. At that same time, their cousins went to live in Palestine. Their grandchildren founded a kibbutz, named Dafneh, in Galilee."

Leila smiled as if she wanted to show him that she understood.

"My grandfather used to say that on Staton Street, where he lived — near Hadar, the Champs-Elysées of Haifa — there were many Jews and that he was on friendly terms with them. I knew Jewish children in Beirut. Tamara, one of my best friends, was Jewish. But in 1947 Palestine stopped being an Arab country. Tamara gained a country and I lost mine."

Leila spoke softly, without passion. She no longer showed any trace of coquettishness or feminine fantasizing.

"What are you talking about?" Sidney exclaimed. "Your friend Tamara was Lebanese, like you. In 1947 there was a division of Palestine, a fair division into two states, one Jewish, the other Arab. The Jews accepted theirs, the Arabs didn't. The Arabs hoped to drive out the Jews and take over the whole territory."

This time Leila's eyes flashed fire.

"You're forgetting Deir Yassin! The massacre of a whole Arab village by the Zionists! Two hundred and fifty-four people, including women and children! The Arabs in Haifa were frightened and left the city."

"But your family left Haifa in 1947."

"True, but I still feel close to that country, the country of my ancestors." She moved her face closer to that of the stranger who had been so friendly at first, but now seemed to be separated from her by a wall of misunderstanding. "I'm twenty-nine, and since 1947, the year of national tragedy for Palestine, I haven't celebrated any of my birthdays."

"My God! You're a real fanatic!"

Their faces were now almost touching. She moved her hand as though to slap him. He grabbed her wrist. They remained motionless like that for a moment, while passersby looked at them with amusement. Then suddenly, without either of them really understanding why, their lips touched. He felt a bite and a taste of blood in his mouth.

"You're crazy!"

"Excuse me," she said, freeing her wrists from his grip. "You shouldn't have provoked me. For me Palestine is a sacred subject."

Sidney paid the check in silence, dabbing his lips with a paper napkin.

"You really *are* crazy," he grumbled.

Leila said nothing. She picked up her handbag and quickly patted her hair into place. What was Sidney going to do? What *should* he do? Leila, standing up, decided for him.

"Do you still want to walk with me to my hotel?"

Silent again, they walked the few blocks that separated them from the Westbury. By the time they reached Sixty-ninth Street, it was getting dark. Suddenly the air felt almost chilly.

They stopped in front of the hotel. Sidney glanced at his watch.

"Damn!" he exclaimed. "I forgot. This is the day of the moon landing. They're going to show the men walking on the moon tonight."

"Well, that's no problem. Why don't you come watch it in my room?"

Her room in the Westbury: yellow and brown lacquer, thick carpet, a gray marble bathroom impregnated with her perfume, a big bed on which Sidney sat down a little awkwardly. *Like in a movie,* he thought as the cratered moonscape and the lunar module appeared on the television screen and Leila put her white hand on his chest. Then she kissed him and pressed her belly against his.

And Sidney, fascinated, discovered Leila's breasts, belly and rounded thighs as she offered herself to him. Which was affecting him more: the first man to set foot on the moon, or the first woman to set foot on the fragile balance of his life? He couldn't hold back a cry of emotion:

"My God!"

Leila laughed — a light, rippling, amorous laugh. Without taking his eyes off the television screen, he murmured words whose meaning he thought he had forgotten. On the moon, a fantastic ballet was beginning. A man was floating around a white module. Another man joined him. Sidney heard their voices and it seemed to him that he could almost touch their faces. Neil Armstrong and Buzz Aldrin exchanged inconsequential words with the base in Houston. How extraordinary! Finally the two spacesuited men planted the Stars and Stripes on the moon. And meanwhile another man, down here on the modest planet Earth, was setting off to conquer another unknown world.

During the night they talked again about Israel and Palestine. They still disagreed, but as their disagreement grew, so did their desire.

"I'm leaving New York in a few hours," Leila said softly when the first glow of dawn was showing through the windows. "Why don't you come to Beirut someday? It's such a charming city, and I . . . I'll be glad to see you again."

Sidney accepted that idea quite naturally. He would come, yes, he would come to Beirut. He had no idea that he just may have sealed his fate.

SDE BOKER, AUGUST 1969

"You want me to tell you about your cousin Hugo?" Ben-Gurion asked me. "I didn't know him very well, actually. He came to see me several times, each time to propose meetings with Arabs. He knew a few Arabs. Leaders. I don't think I saw him after 1959. He was introduced to me by my adviser Israel Beer."

It was two years after the Six-Day War. I had gone to see the old leader at his kibbutz, in the heart of the Negev desert, on the road between Beersheba and Elath. He had been living there since his political retirement, in a simple little wooden house guarded by a sentry.

He had a broad, jovial face haloed by tufts of white hair and was wearing a khaki blazer and trousers that seemed to date from the time of the Haganah. He recalled distant memories, faces from the past. Sometimes he gave me the feeling that he had forgotten I was there, but then he would come back to me and respond with uncommon intelligence and open-mindedness to my questions about some event or situation of the moment.

"You want me to tell you about your cousin Hugo," he went on. "Hugo, yes, Hugo. . . . I can still see him, with his lanky body and his shining eyes. He reminded me of the young idealists in the nineteen thirties. You know: members of the Brit Shalom [Peace Alliance]. Judah Magnes, Martin Buber. . . . They believed in the power of words, too. They hoped they could create a state by carrying on a dialogue with the Arabs. I also thought it was possible. But I didn't wait for that dialogue before laying the foundations of the country.

"It was through them, you know, that I was able to meet the great Palestinian leader Musa Alami. It was in . . . in . . . it seems to me it was in August 1934. And I also talked with George Antonius, in April 1936. At that time, Antonius was the best-known theorist of Arab nationalism. We met, we talked — and it led to nothing. At least your Hugo had specific plans."

"Plans?"

"Plans?" Ben-Gurion echoed, giving me a strange look. "What were we talking about?"

"Hugo's plans."

"Were we speaking Polish?"

Ben-Gurion had been born in Poland, more than eighty years earlier. His mind had obviously drifted away from his conversation with me. The guard signaled to me with broad gestures and quietly stepped closer to us. He told me it was late and that the doctor had forbidden the old man to stay up so long.

When I stood up to leave, Ben-Gurion didn't move from his chair. He was asleep, with his face frozen into a relief as ancient as that of the valley bordering the kibbutz where, far from urban apartment houses, he had chosen to live out the rest of his dreams.

12

BUENOS AIRES

A Precocious Love

Mordecai arrived in Buenos Aires in the spring of 1969. In Israel it was already autumn. Only his son Arieh came with him. Sarah, his wife, wasn't feeling well and had stayed on the kibbutz with Dina, their seven-year-old daughter.

The Sholem Aleichem school had provided Mordecai with a clean but damp little apartment on Montevideo Street, at the corner of Cangallo Street. In Buenos Aires, dampness is everywhere; sugar is kept in metal cans to prevent it from turning into syrup.

Like all visitors, Mordecai was first surprised by the size of the city. Then he was surprised by the size — of a different order, but equally impressive — of the local Jewish community. Because of its language and traditional ways, he found it closer to the vanished communities of Poland and Russia than to "the American way of life." But he was especially struck by its size and vitality.

As for Arieh, he felt both excited and lost. While his father was teaching his classes, he took long, tiring walks in the city, usually keeping up a brisk pace to avoid being recognized as a foreigner. He walked along the Río de la Plata, the famous Corrientes Avenue, the Avenue of July 9 and the Square of the Republic, where an obelisk stands, as at the Place de la Concorde in Paris. He observed, admired and listened. If he hadn't felt so lonely and if he had been able to speak at least a few words of Spanish, he would have been perfectly happy.

The day after their arrival, Doña Regina gave a dinner in their honor. The whole family was there, along with a few carefully chosen friends.

"Zionists," she told her husband with a half-knowing, half-contemptuous look. "To please the cousins from Israel."

Not knowing a word of Yiddish, Arieh was bored stiff. He daydreamed, observed the people around him and slowly became mesmerized by that unknown language, which literally meant nothing to him. This went on till Anna Maria arrived. He first noticed her eyes: dark, shining, very large, ironic eyes. Then her partly open blouse. Then the line of her shoulders, the base of her neck, the touch of arrogance in the curve of her back.

"This is my granddaughter, Anna Maria," Doña Regina said to him. "She's beautiful, isn't she?"

"As if that were what mattered most!" Anna Maria exclaimed irritably.

Arieh blushed. She saw it and asked him, smiling, "Do you speak Spanish?" Seeing him shake his head, she continued in English, "I'm Anna Maria. You're the son of Mordecai the kibbutznik, aren't you? I didn't imagine you like this."

"What do you mean by 'like this'?"

"I imagined you as more of a peasant."

Arieh laughed and thought he had thus regained the advantage, but he blushed again when she remarked:

"Even so, you're not bad-looking, you know." She sat down beside him. "Do you like the tango?"

"That's all I've heard since I've been in Buenos Aires."

"But do you like it?"

"I think so."

"Would you like to see a tango nightclub?"

"But . . ."

"Maybe you're afraid of missing that delicious gefilte fish. My grandmother says that only the Halters from Warsaw can make gefilte fish like that."

Nettled, Arieh stood up. Now that he was on his feet, he was a full head taller than Anna Maria. He was almost seventeen and she was twenty-one, but suddenly he felt more adult, more mature.

"I'm going to show our little cousin what night life in Buenos Aires is like," she announced.

"What! You want to leave without eating?" Doña Regina protested. "You want to hang around the streets at this time of night?" Her voice took on a scolding tone: "Leave the poor child alone!"

"What did my aunt say?" the "poor child" asked.

Anna Maria translated for him. His vanity was stung; he hated being referred to as a child, especially in front of a girl somewhere near his own age, so he swelled his chest, tossed back his hair and said cockily, "Come on, baby, *vamos.*"

Mordecai stared at him, dumbfounded.

Half an hour later Arieh and Anna Maria walked into a huge room packed with people and heavy with smoke.

"This is really a terrific place," she said. "The best in town."

On the ceiling, the blades of a giant fan fluttered festoons of red and pink crepe paper. On one wall an unsophisticated pastel landscape softened the harsh glare of the spotlights. On a pillar in the middle of the room was a picture of Carlos Gardel, the king of the tango, smiling above a polka-dot bow tie. And behind the bar a poster showing a woman singer leaning over a microphone announced, "*Gran concurso de tango.*"

Anna Maria found them two empty seats. On the stage, in a circle of orange light, a pudgy woman who was slightly over the hill was singing *Adiós Muchachos.* Her accompanist was almost entirely hidden behind an enormous piano; nothing could be seen of him except his feet rhythmically bouncing on the pedals.

"Do you like it here?" Anna Maria asked.

Dazed by the noise and smoke, Arieh didn't answer.

"Do you like it here?" she repeated, leaning toward him a little.

"Yes," he said, and, while he was at it, he added, "I like you too."

She eyed him as if he had said something crude.

"Don't you think you're going a little too fast? Remember that we're cousins."

"Very distant cousins."

"Is that how people act on your kibbutz?"

"I think you must have an odd idea of what a kibbutz is like."

"Shh! Quiet!" said a man sitting at a nearby table.

"He's right," a woman wearing glasses chimed in. "Either listen or leave."

A voice was singing, "I sigh for you, Buenos Aires, under the sun of other skies. . . ."

"Let's go," Arieh said.

Outside, neon signs were reflected on the wet pavement: Cine Novedades, Cine Continuado, Pizzeria, and others.

"Are you interested in politics?" Anna Maria asked bluntly.

"Politics? In Israel, everyone is interested in politics. Our lives depend on it."

"In Israel, yes. But what about other countries? Do you know, for example, who the president of Argentina is?"

"No."

"He's a general named Ongania. You see: you're not interested in politics!"

"And do you know who the prime minister of Israel is?"

"No."

"She's a woman named Golda Meir. You see: you're not —"

Anna Maria didn't let him finish. She laughed loudly and gave him a friendly nudge in the ribs. Then, without transition, she asked, "Did you know our cousin Hugo?"

"No, but I've heard about him. He was in the war against the Nazis in Europe. He fought — unlike other Jews from Poland and other countries."

"But what about the revolt in the Warsaw ghetto? Grandfather Abraham . . ."

"That was only a minority." Arieh's voice became impassioned. "Jews must learn to fight, like everyone else, for their country, their self-respect. . . . Now that Israel exists, Jews will never again go like lambs to slaughter."

Anna Maria stopped abruptly, without explanation, like someone who had just been struck by something that should have been obvious earlier. In the dim light of a streetlamp, Arieh noticed her withdrawn expression.

"You never talk about anything but the Jews, over and over," she said. "But what about other people? Here in Argentina, millions of people live in slums, and thousands of others are in prison for their opinions. Do you ever think about them? Or about the millions who are starving in other Latin American countries?"

"Are you really sure you think about them more than I do?"

"Of course. I not only think about them, I'm going to *fight* for them."

"Why?"

"Because . . . because I'm a human being. Maybe also because I'm Jewish."

"If you want to fight, come to Israel. We need girls like you."

"And who will fight here?"

"The Argentinians."

"But I *am* an Argentinian!"

"And who will fight for Israel?"

Arieh was divided between anger and admiration. He found Anna Maria opinionated but very beautiful. Much more beautiful than any of the girls in Kibbutz Dafneh or even Hagesharim. He stepped closer to her, looked at her and thought he saw consent in her eyes. He moved still closer and kissed her. And what had to happen did happen: his amorous ardor was cut short by a big, resounding slap. Humiliated as never before, he stood still for a moment with his arms dangling at his sides, then he turned on his heel and ran away.

When he reached the Río de la Plata he stopped, a little out of breath, and sat down on a bench. He listened to traffic noises, the hissing of tires on wet streets, car horns, the distant calling of ships, and he told himself that he didn't like Buenos Aires. No, he didn't like this city that never slept. Not one bit. And all at once he was dying to go back to Galilee, to his beloved kibbutz. He noticed a big cockroach watching him from the railing of the bridge.

"Are you angry at me, kibbutznik?"

It was Anna Maria. He asked how she had found him.

"I followed you," she said. "It wasn't all that hard. Mind if I sit down?" As soon as she was beside him on the bench, she continued as if she were taking up the thread of a conversation that had been interrupted for some commonplace reason: "My friends keep telling me I should go underground. What do you think?"

What kind of a game was she playing? By confiding in him like that, was she trying to wipe away the incident of the slap? Or show him that she trusted him? Or impress him?

Whatever she was doing, it had a decisive effect on Arieh: his misery, humiliation and homesickness vanished as though by magic, and he asked, "Go underground? What do you mean by that? You want to become a terrorist?"

Anna Maria again felt the dominance she held over this charming but unworldly adolescent whose horizon had never gone beyond the borders of his kibbutz.

"No, I want to become a fighter!" she answered. Then, with a loftiness that bordered on disdain: "I don't know why I'm telling you all this. You're not interested in justice in the world or the war in Vietnam, you know nothing about Latin America, or Che, or military repression, you . . . as far as you're concerned, nothing exists in the world except Israel!"

"That's not true," Arieh protested. After recovering from the first shock of her attack, he had regained some of his self-assurance. "I *am* interested in justice in the world, and that includes Israel. But killing — the way our cousin Hugo was killed, or those innocent passengers in an Israeli airliner at the Zurich airport — isn't the best way to promote justice."

Anna Maria gave a start: three cockroaches were calmly climbing up one leg of the bench in single file. Arieh knocked them off with a wave of his hand. She stood up. He did too. And with a natural movement, having lost all his reserve, as well as all his awkwardness, he took her in his arms and kissed her for a long time.

PARIS, SEPTEMBER 1969

"I didn't know Hugo very well. I mainly knew his wife's family, and especially her brother, Hans Furchmuller. We were at the university together. He's a doctor now, and head of a hospital in East Berlin. He's the one who gave Hugo my name and phone number."

The woman talking to me was about sixty, and as I looked at her I thought a little nostalgically of how beautiful she must once have been. Her name was Ursula von Thadden. At that time I was taking part in an international symposium being held in Paris on human rights in the Soviet Union, and she was covering it for a Munich newspaper, the *Suddeutsche Zeitung*. I had heard her name and remembered seeing it in Hugo's notebook.

"He went to Germany several times, with his wife," she went on. "I was working in Bonn at the time. This was in the spring of 1960. Hugo wanted to meet Chancellor Adenauer. He said that Germany was responsible for the lives and safety of children whose parents it had slaughtered. He thought that Konrad Adenauer, who had excellent relations with Israel as well as with the Arab countries, could help to establish peace in the Middle East by promising to finance a regional development project, a kind of new-style Marshall

Plan. Hugo was a passionate, tenacious man. Obstacles didn't frighten him. It irritated him to be contradicted by someone, but he was too sociable to show it. I think he met Adenauer, but I never found out exactly what came of it because I had to go back to Munich."

I asked what he was like during that period; if he seemed worried, if he gave the impression of being in danger and knowing he was surrounded by enemies. Ursula von Thadden didn't know; she searched her memory in vain. All she could tell me was that Hugo was an incredibly attractive man in those days.

"But don't get the wrong idea," she quickly added. "I was a friend of his wife, as I told you. And besides, I was already too old for those little games. But it's true that no one could see him without being impressed by his magnetism. He had a penetrating, insistent way of looking at you. There was an ironic, almost bitter twist to his mouth; he seemed to be one of those men who have seen and experienced everything, but still have a kind of nostalgia for their ideals. His hair was thick and unruly. His movements were precise. Women always noticed his hands. And he had the look of a constant traveler who was hard to imagine settling down anywhere, or even being married, and . . ."

She stopped short, realizing that she might have said a little too much, and especially that she had shown too clearly how much the memory of Hugo still affected her nearly ten years later. She laughed, made some trivial remark, then said that the symposium was about to resume and walked away from me — without, I must say, having told me very much that I hadn't already known.

13

MOSCOW

Hidar and Olga

SEPTEMBER 1969

"You must be out of your mind! We're involved in a plan that will change the face of the Middle East if it succeeds, and you want to risk ruining everything for a pleasure trip?"

The man talking to Hidar Assadi was Viktor Chebrikov, one of the leaders of the Committee for Solidarity with the Peoples of Africa and Asia. His power came mainly from his friendship with Yuri Andropov, head of the KGB.

The two men were sitting in a big, dark office on the fourth floor of a modern building on Kropotkin Street. The broad bay window that took up almost one whole wall was covered by opaque curtains decorated with yellow flowers. A ray of late sunlight slipped between them and shone on the glass in front of a framed portrait of Lenin.

Hidar shifted his chair a little and answered with a smile, "It's not a pleasure trip, Viktor Alexandrovich, it's part of my work. I've been given a mission and it seems to me that I'm carrying it out to the great satisfaction of our superiors. Olga Lerner's arrival in Beirut will be sure to trouble our adversaries. You know very well that the American and Israeli intelligence services have been keeping close watch on me for the last year. If we want to make our operation in Jordan a success, I must go back to the Middle East. With a woman."

"A Jewish woman," Chebrikov specified.

"Precisely."

"Why do you say 'precisely'?"

"The Israeli services will react exactly like you, and doubt will come into their minds. They suspect me, I know that, but they have no certainty, much less proof. I admit I'm personally attached to Olga Lerner, but I'm asking you to get an exit visa for her because I urgently need her."

Viktor Chebrikov was not a man to be easily convinced. At most, he would transmit the request. He took a pen and a sheet of paper and began writing down Hidar's arguments. When he had finished, he looked up at him and said, "By the way, your report on 'media terrorism' has been judged very favorably by people in high positions. Has Sasha Aronovich mentioned it to you? You spend all your time in his parents' apartment on Kazakov Street. . . ."

"You're well informed."

"I hope it's not a secret."

"No, of course not, but Sasha Lerner and I . . ."

"You're not on good terms with him, and you're right," Chebrikov said with a self-satisfied smile. "He was the only one who opposed your plan. He doesn't think the Arabs are capable of carrying it out." He held out his hand to Hidar. "For your sake, I hope he's wrong, because your friends in Beirut already know about the plan. The next time you see them, they'll present it to you as if it were their own idea. That's what you wanted, isn't it?"

As he went out into the street, Hidar was rather pleased with himself. His report was looked upon favorably, his idea was approved. And his promise to Olga was finally going to be kept: they would go to Lebanon together. He knew the risks of such a trip. He also knew that Olga might have completely unpredictable reactions at the Israeli border. But he drove his anxiety from his mind, making himself lengthen his stride and look up at the old façades of the buildings on this street he liked so much, still known as the Street of the Immaculate Virgin in the early part of the century. In front of Davidoff's house he stopped, as always, to pay silent tribute to Tolstoy.

Then, with joy in his heart, he began walking toward the Moscow river.

Olga was waiting for him near the Borodinsky Bridge.

"Well?" she asked as they embraced.

"It's going to work out. This year we'll have a sunny autumn."

He took her by the arm and they walked across the bridge in silence.

"I promised my parents I'd come by and see them before dinner," Olga finally said. "Will you come with me?"

"Your parents don't like me very much. They think you're ruining your life because of me. Especially your mother. Behind me, she sees a hundred million Arabs threatening her."

"What are you talking about? She knows you have nothing to do with the conflict in the Middle East."

Hidar stopped and looked at her. She had changed, he thought. How? He couldn't say. But he felt that change. It was like a new maturity, a relaxation, a fulfilment.

She moved her face close to his, and for a fleeting moment he saw himself in her gray eyes.

"All right, I'll come with you," he said. "But let's take a taxi, shall we? I don't feel like walking across Moscow."

As luck would have it, a car with black squares painted on it was approaching them — a taxi! They gaily got into it, headed for the Lerners' apartment and arrived there after a ten-minute ride through the near-deserted streets of Moscow.

To Hidar's surprise, Rachel Lerner actually seemed glad to see him.

"Well?" she asked when she had made tea and everyone had sat down around the table. "Well?" she repeated, addressing Hidar.

"What do you want to know, Rachel Davidovna?"

She shook her head several times.

"I know we don't agree, Hidar. I know. . . . When it comes to Israel, we're even adversaries, but you're going to the Middle East and I'm not. One of these days, in fact, I may have to go in the opposite direction, to Siberia." She smiled gravely, sighed and leaned close to him. "I'd like you to tell me about Lebanon, and Egypt. How do people there see Israel? Are they getting ready for war? Is there a chance to prevent it? Please tell me."

Hidar was disconcerted by her frankness and naïveté.

"I'll be glad to tell you what I saw in Lebanon, Rachel Davidovna, but first I want to reassure you. I'm not at all in favor of destroying Israel. And if you don't mind, I'd rather stay off the subject of politics, because it would only get us into an argument."

He began telling her about Beirut and the Palestinian camps, the Lebanon Mountains and Cairo, the Nile and the Pyramids.

Rachel, Aron and Olga listened, fascinated, as if they were hearing a tale from *The Arabian Nights*.

When Hidar had finished, Rachel sighed and said, "For us, you're like that 'branch of Palestine' in Lermontov's poem." Then, straightening her shawl and looking him straight in the eyes: "By the way, what did Hugo look like?"

Hidar stiffened.

"Hugo . . . why Hugo? I was very young when I met him."

"Even so . . ."

"Why are you so interested in a man you never knew, Rachel Davidovna?"

"Because I think he was a bridge between the world of yesterday and the world that's still being born. And also a bridge . . ." Rachel paused, trying to find the right words. ". . . between two abysses, between war and terrorism. But you couldn't understand."

"Why not?"

Rachel stood up, slowly walked across the room to the window, stopped and turned around.

"Because, although it may have changed, your world, the world of your culture and your dreams, has never stopped existing. But we . . . our culture was uprooted by the Nazis. As for our dreams, they were devastated by . . ."

"By Stalin?" Hidar asked with a touch of irony in his voice.

Rachel nodded, came back to the table and sat down.

"Don't you realize," he went on, "that Stalin has been dead for sixteen years?" He turned to Aron. "What do you think about your wife's theory of 'bridges,' Aron Lazarevich? And her constant references to uncle Abraham? In a world that's always in motion, don't you think that's a little ridiculous?"

Aron smiled, passed his hand over his carefully plastered-down hair and said in an almost embarrassed tone, as if he were soliciting indulgence or forgiveness in advance, "You can't understand. We were talking only yesterday with our neighbor, the academician S. . . . When nothing is left of an old world, what rises to the surface is a passionate desire for ancestors." Then, suddenly standing up — a sign that, for him, the discussion was over — he added more resolutely, "Remember this, Hidar: *Omnia risus, omnia pulvis, et omnia nihil sunt:* 'Everything is mockery, everything is dust, and everything is nothing.'"

"You shouldn't have provoked my father," Olga said later, when she was alone with her lover on the shadowy street.

"Why not?"

"He's a false cynic. In a way, it saved him in the time of the great purges at the university, but that time has left him with — how can I say it? — with an incurable melancholy. You have to realize that because you're not a Soviet citizen you can safely say things that he can't say without risk. And you don't live in the same way. For one thing, you can travel wherever you please, and —"

"And with you, darling," Hidar broke in affectionately.

Then he led her toward the Baku restaurant on Gorky Street.

14

NEW YORK

Sidney: A Providential Encounter

SEPTEMBER 1969

Sidney had the feeling that he was going around in circles. His adventure with Leila had affected him much more than he was willing to admit. Since "the day when the first man walked on the moon," he had felt tense and nervous.

Seeing him preoccupied, Marjory had been doing her best to please him and attract him. But instead of being pleased, Sidney was irritated. And, annoyed with himself for his impatience, he became still more irritable. The situation weighed on him so heavily! He wished he could talk it over with someone, but who? How could he confide in any of those true or false friends whose confidences he had always refused to hear?

As he was leaving the hospital on a bright September day, he literally ran into Jerry Cohen.

"Sid!" Jerry exclaimed, hopping on one foot. "You almost broke my toe, you clumsy oaf! But I'll forgive you if you buy me a drink."

Jerry and Sidney had known each other for years. They had been in medical school together, and ever since then they had taken part together in all sorts of political actions organized by doctors in support of the Third World and against hunger, torture and oppression. Jerry was the best anesthesiologist in the hospital, but Marjory found him strange and his colleagues regarded him as an eccentric. He lived in Soho, on Broadway between Broome and Spring streets. He had a magnificent loft in a dilapidated building that smelled of urine, where Hasidim carried on a trade in cameras imported from the Far East.

"Beautiful day, isn't it?" he said. "Looks like it's going to be a great fall. Where'll we go, the Plaza?"

Ever since *The Best Years of Our Lives* came out, the Plaza Hotel's Oak Bar, entirely covered with black leather, had enjoyed a renown that its regular patrons could have done very well without.

"I'd rather go to the Polo Bar at the Westbury: it's closer," Sidney said distractedly.

"That's okay with me," Jerry said, and as they walked he began telling Sidney about his latest conquest. "You won't believe this, but for three months I was madly in love with Sophie — you know, that girl at the hospital, the one who works in . . ."

"The French girl?"

"That's right. We made love everywhere: in storerooms, on laundry hampers, in the middle of cases of medicine. I don't know how her husband found out, but one day he came to me and told me, very seriously, that he was giving her to me. With his blessing. And do you know what happened then? Suddenly I realized I didn't love her. And I felt free as a bird." He took his friend by the shoulders. "Here we are, Sid. I'm going to be magnanimous. Forget the damage you did to my shoe and my toe. I'm treating. Champagne, to celebrate my first taste of freedom in three months!" .

They sat down in red leather armchairs. Jerry ordered the champagne, said, "Cheers!" when it had been served to them, then abruptly changed the subject: "I've just been invited to give some lectures at the American University in Beirut. How does that grab you?"

Sidney started and knocked over his glass.

"I'm sorry. . . ."

"Don't worry, it brings good luck. And champagne doesn't stain," Jerry said, dabbing his jacket with a napkin.

"So you're going to Beirut?" Sidney asked when he had recovered from his surprise.

"I don't know. I haven't made up my mind yet. . . . Why are you looking at me that way?" Jerry emptied his glass, then looked hard at Sidney. "You can't fool me. You're having an affair! When we were in school, I could guess everything, just by reading your face! Remember that Mexican girl we met in El Salvador when we went down there after the earthquake? I liked her a lot, but you were the one she wanted."

Sidney smiled, flattered.

"Let's not bring that up. . . ."

"Why not? Do you think we're here to talk about the future of the world? Or the Vietnam war? Come on, Sid, don't kid me!"

"I'm not," Sidney replied, scratching his chin. "You know how it is: for Jews, things like family, children and faithfulness are sacred values."

"C'mon, Sid, spare me. Being Jewish isn't always a proof of intelligence. How many Einsteins are there among our children? Nowadays, you either make love or do research. Einstein did well in both areas — that was his genius."

"If that's what being a genius means, you and I both qualify!"

They laughed.

"That's how I like to see you, Sid!" Jerry patted his friend on the leg, ordered another round of champagne, then moved closer to him and said, "Tell me about it."

"All right, I will. It's something that hadn't happened to me in a long time. . . ."

When Sidney had finished his story, Jerry leaned back in his chair and lit a cigar, after offering one to Sidney, who refused it.

"Let me tell you something, my friend," he said. "I think *you're* the one who's going to Beirut."

"Don't be silly, Jerry. How . . ."

"I've never been more serious in my life. The story you just told me is beautiful, far more beautiful than my little episodes with the French girl in the hospital or the waitresses at Wolff's. It would be criminal to nip it in the bud."

"But how could I explain . . ."

"You won't have to explain anything. I'll arrange to have you give the Beirut lectures instead of me. Everyone knows that Jews like to travel."

15

MOSCOW

Olga in Beirut

SEPTEMBER 1969

Leaving the Soviet Union! Olga would never have thought such an adventure possible. At the Sheremetievo airport, despite the arrogance of the police and the jostling of the passengers, who were alternatively excited or inert, everything went well. Or almost everything. She had just had her identity checked when a man in his early twenties, claiming to be a plainclothes policeman, imperiously demanded to see her passport again. He took it and, without explanation, disappeared behind a door at the other end of the airport. Olga was frightened. She saw herself being turned back and arrested. Instinctively, she considered herself guilty and quickly thought back over all the petty crimes she had committed, or might have committed. Almost immediately she felt ashamed of that stupid reaction, but the fact was that she had had it. After twenty minutes of waiting that seemed as long as an endless pain, she finally got back her passport from Hidar, to whom an officer had handed it without a word of apology.

It was only a minor incident but she was greatly upset by it. Her anger and anxiety didn't leave her till the stopover in London, when, acting on one of the affectionate impulses she often had, she whispered a few daringly amorous words in Hidar's ear — words of a kind she had sometimes read, over his shoulder, in the spy novels he occasionally brought back from his travels.

When they arrived in Beirut, the sun was there to greet them, as Hidar had promised, along with the plaintive gaiety that Olga had always imagined as being typical of the Middle East. Not very different from Sheremetievo, the Khalde airport was also besieged by a dense crowd. There were porters, idlers, travelers made sullen by their concern with finding their baggage in the midst of chaos, cruising prostitutes, soldiers, shady characters with the look of terrorists and killers. Perfectly at ease, Hidar made his way through that crowd, gesturing to ward off beggars and other bothersome people. He spotted an air-conditioned Mercedes taxi and asked the driver, a young man wearing a T-shirt, to take him to the Hotel St. George by way of the seaside road, known as the Corniche.

Intrigued by the strange couple talking in a language that was totally unknown to him, the driver kept asking them questions in either French or English. Hidar answered in monosyllables, with obvious ill will. This went on until, absorbed in observing his passengers in the rearview mirror, he took a turn too fast, skidded and crashed into a wagon full of chickens. The quarrel between the taxi driver and the owner of the wagon, egged on by a curious and animated crowd, lasted nearly an hour, so that Olga and Hidar didn't reach the hotel till nightfall.

A man was waiting for Hidar there. At first, Olga thought he was a beggar, or maybe some sort of lowly errand-runner. But from the way Hidar spoke to him, she realized that the man had an important message to deliver. There was a rather long discussion. Hidar frowned and looked as if he had just received disastrous news.

Their room was so beautiful, the view of the harbor lights was so romantic . . . but Hidar's mind wasn't on romance.

"My colleagues in the Peace Committee are meeting tomorrow morning," he said, "and they want me to join them."

Olga leaped to her feet.

"What! We got here tonight and you're leaving me the next morning?"

"No, no, darling, I'll only be gone an hour or two, maybe less.

You'll see. I'll leave very early, while you're still asleep, and you won't even know I'm gone."

But inwardly Hidar was upset. He had been looking forward to spending those first two days guiding Olga around Beirut, letting her discover the city. And there was something alarming about the meeting being pushed forward so abruptly.

"No, you won't even know," he went on, as though trying to convince himself. "Forgive me for this little mishap. I promise to be back by the time you wake up."

"If I ever get to sleep! Now that I know . . ."

Hidar put his arms around her and murmured, "Darling . . ." Then he gently pushed her backward, toward the big canopied bed facing the sea.

The meeting was held at the headquarters of the Popular Front for the Liberation of Palestine, on the Corniche Mazra. On the walls of George Habash's office were posters of Che Guevara, portraits of Lenin, and a big map of Palestine on which the name of Israel did not appear.

There were two newcomers among the participants: Ghassan Kanafani, a poet with a pale, thoughtful face; and Bassam Abu Sharif, a dark, lively man of average height who, Hidar had heard, was responsible for "special actions."

"What about Hawatmeh?" Hidar asked as he sat down. "I heard he left the movement."

"He wanted to form a group of his own," Habash replied. "May Allah protect him! But when the time comes, he'll be with us."

"And Al Fatah?"

"Abu Iyad will be here before long."

Turkish coffee was served. A moment of silence was observed. Then, after a few minutes, Wadi Hadad came over to Hidar and sat down beside him.

"What are they saying in Moscow about Ho Chi Minh's death?"

"They've declared a period of national mourning."

"It was a shock for us, too," Hadad said, then looked at Hidar with his dark, lusterless eyes and asked, "What do the Soviets think about the Jordanian operation?"

"They accept it," Hidar answered without batting an eyelid,

"but only if everything is done according to the plans we've drawn up, which I presented yesterday in Moscow."

"What do they promise us?"

"Weapons and information."

"We already have information," Ghassan Kanafani remarked quietly.

"And that's not all," Hidar went on, pretending not to have heard. "They also offer us guarantees against any intervention by the United States, or other Arab countries."

Kanafani raised his voice: "To deal with the Arab countries, we don't need the Soviet Union. With the United States, it's different. Nixon and Kissinger won't turn away from their ally Hussein without serious reasons. But . . ."

Habash was obviously pleased by Kanafani's intervention, and his smug smile irritated Hidar.

"Are you beginning to have doubts, by any chance?"

"I have no doubts about us," Kanafani answered.

Again Hidar pretended not to have heard.

"The Syrians will help us," he said. "They've been given orders. As soon as the attack on the royal palace in Amman is announced, Syrian tanks will move against Irbid."

"What about Moscow?"

"Brezhnev will warn Nixon against any intervention by the Sixth Fleet. But we have to bear in mind that the Soviets won't leave us much time."

"How much?" Hadad asked curtly.

He wore military fatigues and a khaki cap that hid his bald skull.

"A week at most."

"That will be enough," said Jael al-Ardja.

His presence had surprised Hidar. A native of Beit Jala, near Bethlehem, he now lived in Lima, Peru, and represented the Front in Latin America. What was he doing here? What did Latin America have to do with the clash between the Jordanians and the Palestinians that was about to take place?

"I'm the one who asked him to come here," Hadad said, as if he had read Hidar's mind. "He has an interesting plan, too. I thought he should tell us about it."

All eyes turned to Jael al-Ardja, who explained how the Front had decided to kill David Ben-Gurion when he went to Buenos Aires. Ben-Gurion was now only a private citizen, of course, but in the eyes of the world he still was a living symbol of the Jewish state, and therefore of Zionism. All the details of the plan had been settled, including the choice of who would carry it out: a man named Ismail Souhail and a Swedish left-wing militant. What did the group think of it?

"I think you're all crazy!" Hidar exclaimed before the others could say anything.

"Why?" Hadad asked.

"Because public opinion all over the world won't understand the killing of an old man on a private trip to Argentina."

"But public opinion in Israel will understand it very well!"

"You're revolutionary fighters, not murderers," Hidar said as calmly as he could, "and you have to win two battles: one against Israel, the other against the media. With that crazy plan, you'll lose both."

Hadad grimaced.

"Do you really think you know and understand everything just because you've come here from Moscow?"

Voices were raised. Habash intervened. Then Jael al-Ardja. Then Kanafani, who this time was on Hidar's side, but wasn't able to make himself heard.

Only the arrival of Abu Iyad succeeded in relaxing the atmosphere. The greetings and embraces lasted several minutes. With his white sports shirt, his pack of cigarettes in his pocket and his carefully combed hair, the second in command of Al Fatah looked like a kindly college professor who had somehow wandered into a group of conspirators.

Finally they all reached a tacit agreement to leave the thorny matter of Ben-Gurion to the discretion and responsibility of the Latin American comrades.

"That's good," said Habash, running his thumb across his mustache in his usual gesture. Then he leaned toward Hidar as though to share a secret. "I hear she's beautiful."

"She is."

"Don't you think it was a little rash to bring her to Beirut?"

Hidar smiled broadly.

"You know the proverb: 'To love a living woman well, you must love her as if she were going to die tomorrow.'"

"I'm talking about your own safety."

"Olga is my best alibi."

How could Hidar make that fool understand that his remarks annoyed him? How could he make them all understand that aside from being a danger, an alibi or anything else, Olga was *first and foremost* the woman he loved, and that was nobody's business but his, whether they liked it or not? But not wanting to show his irritation and preferring to ignore Habash's bland, ugly smile, he decided to ask the question that had been on his mind for the last hour:

"Why was this meeting called today?"

"Wadi Hadad wanted it called. He has a spectacular plan, something that will occur before the taking of Amman. He wanted to talk it over with us without delay."

"Can you be a little more precise?"

"It has to do with hijacking airplanes. But I'd rather let him give us all the details."

Hidar smiled, suddenly reassured. So that was it! The Soviet comrades had done their work well, and the information had been transmitted.

Hadad came up to them with a cup of coffee in his hand.

"Are you two talking about Hidar's girlfriend?"

"No," Hidar answered, "we were talking about you."

Hadad pulled up a chair and sat down.

"I'm not interesting, whereas your girlfriend . . . I wanted to warn you."

"About what?"

"I understand your strategy. The Zionist secret services may be thrown off the track, but you may have problems."

"I trust Olga completely."

"You shouldn't. As I've already told you, it's a mistake to have any dealings with the enemy."

"But I'm not fighting the Jews!"

"You are, whether you know it or not. The Zionists all over the world are Israel's breeding ground. All Jews are Zionists, or nearly all. Even those who don't know it yet."

"So you want to fight all the Jews in the world?"

"Why not? We can win that war too. We outnumber them."

Hadad stood up, laughing, put his cup down on the desk and, with a vague gesture that seemed to say, "After all, it's your affair and there's no reason why I should try to teach you anything or worry about what happens to you," he began describing the "spectacular plan" that Habash had mentioned.

"What do you think?" he asked Hidar when he had finished.

"It's a very good idea," Hidar answered, holding back a triumphant smile. "We'll be starting an era of media terrorism. A stroke of genius if we succeed. It will force television to promote revolutionary causes!"

"I like the way you put that," Habash said. "If I'm not mistaken, media terrorism can be the cheapest and most effective form of warfare."

Seeing everyone stand up, Hidar raised his voice:

"One more thing before we leave: we must avoid useless violence, and we mustn't discriminate between Jews and non-Jews. Don't forget that millions of men and women will be watching what we do." He turned to Hadad. "And don't forget Samirah, either. She's a brave woman, as she proved a week or so ago when she hijacked that TWA plane out of Rome."

"I haven't forgotten," Hadad said thoughtfully. "But first we'll have to get her out of Syria. The Syrians don't want to let her go. What a stupid idea it was to have the plane land in Damascus!"

"Take care of it," Hidar said decisively. "It's up to you. I want to see Samirah free — and in Beirut."

When he came back to the hotel, he found that Olga had been up a long time. And, contrary to what he had expected, she was in a good mood.

"I found this book in a drawer," she said, showing him a Bible. "I'd never read it. It's fascinating."

"Is that what's made you so happy?"

"Yes, why?"

"I'm surprised, that's all."

"Surprised that I admire something admirable? Listen to this: 'The righteous shall rejoice when he seeth the vengeance: he shall wash his feet in the blood of the wicked.' It's frightening, isn't it? I wonder who wrote that."

"God did."

"Don't laugh, Hidar."

"I'm not laughing."

She stepped toward him, holding the book, opened it at random to the Song of Solomon and read aloud: "'My beloved is white and ruddy, the chiefest among ten thousand. His head is as the most fine gold, his locks are bushy, and black as a raven.'"

"That's a lovely passage and you chose it well," Hidar said. He kissed her lightly. "But for your first visit here, wouldn't it be better to go out and see the city rather than reading beautiful but dusty pages from a book of the past?"

"But these pages talk about Lebanon! Listen: 'Thy neck is as a tower of ivory; thine eyes are like the fishpools of Heshbon, by the gate of Bath-rabbim: thy nose is as the tower of Lebanon which looketh toward Damascus.'"

Dear, darling Olga! She was so beautiful when she read! So beautiful beneath the golden helmet of her hair! And it was so strange to hear her reading about Lebanon and Damascus — maybe in a little while she would find a passage where Habash, Hadad and Samirah were mentioned!

As always when a woman made him feel a little sorry for her, Hidar was seized with one of those powerful impulses to inflict pain that women usually mistook for desire. He took the book from her hands, took hold of her beautiful hair and pulled her head back as if he were trying to break her neck. Then, after undressing her very little and undressing himself only as much as was strictly necessary, he brutally forced his way between her opened thighs.

They spent the rest of the day in the streets. Olga was lighthearted. On the slightest pretext, she kept reciting the passage about the "white and ruddy beloved." They visited Cannon Square, with its tired trees, and the famous Bab Edriss Street, with its flower market. The Al Hamra quarter, with its European galleries, stores and movie houses, drew excited exclamations from her. There was no shop that didn't fill her with wonder, no café that didn't make her want to go into it and sample its delicacies. Near a vast park spread over the slopes of the Ras Beirut promontory, they finally stopped, exhausted.

"Let's rest awhile, my 'beloved with locks as black as a raven,'" Olga said, sitting down on the grass.

"Not here, darling. This is part of the American University of Beirut."

"There's an American university in Beirut?"

"Well, 'American' is just a way of speaking. . . . It was built a hundred years ago by an American Presbyterian mission."

Whether it was "just a way of speaking" or not, the idea obviously enchanted Olga. Her fatigue vanished and she led Hidar off to take a look at the university. The entrance hall was filled with students talking, exclaiming and calling out to each other in a wide variety of languages.

"Let's go and see," she said, nodding toward a big bulletin board with a crowd of young people in front of it.

When they had gone to it, she excitedly pointed to a small poster attached to it with thumbtacks.

"Read that! Isn't it amazing!"

Hidar read it, and even in this turbulent, unpredictable world what he read did indeed seem amazing to him: "On September 22, 1969, in the main lecture hall of the School of Medicine, there will be a lecture by Dr. Sidney Halter of the Manhattan Eye, Ear and Throat Hospital in New York."

16

BEIRUT

A Game of Chance

SEPTEMBER 1969

What a bore! Sidney thought when he found the note that Olga had left for him at the Hotel St. George. The longer he stayed in Beirut, the less he liked it. Not only had he had to cancel a trip to Ethiopia that he had promised to make, but he had also abandoned his plan to attend the big medical conference in Frankfurt. And lying to Marjory hadn't been very easy, either. Images of her and the two children, remorse, a guilty conscience . . . but at least this trip had the merit of taking him away from "the scene of the crime." Ever since his arrival, he had kept repeating Jerry's comforting words to himself: "Beirut is so far away! No one will ever know anything, because no one knows you there." But then came that note, and he had a relative on his hands. He would have been glad to meet her in other circumstances, but not here, not like this, not in this situation.

Two days after he received the note, he still couldn't take a step, go into a public place, or sit down at a sidewalk table of La Grotte aux Pigeons with Leila without thinking that his cousin was about to appear, call his name, come to him and . . . he preferred not to imagine the rest.

Did he at least like Beirut itself? Well . . . he wasn't sure. Since coming there, he had seen the wretched poverty of some neighborhoods, the children swarming around passersby in the hope of getting money from them, the cripples and old people begging in the streets. That morning, not far from the Great Mosque, which he wanted to see, he had passed a group of American tourists, watched them and envied their cheerful detachment. *Only Americans,* he had thought, *can be so much at ease when they're surrounded by dirty, hungry, miserable people. Actually, they're true optimists. I must have something wrong with me, to be so gloomy.*

So he had good reason to feel dejected when he arrived at La Grotte aux Pigeons, and for a moment he found himself wishing that Leila wouldn't keep their appointment, that some mysterious obstacle would arise to keep her away. But there she was, of course, sitting under a beach umbrella. When he saw her, he couldn't repress a surge of emotion: she *was* the most beautiful woman in the world. But when he went up to her and tried to kiss her, she pushed him away.

"Not here, Sid, not in public. We're in the Middle East. Let's go to your hotel."

"You don't want to have dinner?"

"We'll have something sent up to your room. I'm afraid, Sid. My husband seemed strange this morning. He made a few remarks about my trip to America. . . . He's very powerful here."

Sidney looked at her intently.

"Are you afraid of your husband, or are you afraid of being seen with a Zionist?"

"Don't be silly." She quickly brushed her pale fingers across his hand. "I'm glad you're here, but you have to understand. . . . Here, everyone knows my husband. He's as well known as you are in your hospital in New York."

They were about to leave when a voice exclaimed in English with a strong Russian accent, "My God! It's you! You're my cousin Sidney!"

Leila, a little surprised, gave Sidney a questioning look.

"Don't worry," he said, terribly embarrassed. "I think she's the daughter of my Soviet cousin."

Olga came up to their table and said how glad she was to meet him and his "beautiful wife." He replied curtly that Leila wasn't his wife, but only a "Lebanese friend." Olga told how she had checked nearly every hotel in the city before finding out that he was staying at the St. George. Yes, he remarked, that was where American tourists, journalists and businessmen often stayed. She was delighted to have recognized him instantly, although all she had to go on was an old photograph that her mother kept in the family album. And he replied that yes, it was strange: probably the miracle of family ties, one more proof of the saying that "blood is thicker than water." He had recognized her too, without a photograph or anything else, simply because of a slight but obvious resemblance.

Finally she took hold of his arm and said winsomely, "Please don't leave. Come and have a drink with us. I'd like to introduce you to my . . . friend, Hidar."

Sidney consulted Leila with his eyes, pretended not to see her dismay and, hopelessly trapped, heard himself say, "All right, but we can only stay a few minutes."

He and Leila stood up and went to Olga's table. And there, of course, he met Hidar Assadi.

Hidar was surprised by that red-haired, six-foot-three Jew, but Leila's presence surprised him even more. What was the wife of the powerful Michel Chehab, the press magnate, doing with that Zionist? For once, he didn't curse the workings of chance.

Olga was happy as a child.

"My parents will never believe me! They were so afraid for me — you know, a Jewish woman in an Arab country. And now I've met cousin Sidney, from New York, and we're having a drink together in the most famous café in Beirut. Isn't it amazing?"

"How long are you staying in Beirut?" Hidar asked Sidney.

Sidney leaned back in his chair, ill at ease.

"For a few more days. I've accepted an invitation to give a lecture tonight at the American University."

"I know. We saw your name on the bulletin board there. Did you come to Lebanon alone?"

Hidar spoke English with a harsh accent, half Arabic and half Russian.

"Yes," Sidney answered, more and more embarrassed. "My wife couldn't come with me because she just had a baby."

He glanced at Leila and felt his face turning red. Then he emptied the glass that the waiter had put on the table in front of him and asked, "And you?"

"I'm here with Olga."

"Yes, but are you married?"

"To Olga?"

"Yes, to Olga."

"No, not really."

"I thought they were very strict about such things in the Soviet Union."

"All kinds of things are said about the Soviet Union."

There was a silence, as if that rapid exchange had exhausted all possible topics of conversation.

"What is your name, exactly?" Sidney finally asked.

"Hidar Assadi."

"Assadi . . . Assadi . . . Will you please spell it for me?"

"Why?"

"Because that name reminds me of something."

"You may have read Hidar's name in the newspapers," Olga intervened. "He's very important in the Committee for Solidarity with the Peoples of Africa and Asia. Sasha works for that committee. You know: my brother Sasha. Hidar travels often, and organizes conferences."

Hidar affectionately put his hand over her mouth and said, "She's exaggerating."

But Sidney, absentmindedly running his fingers through his red hair, seemed lost in thought.

"Assadi . . . Assadi . . . are you Tunisian, by any chance?"

"Yes, why?"

Sidney smiled radiantly.

"Then you must be the Hidar Assadi my cousin Hugo talked about!"

Two men sitting at a nearby table looked around as if they had been following the conversation. To gain time, Hidar took a sip of his arrack.

"Yes, of course," Olga answered in his place. "They were friends, although Hidar was only thirteen or fourteen at the time."

"Did you ever see him again?" Sidney asked.

"No." Hidar put down his empty glass. "But I was very sad when I learned of his death."

"You mean his murder!"

Hidar smiled with a fatherly expression, which irritated Sidney.

"Whether he was murdered or not, the result is unfortunately the same."

"But it was your friends who killed him!"

Sidney felt anger rising inside him. He disliked this handsome, curly-haired man, and he wondered what Olga was doing with him.

Hidar signaled to the waiter, ordered another round of drinks and said quietly, "No, Dr. Halter, it was not 'my friends' who killed Hugo. The opposite is true, in fact: the people who killed him are among my enemies." And he asked in a tone that he tried to make neutral, "But you have a brother in Israel, don't you?"

"How do you know that?"

"From Olga's mother. She has a strong interest in everything that concerns her family."

Hidar stopped the waiter, who was about to walk away, and handed him a hundred-pound bill. Sidney tried to protest, but Hidar said, "No, please allow me to pay. It's my pleasure. I hope we'll see each other again before you leave."

"I hope so too," Sidney replied. And, remembering Benjamin Ben-Eliezer, he ventured, "I'd be very glad if you could talk to me a little about Hugo before I leave Beirut. I've always been fascinated by him."

Hidar hesitated for a second.

"I'll try, but I'm afraid I'll disappoint you. I knew Hugo more than twenty-five years ago. He was a friend of my father's. You might get more information from his wife's family. Did you know her?"

"No. Our family refused to see her."

"Why?"

"It was foolish, but you have to realize . . . it was right after the war, and she was the daughter of a Nazi general."

"That's not an unforgivable sin. Sigrid was a fine woman."

Sidney started.

"You knew her?"

"I heard about her." Hidar stood up. "We really must go now." He held out his hand.

"We have to go too," Sidney said, gripping Hidar's hand. "But Olga's right: it's not every day that a Jew meets a Soviet cousin in an Arab country. Our families have been shattered, like one of the ancient vases on display in the museum here, in the room where treasures from Byblos are kept. It takes very strong glue to put a shattered family together again. I think Hugo had enough tenacity. But desire isn't enough: you also have to find the pieces."

BEIRUT, SEPTEMBER 1969

It was the day after the meeting between Sidney and Olga. Why was I also in Beirut? What had I really come to do there? Who was I this time: the tireless pilgrim for peace carrying on an endless dialogue with Palestinian leaders, or Salomon's son coming to honor a sacred promise and take advantage of those relations to pick up Hugo's trail? The truth is that I didn't really know, and that, as always, it was hard for me to sort out those two preoccupations within me. In any case, I was there.

I had landed at the Khalde airport early in the afternoon, to the familiar welter of overwhelmed customs officials, travelers in djellabahs and white turbans waiting for a plane to Kuwait, crying children, and cages crammed full of terrified chickens. And in the midst of that pandemonium, a gesticulating man pushed his way toward me through the crowd.

"Marek Halter? I'm Jacob, your Sephardic uncle, the uncle of your cousin Martín's wife Gloria in Argentina. She told me you were coming."

Uncle Jacob had reserved a room for me at the Hotel Alcazar.

"It's right next to the Hotel St. George," he said proudly, "and it's cheaper."

He took me there in a taxi, showed me to my room, tipped the bellhop, locked the door and waited awhile in silence, apparently listening for something. Then he came over to me and murmured in a conspiratorial tone, "Do you know that cousin Sidney is here?"

"Cousin Sidney?"

"Yes, our cousin from America. Look."

He took a newspaper from his pocket, opened it and showed me a paragraph that had been carefully circled with a blue ballpoint pen.

"Read that," he said. "Go on, read it. That's him: Sidney Halter. He gave his lecture last night. Too bad you weren't here then. You'd have loved to hear him." Then, drawing himself erect and doing his best to enhance his dramatic effects: "And that's not all. Our cousin Olga is also here. You know: Olga, Rachel Lerner's daughter. No, Olga and Sidney didn't come together. They're here at the same time only by chance. But she was at the lecture last night and I saw the two of them together. I told them you were coming, of course. I must say that Sidney didn't exactly seem overjoyed to hear it. I'd say he was worried about something — unless he was just uncomfortable, the way Americans sometimes are. Anyway, I arranged everything. 'Look here,' I told him, 'you don't get a chance to enjoy yourself every day. Day after tomorrow night, we'll have a drink at a sidewalk table of the St. George with our French cousin Marek.'"

I thanked uncle Jacob and complimented him on his diligence. I also smiled inwardly at the thought of those unknown relatives who hadn't been revealed to me till I came to Beirut this time. But that wasn't the main point. I was there for much more serious reasons.

My mind was elsewhere and my tone was probably indifferent when I answered, "Yes, uncle Jacob, I'm looking forward to that."

I then picked up the phone and began my investigation.

I had come to Beirut with a few introductions and mutual friendships. A French writer had recommended me to Marwan Dajani, a Palestinian businessman who owned the Strand Building, an enormous commercial complex in the fashionable Hamraa neighborhood, where Arafat and his friends regularly met. I went there. The receptionist directed me to a door in front of which armed fedayeen were filtering visitors. This was Marwan's office. Modern furniture, telephones, hypersexy secretaries. Marwan embodied, with obvious satisfaction, the image of the capable, dynamic businessman.

"Arafat and Abu Iyad will be here tomorrow," he said. "Call me in the morning and I'll tell you when you can come."

He then called George Habash's office, talked for a few moments in Arabic and said to me without hanging up, "Habash has gone to Baghdad. In the meantime, Kanafani will see you."

That was all right with me.

Kanafani received me in Habash's office. Preliminaries, arrack, all sorts of polite conversation. Then, after a brief exchange on the relative merits of French and Arabic poetry, we finally came to the point.

"The Arab revolution may break out anywhere besides Palestine," he said, "but Palestine is its leaven."

"Do you mean it may happen in Jordan?"

"That's a possibility."

Ghassan Kanafani was full of contradictions. And, maybe for that reason, he was more interesting and likable than his comrades. As a poet, he loved words; but as a militant, he mistrusted them and preferred action.

"Isn't talking a form of action?" I asked.

He didn't think so, and he therefore didn't believe in the value of a dialogue with the Israelis. To him, talking with the Israelis was tantamount to recognizing them, which he wanted to avoid at all cost.

I asked him what he thought of my efforts in this case.

"You never know," he answered. "Keep trying. Maybe the Israelis will give up Zionism, who knows?"

The truth is that he preferred the Jews to the Israelis. The Jews were far away. They lived in Moscow, Buenos Aires, New York, whereas the Israelis . . .

"Shall I take you back to your hotel?" he offered when he judged that he had said everything. Then, ironically: "Unless you're afraid . . ."

"What would I be afraid of?"

"I don't know. . . . My car is old and its brakes are uncertain."

"And what else?"

"Maybe you're afraid of terrorists."

"So you're a terrorist?"

He laughed.

"No, I'm not. I'm a resistance fighter. I fight against imperialist oppression."

"What imperialist oppression?"

"Israel's."

"And you fight by killing innocent people?"

"Why innocent?"

Thinking I would trouble him, or at least disconcert him, I told him about Hugo's death.

"Hugo Halter . . . Hugo Halter . . . ," he repeated thoughtfully. "It must have been a misunderstanding. That's how it is: when you fight a war, there are stray bullets."

"I see you already knew about it. Tell me what you know."

Kanafani smiled faintly.

"It's all so long ago now — and it was a misunderstanding, as I said." Then, when I insisted: "All right, I'll give you a lead. And you'll see that we're well informed. You have some cousins named Lerner. Don't look at me like that — our records are kept up to date, you know. Well, young Olga Lerner is here. Yes, here in Beirut. And the amazing part of it is that she's here with a close friend named Hidar Assadi, who knows a lot about . . . what interests you."

Hidar Assadi . . . of course. Always the same ones! Hadn't he been among Hugo's friends or contacts?

"You know that hoodlum?" uncle Jacob asked me when I saw him again.

"What hoodlum?"

"The one who brought you to the hotel. *I* know him. They want to destroy Israel, but they'll destroy Lebanon, you'll see. I just hope they won't do you any harm. Be very careful."

"Don't worry, my dear uncle," I said, laughing.

After being so uninterested that morning in his stories about

cousins who had miraculously gathered in Beirut, I now questioned
him closely. I asked him what Sidney was like, how Olga looked, if
he knew the man she was with, if he had seen him. And, to my own
great surprise, I asked him to reschedule our family meeting at the
St. George for tonight.

17

BUENOS AIRES

A Precocious Love (Continued)

SEPTEMBER 1969

"I just got a letter from my uncle Jacob," Gloria announced at dinner. "He's met our French cousin and everything is going well."

"What's our cousin doing in Beirut?" Anna Maria asked.

"Uncle Jacob doesn't say. He just says he's trying to stop him from 'doing anything foolish.'"

Anna Maria laughed.

"For your old uncle, doing something foolish means being involved in either politics or love. Which is it? Which one is more likely for our French cousin: politics or love?"

As she said this, she rubbed her knee against Arieh's under the table.

"At your age, what do you know about either politics or love?" Martín asked her ironically.

"I know a lot of things, Papa. For example, I know that you're against both love and politics. Isn't that right?"

Without meaning to, she had raised her voice. No one was better at making her angry than her father.

"For love, you're still too young," he replied. "As for politics, we know what its results are. Auschwitz, Hiroshima, the gulag — do those mean anything to you?"

Anna Maria's eyes became still darker.

"Those are horrors of the past. We're struggling to keep them from ever happening again."

"By killing people?"

"By killing murderers."

"Who decides who's a murderer?"

"Certainly not a petty bourgeois like you!"

After beginning playfully, the discussion had become almost violent. Anna Maria, furious, pushed back her chair.

"I can never eat in peace here!" she shouted with the spectacular unfairness she always showed in such cases; she wasn't far from regarding it as a form of "the dialectical spirit."

"You see what this kind of conversation leads to," Gloria said to Martín while their daughter took her coat and prepared to leave.

"I'll go with you," Arieh said.

He stood up and hurried out of the room behind her.

"I wish you'd stop running after me," she said irritably when he had caught up with her at the corner of Rodríguez Peña Street.

"I'm sorry, I didn't know you wanted to be alone."

Anna Maria took a few more steps in the direction of Corrientes Avenue, then stopped and turned around.

"Do you plan to just stand there till it's time for you to go back to Israel?"

Arieh came toward her.

"I thought —"

"Don't think!"

Corrientes Avenue was a broad, busy street lined with cafés and all kinds of stores. Arieh sometimes lingered there on his way home from the school.

"I'm glad to be here with you," he said in a subdued voice. Then, when she didn't answer but seemed calmer: "I don't want to make you angry again, but aren't you a little hard on your father?"

"You're not trying to defend that petty bourgeois, are you?"

"Why not, if he's right?"

"He's wrong!"

They walked awhile, then stopped again to wait for a break in the stream of cars on the Avenue of July 9.

"When you started arguing with your father, you seemed to be saying . . ."

"What did I seem to be saying?"

"That, for you, love and politics are the only things that give meaning to life."

"Yes, it's true." She kissed him lightly. "You Israelis are good as far as love is concerned, but when it comes to politics you don't know which end is up. You think that by defending your country you're solving all the problems of the human race."

"Please, let's not get into that again. You don't know Israel, you can't deny it! Do you think the Israelis don't demonstrate against the war in Vietnam, the way you do here in Buenos Aires? Do you think we don't know that people are dying of hunger in Brazilian slums?"

"You can't even protect Jews who come to visit you!"

"Are you talking about Hugo?"

"Yes, Hugo, the man you admire so much!"

The traffic light turned green and they moved along with the crowd toward the elegant Florida Street. Anna Maria stopped and looked at her watch as if she had just awakened from a dream.

"Oh, no! It's stopped! Do you know what time it is?"

"Yes, it's ten past ten," he answered.

"Ten past ten? My God, that's terrible! I didn't know it was so late! Let's go back! Come, hurry!"

"Why hurry? It's still early."

"No! Come! Don't ask questions, I'll explain later."

They had gone no more than a hundred yards in the incredibly dense crowd on the sidewalk, and had said only two or three sentences to each other, when they heard a powerful explosion. The display windows of the shops near them were shattered. The crowd went mad. Within seconds, panic stirred it into irresistible swirls, and waves going in opposite directions. Car horns blared, children cried, the sirens of ambulances and police cars were heard in the distance.

"What happened? What happened?" people around them asked.

"A bomb!" someone said.

"A bomb!" the crowd repeated.

"Yes, a huge bomb went off in front of the United States embassy on Sarmiento Street. Two people were killed. . . . No, ten. . . . No, a hundred. . . ."

Arieh, dazed, followed Anna Maria like an automaton.

"Where are you taking me? Tell me, where are you taking me? Where are we going?"

Wild-eyed and disheveled, Anna Maria didn't seem to hear him. She ran as fast as she could and didn't stop till she came to an old colonial house with a carved wooden door, on Lavalle Square, far from the main thoroughfares.

"Yes, yes, here we are," she said, as if she had only just realized that he was with her. "Wait for me. I have to go inside for a second. I'll be right back. Don't be afraid."

For a few minutes Arieh waited in front of the door as she had asked him to do. Then, curious, he crossed the street to see the house better. Windows on the second floor were lighted. He saw several people coming into a room. In the midst of them he thought he recognized Anna Maria gesticulating violently. What were they doing? Were they arguing?

Arieh was still trying to decipher the meaning of that strange shadow play when he suddenly heard the siren of a police car on the next street. Instinctively, he moved a short distance away and took refuge in the shadow of a doorway. The police car screamed to a stop in front of the house Anna Maria had gone into. Five policemen hurtled out of the car and rushed into the house. Arieh heard hurried footsteps, shouts, orders. Then a group of young people streamed out of a side door, followed seconds later by the policemen after them. More hurried footsteps. Shots, followed by a cry and angry swearing.

"Anna Maria!" he called out softly as the young people raced past.

She heard him. She stopped, saw him and stepped quickly into the dark doorway. As in a scene that he had seen many times in the movies, he put his arms around her and kissed her for a long time while the policemen raced past after the others. A pistol shot. Another. A car started, then another. When he finally let go of her, the street was empty.

"It's safe to leave," he said, amazed at his own calm.

But Anna Maria didn't relax till they had melted into the crowd on Corrientes Avenue.

"Thanks," she said. "You were great." Then, after taking a few steps and feeling a return of the strange thirst that only action could quench: "Now we have to see if anyone was caught." She saw him question her with his eyes. "Yes, as you can see, we're at war too."

His face tensed.

"So it was you!"

"Of course."

"We fight when we have no choice, *b'ein breira,* as my father says, but you . . ."

"It's the same with us, Arieh."

He flushed with anger; his eyes narrowed and he raised his voice:

"How can you say that? It's crazy! It's contemptible!"

"Calm down. Don't shout, people will hear you."

He moved closer, till his face was almost touching hers.

"In a war, armed soldiers fight each other. You people kill unarmed people, passersby, maybe your own friends. How can you support such irresponsible acts?"

Tears were welling; he didn't know if it was from rage, fear, or love — or all three.

"Control yourself," she said. "I could tell you didn't understand anything about politics."

She tried to maintain her resolute manner, but her heart wasn't in it. She too was overwrought. Her big, dark eyes had lost their spark of irony and she was now walking with abrupt, nervous steps.

"How can you defend such a thing?" Arieh asked again, behind her. "How?"

She didn't answer. When they came to the San Martín municipal theater, she simply said, without daring to look him in the eyes, "You can go home now."

"And you?"

"I have another appointment."

"The same kind?"

She shook her head and smiled sadly.

"I promised a Communist friend I'd stop by and see her. Some Cubans and Soviets will be there."

"Communists? That's what I thought: the same kind of people as before."

"No, you're wrong. Here, the Communists get along very well with the military. They even do good business together."

"But . . . don't they help the guerrillas?"

She affectionately ran her hand through his dark hair.

"I've already said you don't understand anything about politics. Run along now, I'll see you tomorrow."

"I thought . . ."

He leaned against a tree and looked straight into her eyes with an insolence she had never seen in him before.

"What's the matter?" she asked.

"I'd like to go with you."

"Well, I suppose . . . all right, if you want to."

Two rooms on the fifth floor. Cigarette smoke. A spotlight dimly illuminating a picture by the Argentinian Communist painter Castanina. Men and women, most of them young, talking with drinks in their hands.

"Here's Anna Maria!" exclaimed a plump woman with glasses. "Who's this young man?"

"My cousin."

"Welcome to Anna Maria's cousin," the woman said with a big smile.

She took a pack of cigarettes from a pocket of her jeans, lit one of them and said in a falsely confidential tone, lowering her voice, "The discussion was really fascinating. Those Soviets are admirable. Three cheers for a country that produces people like that!"

18

BEIRUT

In Search of the Past

Sidney had been deeply troubled by both those two encounters: first Olga at La Grotte aux Pigeons, then his French cousin two days later at the St. George. How was it possible? What destiny was capable of bringing together, in the hostile territory of Beirut, three survivors of a Jewish family that had been scattered all over the world?

Although he had been instantly attracted to Olga, with her gaiety and spontaneity, he was wary of Hidar, who obviously knew more about Hugo's last years than he was willing to admit. As for Marek, he had found him likable, even though Sidney rejected his approach to the problem of peace in the Middle East. He didn't believe in the power of words against the onslaught of violence. Being determined to talk peace with terrorists who thought only of killing seemed to him a kind of foolhardiness that was all the more unforgivable because it involved heavy risks. "You remind me of Hugo," he had said to Marek. Why? He couldn't have explained it exactly. It was just an intuition. But it was enough to put a distance between them that made real mutual understanding impossible.

Trying to make peace by talking . . . Sidney thought disdainfully when he was alone in his room, after they had all left. *And while you're at it, why not try to win the war by talking? If that worked, we wouldn't need to send any soldiers to Vietnam, we could send speech-makers instead.* That idea amused him. He undressed, took a shower and again thought back over the events of the last few days. *Incredible. Yes, incredible. Life is really made up of irony.* And since he absolutely had to tell someone about his "fantastic" life, he suddenly decided to call Jerry Cohen.

Jerry answered the phone. "Hey, how nice of you to call me," he said. "What a surprise! Tell me, how's your love life?"

"Guess who I met in Beirut today."

"Not Marjory. I saw her on Madison a little while ago, with your daughter — who looked adorable."

"Really? How are they?"

"They're fine. But I assume you didn't call me to ask about them. Who was it you met?"

"My cousin from Moscow and my cousin from Paris."

"You having a family reunion?"

"It's nothing to laugh about, Jerry."

"You mean it was boring?"

"Let's say it's complicated my life as far as Leila is concerned. You can see what I mean: if you want to be discreet about a love affair, this isn't exactly the way to do it."

"It's all right, things will be better tomorrow. You'll manage."

"Yes, but there's something else."

"Let's hear it."

"You remember my cousin Hugo?"

"The one who got killed in Israel?"

"That's right."

"Don't tell me he's in Beirut too?"

"Come on, Jerry!"

"Okay, sorry. But get to the point: what's the news about your cousin Hugo?"

"It's . . . hard to explain. I saw both these cousins and we had lots of things to tell each other. But even though Hugo's been dead eight years now, we talked about him more than anything else. Doesn't that seem strange to you?"

"Family matters always seem strange to me."

"This is no ordinary family matter! And here's the strangest part of it: the more we talked, the more information we exchanged, the less we seemed to know. Instead of getting answers, I had the feeling that I was bumping up against my own questions."

"What's that supposed to mean, Sid?"

"I know it's confusing, but bear with me. Uncle Abraham gave Hugo the responsibility of taking care of the family book. It's as if Hugo's death had taken away the family's knowledge of its own history, given all its members a feeling of having lost their past. It's like some Agatha Christie novel that keeps you in suspense till the end. Hugo's murder has turned all his cousins into detectives trying to find clues that will save the past from oblivion."

Sidney was right, because at the same time he was telling Jerry about his uneasiness, I was talking with Hidar, at last, in the Pierrot pastry shop on Georges Picot Street, not far from the Hotel Alcazar. Around us, secretaries from the nearby embassies gossiped as they ate their honey cakes.

That meeting with Hidar was important. He obviously didn't trust me. Did I belong to an Israeli, American or French intelligence service? He didn't know, but he was convinced that I belonged to one of them. Why else would a young man who was neither an Israeli nor an Arab venture into this quagmire? Although Hugo . . . Hidar, too, told me it was amazing how much I reminded him of Hugo. Not physically, but in my way of talking, looking and acting, as well as in my accent. Could one man come back in several incarnations? he asked me, laughing. Despite his attempted levity, I sensed that he knew more than he let on. He held at least part of the secret. And since destiny, in the person of my cousin Olga, had made our paths cross . . .

In an effort to gain his trust, I began by telling him about Hugo's notebook.

"It's an address book?"

"A kind of address book."

"And my name is in it?"

"Yes, it is."

"Along with other names?"

"Yes."

Hidar leaned heavily on his elbows, nearly tipping over the table, and looked at me intently with his dark, almost slanting eyes.

"And have you found all the people whose names are in the notebook?"

His tone put me on my guard. I took a moment to answer.

"Almost."

"Why almost?"

"Because . . ."

"You haven't found all of them?"

"That's right."

Hidar relaxed.

"It's an incredible story. If you had the notebook with you, I might be able to tell you some helpful things about the names you don't know."

I smiled.

"No, that notebook is the only source of our family knowledge. I'd rather not let it circulate." And when Hidar frowned, obviously feeling that I'd attacked him, I added, "Personally, I'm convinced that you know the reasons for Hugo's death and are either unwilling or unable to tell me about them."

He gave a start.

"What are you talking about?"

"Excuse my frankness, but you know things I don't know, and . . ."

"What makes you think so?"

"It's just a feeling."

"Since you've been frank with me, I'll be frank with you: I don't like clairvoyants and prophets." Then, taking hold of my shoulder after a silence: "I liked Hugo very much. He was my father's best friend. It was because of his generosity that I was able to begin my college education."

"Then you saw him again after the war?"

Hidar appeared to meditate. His lips slowly formed a smile.

"I've told you that you remind me of Hugo. He also had that kind of aggressive but friendly frankness. He was someone who believed in the power of truth. . . . Take my word for it, with his notebook you have much more information than I do, even though I knew him!" He changed the subject. "I know you're acquainted with many people. How's Golda Meir? You've met her, haven't you? And Moshe Dayan?"

But it was getting late and the days are short in October. All at once, light burst from neon signs. Dazzled, we closed our eyes and opened them again at the same time, laughing loudly.

"As far as contacts between Israelis and Palestinians are concerned, you can count on me," Hidar said almost solemnly. "Moscow is interested. There's probably no other solution to the conflict."

Just then someone rapped insistently on the window of the pastry shop. Hidar stood up. It was Olga.

"Hello, cousin," she said, hugging me. And to Hidar: "I was beginning to lose patience." She looked at the tray loaded with pastry and exclaimed, "Thanks for not eating it all up!"

Back in my hotel room, I called my mother to tell her about my conversation with Hidar, and also to ask her to take Hugo's notebook from my apartment and put it in a safe-deposit box at the bank.

BEIRUT, OCTOBER 1969

"Hugo was your cousin? Well, excuse my frankness, but I won't congratulate you on that." Rabbi Ben-Moussa pointed his beard at me, like a bird pointing its beak. He was quivering with rage. "It's written in *Pirke Avot,* 'Be on your guard in your relations with the powerful, for it is in their own interest that they make themselves accessible.' Your cousin was so glad he'd succeeded in associating with powerful people that he didn't see the danger he was in. And, even worse, he didn't see that he'd also put others in danger. Listen to me carefully: to reach the powerful of this world, he used people, *humble* people, without thinking about the risks he made them run. I'm telling you that Hugo Halter was a dangerous lunatic."

The conversation took place in a little synagogue in East Beirut. A dark room with a few benches, and a cabinet that held the Scroll of the Law.

"Here's an example," Rabbi Ben-Moussa went on. "To contact Kamal Jumblatt, Hugo used a Jewish merchant, David Stara, who supplied flour to bakers in the Shuf Mountains. Since Hugo later met with the Frangiehs and the Gemayels, the Druzes thought he was spying for the Christians, and whom did they blame? Stara!"

"Then what?"

"Then poor Stara was found with his throat cut, near Mukhtara."

"And you feel that Hugo was responsible for it?"

"It's not sure that he was and it's not sure that he wasn't. Money was stolen from Stara, but that doesn't prove anything. His death is a fact. Hugo went on showing himself with powerful people while poor Stara was dead."

"Hugo was also killed."

Rabbi Ben-Moussa obviously hadn't known that.

"Killed? Where?"

"In Israel. He was murdered by Palestinians."

He rapidly ran his hand over his beard, then quoted from a psalm: "'They have prepared a net for my steps; my soul is bowed down: they have digged a pit before me, into the midst whereof they are fallen themselves.'"

Then, as he was showing me to the door, he said, "Hugo is dead, so let's say no more about him. We'll respect the commandment, 'When the dead man rests, let the memory of him rest.' But pay attention, young man: there are no saints or heroes, and no perfection, in this vale of tears. It would be a great mistake for you to idealize your cousin to the point of making him one of our prophets. That's what I wanted to tell you."

19

NEW YORK

God Willing

Trinity School stood at the corner of Ninety-first Street and Columbus Avenue. It was a big, square, red-brick building whose long halls
were lined with hard benches. Richard liked the "traditional" atmosphere of his school, one of the oldest in New York. He was amused
by the slightly tarnished plaque at its entrance, which indicated its
original name: "The Episcopal Charity School, 1794." It was now a
private school for the rich and, in spite of its name and tradition,
almost half its students were Jewish.

When Richard had two close friends, John Kinsey and Alex Seaver,
both goyim and both on his soccer team. Trinity was for boys only.
Friendship replaced love there. And though Richard sometimes met
girls at the Green Bar, a block from the school, the truth is that they
didn't interest him very much. Schoolwork, sports and friends were
enough to take up his time and fill his thoughts.

When Richard, John and Alex left the school at the end of a
sunny but unseasonably cold afternoon in October 1969, their attention was caught by a group standing on Columbus Avenue. It was
the feverish part of the day in New York when everything seemed to
speed up: people, traffic and time. A diffuse feeling of violence

emanated from the crowd. The noise of sirens and car horns ripped through the chilly air. People came and went, passing and bumping into each other in seemingly aimless and endless motion. Richard liked that electric atmosphere. And it seemed only natural to him to approach the group.

Half a dozen bearded young men were there. Below their black hats hung earlocks, curly locks of hair in front of their ears. And they were trying to persuade a boy in the senior class of Trinity School to put on tefillin.

Richard vaguely knew what tefillin (or phylacteries) were. He had seen them in his grandfather's synagogue in Winnipeg. He remembered how religious Jews wrapped them around their left arms before prayer. They were two black leather hollow cubes, each with a leather strap attached to it. According to his grandfather, the faithful revitalized their faith by strapping on those cubes every day. "When you put on tefillin," he had said, "you engrave His name on yourself." Still the operation had always seemed mysterious and sacred to Richard.

The Trinity School senior appeared to be ill at ease. He fidgeted nervously in front of the bearded young men, evidently not wanting to offend them, but earnestly wishing he were somewhere else.

"I . . . I'm in a hurry," he stammered. "I have to go home."

"It will only take five minutes," one of the religious young men said soothingly.

Near them, a white van was parked next to the curb. Painted on its side, in both Latin and Hebrew letters, was the word *Lubavich*.

"I'm in a hurry," the senior repeated awkwardly.

He had repeated it so often that by now it had become comical, and there was laughter from the crowd gathered around the group.

"You are Jewish, aren't you?" the religious man asked gently.

"Of course I'm Jewish, but —"

"And you're not ashamed of it?"

"No, but —"

"Do you know that, to be a Jew, you must respect the Mitzvoth, the Jewish religious and moral obligations?"

"I do respect them."

"Good, but you must also respect the Mitzvah toward the Almighty."

Alex tugged at Richard's sleeve.

"Let's go. I'm getting cold and this looks like it's going to last a long time."

Alex Seaver was a tall, dark-haired boy with blue eyes that always looked surprised. He lived a few blocks from the school, at the corner of Ninety-third Street and Central Park West.

"Let's go to my place," he said.

His two friends accepted the invitation without comment, knowing that in his apartment the snacks were better and time usually passed more pleasantly.

"I thought Jews didn't proselytize," John said when he had sat down in Alex's room, which had Warhol prints on its walls.

John, the son of a Protestant minister, was the smallest of the three, and also the least tactful.

"They don't," Richard replied. "Those Jews weren't trying to convert a Christian: they were trying to bring another Jew back to his own religion."

"What happens if they talk to a Christian by mistake?"

"They always start by asking if the person is Jewish or not."

"Have they ever talked to you?"

"No."

Alex turned on the television. The room was filled with the excited shrieks of a young woman who had just won five thousand dollars on a game show. Alex turned off the sound with annoyance. The screen continued to show a face grimacing with joy, a wide-open mouth and a body on the verge of going into convulsions.

"What if you put on those straps, those tefillin," he asked, "and then said you weren't Jewish? I'd be curious to see how those fanatics would react!"

"Try it and find out."

"No, *you're* the one who should try it. It would be more fun, because you're Jewish in a way, but not really — isn't that what you told us?"

"All right, I'll do it!"

A week went by. Every day, when they came out of school, the three friends vainly looked for the Lubavichers and the white van that they had nicknamed "the Mitzvahmobile." It wasn't till two weeks later, when they had almost forgotten their plan, that they found the Lubavichers near Trinity School. This time there were only two of them. Unluckily for them, it was raining lightly and they were having great difficulty attracting the attention of passersby. Their faces brightened when they recognized Richard and his friends; they were obviously glad to be on familiar ground. Richard saw it and felt remorseful. He slowed his steps, but John and Alex pushed him forward.

"You're not going to chicken out, are you?"

One of the Lubavichers, a husky young man with a fan-shaped beard, wearing a wet black coat over a white shirt, hurried toward Richard.

"You're Jewish, aren't you?"

"Yes."

"Have you ever put on tefillin?"

"No."

"But it's the supreme Mitzvah for any Jew!"

"I know."

"What's your name?"

"Richard, Richard Halter."

The bearded man smiled.

"I'm Mendel Fogelman."

He was only a few years older than Richard and, actually, he seemed rather likable.

"It's raining — would you like to come into our van?" he went on. "We'll be dry there."

"I don't mind the rain," Richard said uneasily.

Had Fogelman guessed what he intended to do? At any rate, he began explaining the meaning of the tefillin in a singsong, hypnotic voice, like that of an Oriental storyteller:

"Tefillin are a neglected Mitzvah nowadays, yet few rites are as rich, few have such a power of edification and sanctification."

A crowd had gathered around them. Fogelman obviously liked speaking in public. He raised his arms, shook his head, stepped forward, backward, then forward again, pretended to call to witness the people listening to him:

"When Rabbi Khiya Bar-Abin was asked by Rabbi Nachman Ben-Isaac, 'What is contained in the tefillin of the Master of the Universe?' he replied with this verse: 'Who is like thy people Israel, a nation unique on earth?' And to the question 'Does the Almighty, blessed be His name, glory in Israel's praise?' he answered, 'Yes, because the Almighty, blessed be His name, said to Israel, "You have given me a unique character by proclaiming, 'Hear, O Israel, the Lord our God, the Lord is One,' and in return I grant you a unique character: 'Who is like thy people Israel, a nation unique on earth?'"'"

The rain had stopped and a streak of sunlight had timidly slipped between two gray clouds. Fogelman lowered his arms one last time and smiled at Richard.

"Now do you understand? The tefillin are like a wedding ring between the Almighty, blessed be His name, and man. What could be more beautiful than to link yourself with Beauty? What could be stronger than to associate yourself with Justice?" He stepped closer to Richard, who smelled the musty odor of his wet coat. "First you put on the *tefillin shel yad,* the arm phylacteries, then the *tefillin shel rosh,* the head phylacteries. This shows that action and practice take precedence over meditation and theory. It is written, 'We will do and understand everything that the Almighty, blessed be He, has said.' It's by obeying the Commandments that we truly understand their meaning."

Fogelman stopped talking and looked straight into Richard's eyes. Richard looked back at him and discovered that he had green eyes. *It's funny,* he thought: *he has beautiful green eyes.*

"Well?" the Lubavicher asked.

Richard turned his head a little and, as though in a dream, saw his two friends smiling at him. Then, feeling like a sleepwalker, not knowing very well what he was saying or doing, he heard himself answer:

"All right."

Richard lay on his bed that night, unable to sleep. It seemed to him that the streetlamps shone through the blinds of his room more brightly than usual. He wasn't proud of himself. No, not at all! He had followed all of Mendel Fogelman's instructions. He had put on the tefillin and, as he wrapped a strap around his middle finger, like a wedding ring, he had recited a Biblical passage that made a deep impression on him: "And I will betroth thee unto me for ever; yea, I will betroth thee unto me in righteousness, and in judgment, and in lovingkindness, and in mercies. I will even betroth thee unto me in faithfulness: and thou shalt know the Lord." He remembered how troubled he had been, and how respectful he had suddenly become, and how he had been awed by the rite and the Lubavicher's voice. And he remembered Fogelman's surprise when, after the ceremony, he had told him that he wasn't Jewish. He had expected an angry outburst, but he had received only a sad look and a sorrowful smile. The memory of it made him feel heartbroken and ashamed.

He didn't fall asleep till dawn, and when his mother woke him he felt as if he hadn't slept at all. He took a shower, drank a cup of coffee, went back to his room and called information for the number of the Lubavichers in Brooklyn. He wanted to talk to Mendel Fogelman, but the man who answered in Brooklyn said that he wasn't there, he had gone to Boston.

A week went by before Richard was able to speak to him on the phone. Fogelman listened to his confession in silence, then quoted Proverbs: "'He that covereth his sins shall not prosper: but whoso confesseth and forsaketh them shall have mercy.'"

Two days later, on a Sunday morning, they met in front of the Plaza Hotel. "We'll walk across Central Park," Fogelman had said. And Richard was apprehensive when he came to keep the appointment. It was cold that morning. The park, a vast stretch of greenery hemmed in by concrete and steel, showed all the colors of Monet's *Les Nymphéas*. The eye was caressed by the whole range of greens, blues, browns, grays and reddish-browns. Along footpaths patrolled by mounted policemen, hundreds of New Yorkers were calmly jogging. Fogelman wore his usual black hat and threadbare black coat. He had the same beard, though it was perhaps a little more orderly now. He was cheerful and seemed to have no resentment against Richard.

"Do you know what a Hasid is?" he asked abruptly.

"No."

"Or who Baal Shem Tov was?"

"No."

Fogelman's half-closed eyes showed a beginning of surprise.

"Baal Shem Tov was born in the year 5458 after the creation of the world by the Almighty, blessed be He — in 1698 of the common era." His voice had resumed its incantatory rhythm. His body swayed and his eyes closed completely. "It was after the great massacres by Bohdan Khmelnytsky's Cossacks. Millions of Jews in central and eastern Europe were living in wretchedly poor little villages. Children had to work hard for long hours and had almost no time for school, so hundreds of thousands of Jews grew up with very little knowledge." He raised his arms as if he were about to take flight. "Knowledge, knowledge . . . for Jews, it's the supreme duty. It's written, 'Above all, study. Whatever your motives at first, you will soon love study for itself.' Then Baal Shem Tov came. He saw that the Jews were in despair and tried to restore their faith. He told them that what was agreeable to the Almighty was the intention and not knowledge itself; he told them that sometimes a sincere song or a cry filled with piety came closer to the will of the Almighty than an insensitive reading of a holy text, even if it was done in a beautifully dramatic way. And the poor began to dance. . . ."

Near Bow Bridge, which rose above the lake, Fogelman stood still for a moment and then, to Richard's great surprise, began dancing with his hands raised, his head tilted slightly forward and his eyes still closed. People around them stopped and seemed astounded by what they were seeing. And the truth is that Richard felt terribly embarrassed.

He soon realized, however, that the onlookers were much less embarrassed than he was. They weren't laughing or making fun of Fogelman; their faces clearly showed respect. Fogelman's dance wasn't a game, not at all. It was a rite, a ceremony, a communion with the Almighty. As he went on whirling, his body became light and airy, and he was like the birds flying above the lake.

Captivated by the scene and caught up in the rhythm of the dance, Richard began accentuating it by clapping his hands. The crowd followed his example. A man with a guitar turned up from somewhere and started playing. Richard recognized a Jewish melody that he had heard long ago in his grandfather's house in Winnipeg. Swept along by a mysterious nostalgia for ancestors, as well as Fogelman's increasingly rapid gyrations, he began dancing too.

Later, when they were both sitting, out of breath, on a bench in the Shakespeare Garden, across from the American Museum of Natural History, Fogelman said simply, as if it were a matter of course, "Next Sunday we'll go to see the Lubavicher Rebbe in Brooklyn."

20

BEIRUT — NEW YORK

Return to New York

NOVEMBER 1969

Sidney left Beirut, feeling sick with anxiety. He had become a divided man. Even before saying goodbye to Leila, he had begun to miss her body; he wondered apprehensively how he could go back to having normal relations with his wife. Also, that unexpected family meeting had only upset him. What Olga had told him about her parents, their lives, their desire to go to Israel, and their difficult relationship with Sasha seemed tragic to him. He was deeply affected by Salomon's poignant race to recover the past, and his death before he could achieve his goal. Hugo's address book intrigued him and he was frightened by the Palestinians' mysterious preparations, which I may have been wrong to tell him about after I had gotten wind of them. Frightened for Israel, for everyone, for Mordecai on his Kibbutz Dafneh in Galilee.

Sidney didn't believe that those Palestinian terrorist organizations could ever become oriented toward peace. He knew, of course, that I kept seeing all those people for a good cause, in the hope of achieving peace someday, even if it meant granting them the right to have an independent state beside Israel. But were all those efforts worth making? Israel's military strength was her best, her only, guarantee of survival. Sidney was convinced that if peace ever came, it would be through the triumph not of morality, but of various countries' enlightened self-interest. And that, he believed, was a very distant prospect. What should be done in the meantime? In the meantime, Israel should be helped to defend and develop herself. Just before leaving, he had been impressed when he saw a demonstration by Palestinian students at the American University. At first he had been attracted to them and felt like defending them, liking them. Seeing them fill the campus with their flags and their singing, he had spontaneously thought of young Zionists before the birth of the State of Israel. But why, when he spoke to some of them, did they have to launch into anti-Jewish diatribes? Why did that young woman, so provocatively beautiful with her gray eyes, her dark braided hair, tell him that the Holocaust was an invention of the Zionists? Why, in demanding the right to have a state of their own, did they deny that same right to the Jews? And why, even worse, did they deny the Jews a right to a past, *their* past?

Dinnertime came. It was the best part of traveling in a plane or being in a hospital — the only two places where it was good to let others take charge of you. He asked the stewardess for a Scotch. Seeing that the man beside him had champagne, he immediately regretted his choice, but foolish pride kept him from changing his order. He emptied his glass and found the whiskey particularly bitter. He then waited for the stewardess to take away the tray and for the captain to stop droning on about trivial details. When the loudspeaker was finally silent, he stretched voluptuously and tried to put Beirut out of his mind.

"Are you from New York?" the man beside him suddenly asked.

"Yes," Sidney answered reluctantly.

"Were you in Beirut on business, or just visiting?"

"On business."

The man carefully blew his nose, said apologetically, "I have a cold," and asked, "What kind of business?"

"Lectures at the American University."

"You're a professor?"

"No, a doctor."

The man spoke English with a pronounced Arabic accent.

Sidney observed him for a moment. He was paunchy, with a receding hairline, slightly bulging eyes and a sweaty face.

"Are you Lebanese?" Sidney asked him.

"No, Peruvian."

"Ah. But before?"

The man laughed.

"Before what?"

Sidney didn't answer; he had no desire to go on and wished he hadn't said that "before." But the man obviously wanted to become better acquainted.

"I've lived in Lima for several years. But you're right, I'm not originally from Peru."

"Then you're an Arab."

"How did you know?"

"From your accent."

"Yes, I'm an Arab. But can you tell which Arab country I'm from?"

"No."

That admission of ignorance seemed to close the conversation. Sidney dozed off in the silence that followed. But no, the man hadn't given up.

"Do you know Bethlehem?"

"Hm . . ."

"I'm from Beit Jala, near Bethlehem."

"Really?"

"Yes." The man from Bethlehem ceremoniously held out his hand. "My name is Jael al-Ardja."

"I'm Sidney Halter."

"You're Jewish?"

"I'm Jewish."

"Do you like Israel?"

"Of course."

"It's an American colony!"

"Ah, yes. . . ."

Sidney did his best to avoid a discussion, but the man was evidently in a talkative mood.

"Actually, I admire the Jews. They're the only ones who have enough genius to rewrite history."

"What history?"

"The history of the Second World War. Their story about Nazi gas chambers, for example, made it possible for them to carry out a gigantic political and financial fraud that mainly benefited Israel and international Zionism."

This jolted Sidney out of his apathy. He opened his mouth to answer, but he was stopped by a violent lurch of the plane and the captain's voice asking the passengers to kindly fasten their seat belts. For the second time in forty-eight hours, he had encountered in an Arab that strange will to deny, not out of liking for the murderers, but out of hostility against the victims.

Jael al-Ardja went on talking. In spite of his anti-Americanism, he liked to visit the United States. On the way to Lima, he always stopped over in New York, where he stayed at the Meridien. Did Sidney know the Meridien? The Hilton? It wasn't the same, of course, for an American. . . .

"I'd be glad to see you again," he concluded when the flight was nearly over.

"But I've told you that I'm Jewish."

"My best friends are Jews." Then abruptly: "Do you know Ben-Gurion?"

"I know who he is, needless to say."

"But you don't know him personally?"

"No, I haven't had the good luck to meet him."

"It seems he's about to go to Latin America. Maybe I'll have the good luck to meet him."

"Oh?" Sidney said.

He had the impression that Jael al-Ardja gave him a mocking look, but he was feeling sleepy and soon dozed off again.

He found New York paralyzed by an enormous demonstration against the war in Vietnam. The newspapers spoke of a historic day. The organizers of the demonstration called it "an unprecedented success." Sidney's taxi crawled laboriously through the snarled traffic. Its radio was on and he heard an announcement that President Nixon would make an important speech on November 3.

Marjory was waiting for Sidney when he arrived home. She had bought flowers and made his favorite cheesecake.

"Your brother Larry and his wife are in New York," she told him. "I invited them to come over for a welcome-home party. Your nephew David is also coming, with his new girlfriend. She works at the UN. I hear she's very nice."

All of a sudden, Beirut seemed very far away.

21

BUENOS AIRES

A Precocious Love (Conclusion)

NOVEMBER 1969

It was a clear, hot Sunday. Doña Regina had replaced the usual hot
bouillon with cold gazpacho. Don Israel wore wide red suspenders
over his undershirt and stood with sensuous pleasure in the stream
of air from the ancient fan buzzing steadily on the dresser. The family had gathered for Arieh's birthday. Seventeen — that was worth a
celebration!

As usual, Anna Maria teased her grandmother. Martín scolded
her. She answered him sharply. His temper flared and he tried to
quell his anger by changing the subject.

"Gloria got another letter from her uncle in Lebanon," he
announced to the whole assembly. "He had some surprising news:
in addition to meeting Marek, he's now also met cousin Sidney from
New York and cousin Olga from Moscow."

"Olga, Sasha's sister?" Doña Regina asked.

"Yes."

"Sasha the Communist?"

"That's right."

"We've got so many relatives that I feel as if they were swarming
all over us," Anna Maria remarked.

Arieh pretended to be offended.

"Thanks for the compliment!"

His Spanish was improving every day and he was even developing the highly distinctive Buenos Aires *porteño* accent.

"Don't be so touchy," Anna Maria said, pinching the tip of his nose.

Gloria began reading the letter aloud. When she had finished, they all started talking at once. Don Israel expressed surprise at that sudden expansion of the family. Anna Maria made caustic comments about uncle Jacob's "simple-minded hostility" to the Palestinians. And Arieh, who knew Sidney, wondered what he was doing in Beirut. But Mordecai was the one most obviously affected by uncle Jacob's letter.

"What's the matter, Papa?" Arieh asked.

Mordecai, who had remained silent since the beginning of the meal, narrowed his eyes.

"Hidar, Hidar Assadi . . . ," he said in a voice touched with emotion. "Isn't the Hidar mentioned in the letter from Gloria's uncle the same one who knew Hugo in Tunis when he was still almost a child?"

"The cousin Hugo who was killed in Israel?" Martín asked.

"Yes. He and Hidar's father were close friends during the war. And I heard . . . yes, I was told in Israel that Hidar probably knew who killed Hugo."

The information given by Mordecai took up the rest of the afternoon. Some friends of Doña Regina's who came for tea noisily took part in the debate. Other subjects discussed were the Arab-Israeli conflict, prewar Warsaw and the quick passing of time. Don Israel, who liked jokes, told a few.

After a time, Anna Maria sat down beside Arieh and said quietly, "I have to go."

He thought he heard repressed anxiety in her voice.

"I'll go with you."

Had he been firm enough? Had he shown enough masculine determination?

His pretty cousin resolutely shook her head.

"No."

"Is it a secret meeting?"

"Very secret."

"Will I see you again?"

"I'll call you."

Doña Regina had been watching them with a mixture of indulgence and curiosity.

"Are you two hatching a plot?"

Anna Maria stood up.

"I have an appointment."

"Will you come home late?"

"I don't know yet."

"Ah, these young people!" Doña Regina said with a sigh. And, addressing the whole room: "It's wonderful to be young, isn't it? When I was their age . . ."

The meeting took place on Chacabuco Street, in a big apartment recently rented by the movement. It was a simply furnished middle-class apartment. The dark red flowers on the heavy curtains also appeared on all the upholstery. Only a poster with a picture of Che Guevara gave evidence of the new occupants' convictions. Leaders of the FAR (Perónist armed forces) and the Montoneros (Perónist youth) had been meeting there for several days to coordinate their actions.

When Anna Maria came in, they were all there, except for the poet Julio Feldman, who was to come with a new weapons supplier. The two men arrived a few minutes later. Julio was a tall young man with brown eyes and a mustache that was already turning gray. His swarthy companion wore dark glasses that didn't completely hide his bulging eyes. He seemed to be always in motion and kept talking into Julio's ear while Julio, very pale, listened with discreet attention.

Mario, who was apparently the leader of the group, began:

"The struggle we're carrying on isn't easy, and it will be less and less easy from now on. It's safe to predict that there will be terrible repression after the series of forceful actions we're planning." He looked around him. "So anyone who wants to back out can still do it."

"No one's going to back out, Mario," Julio said, with an apprehensive glance at his companion in the dark glasses. "We're not going to put our struggle in danger because of the weakness or cowardice of this or that person."

"Are you afraid we'll be betrayed to the police?" someone asked.

Julio didn't answer at first. He had a somber expression and everyone waited for him to speak.

"No, I'm not afraid of that," he finally said. "I'm afraid of human weakness, natural human weakness. There are people who prefer to be cowardly rather than unhappy."

"You're a poet, and now you're talking like one!" Mario said, putting his hand on Julio's shoulder. "We're not concerned about cowardice or unhappiness. Fighting for a better society is one kind of happiness, and not everyone is lucky enough to have it. But we must realize that our struggle is difficult, so I may as well warn —"

"Happiness has nothing to do with it," Julio insisted. "What we're doing is a duty, and we're here because we accept its risks."

"Enough! Enough!" cried a chubby little man at the back of the room. "We don't have any time to waste on empty chatter!"

"Empty chatter?" Mario said, tossing his head to throw back the hair that had fallen over his eyes. "A revolutionary isn't a killer. When he agrees to plant a bomb, he must know why, and do it with full awareness of —"

"I still say we have to stop the chatter!" the chubby man interrupted, stepping forward. "There's a time for theory and a time for action. The time for theory was yesterday. Julio has brought the Palestinian comrade to us. Let us listen to his proposals."

The man with the dark glasses drew himself erect, as if he were about to speak, but after thinking for a moment he slumped a little, put his hands in his pockets and waited placidly, as if the matter concerned someone else. Julio answered for him:

"Comrade Jael has supplied us with four cases of dynamite, fifty-two pistols and a thousand cartridges."

"What are we giving in exchange?" Mario asked.

"We agree to pay all the expenses of transporting the weapons."

"And who will pay for the weapons?"

Julio rubbed his forehead several times, as he always did when he was faced with an awkward situation.

"Palestinian comrades are struggling against imperialism in the Middle East. Their representative in Latin America, Jael al-Ardja, is with us tonight. But the struggle against imperialism is now worldwide, so they need — how shall I put it? — they need a relay in Latin America. We'll be that relay."

"What does that mean?" asked Anna Maria, who till now had said nothing. "Will we have to blow up the Israeli ambassador?"

There was a stir among the others. Julio rubbed his forehead again and said, "No, our Palestinian friends aren't asking us to do that. They want us to help counteract Zionist propaganda, make the Arab revolutionary positions better known, and —"

"I protest," the chubby little man broke in. "I protest with all my strength! I want . . . I want us to say frankly to our Middle Eastern comrades that we support them, that we're willing to go to the Palestinian camps in Jordan to train them, if our help is needed, but that the international action of an Argentinian revolutionary can't be limited to anti-Israeli propaganda. Especially since in Israel there's also a struggling proletariat, a Left that shares our views." He paused to catch his breath, then blurted out, "Damn it, comrades, what you're suggesting that we do is stupid! Your attitude isn't revolutionary — no, not at all!"

Mario intervened brusquely:

"Stop yelling, Roberto! You want action, not theory? Then get it into your head that for action we need weapons, and for weapons we have to pay, and to pay. . . . To hell with you! You're getting me all mixed up!"

The discussion went on for a long time. The Palestinian didn't open his mouth, but they all understood that if they wanted weapons, they would have to pay the price.

Throughout the discussion, Anna Maria thought of Arieh, and the thought made her unhappy.

Had Julio, the poet, guessed her distress? Before leaving her, he advised her in a friendly but firm tone, "At this stage in our action, you'd better break off with your Israeli cousin. Unless you decide to abandon us. You can't reconcile him and us."

"What if I decide to give up political action?"

Julio looked at her a long time and his smile became ugly.

"You know very well that no one has a right to abandon the cause."

Poor Arieh, thought Anna Maria.

TEL AVIV, JUNE 1970

On the day before the feast of Shavuot, I got out of an Air France
747 at Lod airport, where, having been notified by my mother, my
cousin Mordecai was waiting for me. It had been more than two
years since my last trip to Israel, and just seeing Hebrew letters on
the front of a building gave me a wonderful feeling.

This was the first time I had seen Mordecai. He hadn't been
able to come to Tel Aviv the last time I was there, and since my stay
was very short I hadn't had time to visit him on his kibbutz in
Galilee. Was I glad to see him? Yes and no. This trip, like the one
before, was motivated by my fight for peace. After meeting with
nearly all the Palestinian leaders, including Arafat, in Beirut, I had
come to tell the Israeli leaders about it. And, for that, I could
obviously have done without this loud-talking cousin. I had my
mother to thank for my meeting with him. She and her mania for
keeping the whole family informed of our slightest doings! Would
she ever understand that you could love your house without sitting
on its roof?

Luckily, though, I liked Mordecai from the start. Garrulous but
capable of seriousness, he fitted the classic idea of a kibbutznik: he

had the concerns of an intellectual and lived like a peasant. He had just come back from Argentina and was still excited by his stay at the other end of the world. He told me about Doña Regina and "little" Anna Maria, but the bulk of our conversation was about the situation in Israel. I knew few countries in the world where most citizens were as passionately interested in politics as they were in Israel.

"Do you know about the Goldmann affair?" he asked me as we were coming into Tel Aviv. Then, noticing my blank expression: "I can see you don't. I'll tell you about it at your hotel. That reminds me: where are you staying?"

"At the Bazel."

"Why not the Dan? Sidney stays there."

"Because the Dan is too expensive for me."

The Bazel Hotel, like the Dan Hotel, was on Hayarkon Street, next to the sea. It was a six-story hotel, new and clean, but without a view of the beach. I left my suitcase there and we went to eat at the corner of Frichman Street.

"Well, what about the Goldmann affair?" I asked when we had sat down at one of the sidewalk tables of a little Oriental restaurant.

Mordecai pushed up his glasses as though to see my reaction better and announced, "Gamal Abdel Nasser has invited Nahum Goldmann to come to Cairo."

I didn't share his enthusiasm.

"Meetings like that should be announced only when they've taken place."

He shrugged as if he wanted to apologize for having given me the news.

"You think it won't come off?"

"That's right."

"Golda seems to agree with you. She's refused to give him her blessing."

Mordecai seemed surprised by Golda Meir's refusal to back Nahum Goldmann, but what surprised me was that Goldmann, who was the president of the World Jewish Congress and held three passports, should need permission from the Israeli government to go to Cairo. Unless he intended to officially represent Israel there.

"Goldmann," I said, "is an eminent Jew with an attractive personality. A meeting between him and Nasser would probably stir up some excitement. But the Egyptians are fighting the Israelis, not the Jews, and I think it's in their interest to talk with their adversaries."

"Aren't the Israelis Jews?"

"Yes, but Israeli Jews." I laughed.

"What's funny?" asked Mordecai, surprised.

"I just realized that I've repeated to you what I said exactly three days ago to an Egyptian diplomat in Paris."

"He invited you to Cairo?"

"Yes."

"And do you intend to go there?"

"Yes."

"Then why are you against Goldmann's going there?"

"Because I won't have any personal stake in going to Cairo. I can only be a modest intermediary, and maybe a bridge between enemies who will have to meet someday if they want peace."

"A bridge? It's odd, you talk like Hugo. He also wanted to be a bridge."

Twenty-four hours later I introduced myself to the prime minister's chief of staff. He listened to me, asked me to wait and came back a short time later.

"Golda has good memories of your last argument," he said. "She'll see you now."

Golda was there. Strong and square, she seemed to be part of the big desk in front of her. She smiled, crushed out her cigarette, stood up, held out her hand to me and said simply, "I'm glad to see you again."

What an amazing change had taken place in her! Two years earlier, I had met a sick old woman who had to be supported and kept from overtaxing herself. I now found her solid as a desert rock, willful, determined, smoking one cigarette after another. I told her my impression and wondered aloud if the exercise of power might not be the most powerful tonic. We philosophized a little and took pleasure in speaking Yiddish, exchanging a few unimportant remarks.

After those preliminaries, she finally asked me what had brought me to Israel. I now spoke slowly and deliberately, knowing that all my words would be loaded with meaning and ambiguity. I proposed a meeting between an Israeli diplomat and President Nasser of Egypt, which, I believed, might pave the way for a visit to Israel by Nasser.

"You're out of your mind!" she exclaimed. "Completely insane!"

I argued that this was the kind of insanity with which it was sometimes possible to break the order of the world, and that ideas like this always seemed senseless at first, but then seemed obvious after they had succeeded.

She looked at me thoughtfully and said, "It's funny, you remind me of your cousin Hugo. He *was* your cousin, wasn't he? Well, after all, why not? Yes, why not?" Then she laughed, as though she wanted to avoid giving too much weight to what she was about to say. "Have you talked about your idea to an Egyptian leader?"

"Yes, to Mohammed Hassan al-Toukhami. He's a 'free officer' who took part, with Nasser, in the revolution against King Farouk. I met him in Paris."

"I can't ask you to give me any guarantees, of course," she murmured after what seemed to me an endless silence. "But I hope you understand how hard it is for me to plunge into such an adventure."

I answered that the Israelis had nothing to lose and everything to gain by proving their willingness to take any chance for dialogue, and I told her that ever since my arrival everyone had been telling me about that "Operation Goldmann" whose failure seemed to be attributed to her personally.

"Did your Egyptian friend feel that a trip to Cairo by an Israeli diplomat was a real possibility?" she asked.

"Yes, he did."

She was silent again, then said, "Personally, I have nothing against it. Anything that can promote peace is important. Ever since I became responsible for this country and all the Jews who live in it, that's been constantly on my mind, believe me. We have a coalition government. If your attempt is successful, the government will fall apart. I don't care about that, but I wouldn't want it to fall apart for nothing. I'd like to be sure we have some chance of success. I'm going to meet with a few friends in the cabinet. Come and see me at five o'clock tomorrow afternoon, in my office in Tel Aviv." She stood up. "Will you please write down that Egyptian diplomat's name for me?"

When I had done as she asked, she held out her hand to me and said, "Good luck."

"Good luck to you too."

I had twenty-four hours ahead of me. Twenty-four hours to kill. I didn't understand how anyone could kill the most precious thing we have ever received: time. But that was what I had to do. I went back to my hotel and looked over the list of Israeli and Arab names that I had drawn up on the basis of Hugo's notebook. Many of them were already crossed out: those people either were dead or didn't have much to tell. Others meant nothing to me. Still others seemed to me so mysterious that I felt in advance that they were indecipherable. And my eyes stopped, God knows why, on the name of Dr. Jemil al-Okby, in Gaza. Why did that name catch my attention? As I said, only God knows. But a sudden intuition told me there was something to look for in that direction. Fifty miles to Gaza; a hundred there and back. Not too hard to do in one afternoon, even on a road with heavy traffic. I decided to go.

Early June is the best time to visit Israel. The light is transparent, the sun is blond in a blue sky, and it's not too hot. All the way to Yavneh, the road wound its way among vineyards, then the vineyards were replaced by orange groves. I drove calmly, without hurrying, taking time to stop here and meditate there, and invoke the holy memory of Yokhanan Ben-Zakai, who foresaw the destruction of Jerusalem, asked Titus for permission to found his school and abandoned the insurgents so that Judaism could survive. He turned his back on flesh-and-blood Jews so that the Bible would be saved and the first book of the Talmud would be written. What a choice! What a terrible, tragic dilemma!

I had reached this point in my reflections when I arrived at the gates of the city of Gaza. An Israeli patrol asked for my papers. I parked my car on the main public square, near the mosque. A light wind was blowing dust toward the lower part of the gently sloping square, in the direction of the marketplace. The square was crowded, even though it was siesta time. I was quickly surrounded by men who were nearly all from a Palestinian refugee camp next to the city.

"Which way is the hospital?" I asked.

They all talked at once, but no one answered me. Standing off to one side, two Israeli soldiers watched us. Finally a rather young man, wearing jeans, a white shirt and sandals, stepped toward me.

"Why the hospital?" he asked in English.

"I'm trying to find Dr. Jemil al-Okby."

Without looking at the others, he motioned me to follow him. We walked awhile in silence, went into a café with a beaten-earth floor and sat down on low stools at a little wooden table next to an opening that served as a window.

"Coffee?"

I nodded.

"Do you know Jemil?" he asked after two cups filled with a black liquid had been put down in front of us.

"No," I answered. "He was a friend of my cousin Hugo."

He gave a start.

"Just before the war, someone who said he'd been sent by Hugo came to see Jemil." He looked me straight in the eyes. "Who is Hugo?"

This time it was my turn to be surprised. Who could have said he had been sent by Hugo? Who had been there before me, as usual? To ask the question was to answer it.

"Was the man who came to see Jemil tall and rather handsome, and did he have a stiff leg?"

"That's right. How did you know? Is he also one of your friends?"

"In a way. . . . He's a Tunisian named Hidar Assadi. And where's Jemil?"

"You don't know?"

"No."

He lowered the cup he had raised to his lips and delicately set it down on the table.

"He died in the taking of Gaza. Killed in his car, by a shell. He was on his way to the hospital."

I absorbed this news and asked, "What about the Tunisian, the man who came to see him just before the war? Did he talk to him?"

"I don't know, but I think he did."

"Did he have any relatives here?"

"Who?"

"Jemil."

"No. He was originally from Tunis. He came here in 1959 or 1960, I'm not sure which. He wanted to work at the hospital and help the refugees."

"Did you know him?"

"Of course, everyone did."

"I mean, did you know him personally, did you know about his life and his family?"

He shrugged.

"No. But I know he was a good man."

He obviously hadn't told me everything, but I could see I wouldn't get anything more from him. What a shame to be so close to the goal and then see it slip away! Discouraged and a little sad, I couldn't help thinking that there was some sort of evil spell on me and my investigation.

When I came back to my hotel that evening, I crossed the name of Jemil al-Okby off my list.

The next day, tired and preoccupied, I went to Kirya, the part of Tel Aviv where the government ministries were located, long before the time of my appointment. At least a dozen times I went in and out of the café at the corner of Ibn Gvirol and Kaplan. Finally, fifteen minutes early, I went to Golda Meir's office. Twenty more minutes went by. I saw General Dayan come out. And five minutes later Golda Meir received me, smiling broadly.

"My friends have accepted your idea," she said. "We trust you. I'd like you to report to me directly on what happens. I hope for you that you succeed. And for us, for the Arabs, for everyone."

How can I express the joy I felt as I left that little office. I ran — no, I flew, I felt as if I had wings. And if I hadn't been restrained by the need for secrecy, I would have shouted out my happiness to everyone around me.

When I came into the lobby of my hotel, I saw Mordecai with a dark-haired young man.

"This is my son Arieh. I wanted you to meet him before we go back to the kibbutz." Seeing that my mind was obviously elsewhere, he took me by the arm and added, "I hope we're not disturbing you."

"No, not at all," I said, "I'm glad to see you."

"Do you have time for a drink?"

When we had sat down at an outdoor table of our "usual" restaurant, he asked with a shrewd smile, "Well?"

I looked at him in surprise.

"You were in Golda's office just now, weren't you?" he said.

"How did you know?"

"I have a friend named Benjamin Ben-Eliezer. It's his job to . . . know things. So you're going to Egypt?"

"Yes."

"And Golda has agreed to it?"

"Yes."

"Then you've won!" he exclaimed, shaking my hand.

But I realized that I hadn't won anything at all, that the main part of my plan still had to be accomplished. I was like the marriage broker who spent hours and hours trying to convince a poor peasant to let his daughter marry Rothschild's son; when he had used all his talent, experience, persuasiveness and arguments, and finally got the peasant to consent, he said, "Good, now all I have to do is convince Rothschild."

22

FRANKFURT

On Hugo's Trail

SEPTEMBER 1970

In a year, Sidney saw Leila only once. It was at the end of May, when she stopped in New York for two days on her way to join her husband in Mexico City. Claiming that he was going to a convention, Sidney took her to Washington. They stayed in their room at the Four Seasons Hotel with no thought of going out to admire the blossoming trees or walk through the animated streets of Georgetown. She still proclaimed her anti-Israel feelings and he still desired her as much as ever.

At the beginning of the month, the American army had invaded Cambodia and, unlike his friends, especially Jerry Cohen, he hadn't objected to it at first. "When Cambodia agreed to be a base for the Viet Cong," he said, "it came into the war, actually if not officially." And while he recognized that the war was "ugly" (the news media gave proof of it every day), he asked anyone who would listen if there had ever been "a pretty war." He didn't change his opinion till two weeks later, when David, his brother Larry's son, was drafted. Although he was still hostile to the Hanoi regime, he came to have doubts about the justification of American involvement in the war. That wasn't enough to keep him from having a few arguments with

Leila, who was an unconditional supporter of the Vietnamese "revolution." Their political differences seemed to increase the desire they felt for each other.

After Leila's departure, life in New York seemed so dull to him that, to Marjory's surprise, he suddenly consented to go to a medical conference in Frankfurt. The invitation had been lying on his desk for months. It was for the annual conference on ophthalmological surgery, which he had missed the year before because of his trip to Beirut. The idea of attending it this year seemed to him both exciting and disturbing.

He arrived in Frankfurt on September 2, 1970. As planned, he stayed at the Intercontinental. In the bustling lobby, under an enormous chandelier, two blond hostesses received the delegates with smiling efficiency. As in the United States, each one was given a name badge, a program of the discussions and a guide to the city.

It was Wednesday morning. The conference wouldn't really get under way till that evening. Seeing the addresses of several synagogues in the guidebook, Sidney decided to visit one of them. The nearest one was on Freiherr von Stein Strasse. Good, it would do.

The building was guarded by several uniformed policemen. Sidney was appalled to discover that, twenty-five years after the war, Jews still had to be protected in the land of Nazism. In the entrance hall he encountered a group of believers chatting after *shaharith,* the morning prayer. There were young people, but also some old ones, and, for the first time in Germany, he spoke to Jews in his defective Yiddish:

"Why are you still living here?"

The old people smiled, embarrassed, and questioned him in return. They wanted to know where he came from, what he was doing in Frankfurt and what he intended to do there later. But they didn't answer his question.

A young man caught up with him in the doorway as he was leaving.

"You must understand them," he said. "They're all sick — sick in the head. They live in Germany, but they're ashamed of it. For most of them, this isn't the country of their forefathers, it's the country of their torturers."

That evening, after several opening speeches had been read,

Sidney sat down at a table in the immense hotel restaurant with seven other delegates of different nationalities. To his left was Rabbi Lewinson, the chief rabbi of Baden and Hamburg, with his wife, an ophthalmologist in Heidelberg. Born in Germany, Rabbi Lewinson had gone to the United States in 1933, then come back to Germany as an American soldier. He confirmed the diagnosis of the young man in the synagogue:

"Yes, it's true, the Jews now living in Germany are sick, but I hope they'll stay here, to keep Hitler from achieving one of his main goals: a *Judenrein* [Jew-free] Germany."

"That's a good point," said a man of about sixty, with carefully parted white hair, sitting on Sidney's right.

Sidney turned his head; the man gave him a friendly smile and pointed to his name badge: "Hans Furchmuller, German Democratic Republic."

Sidney had a feeling that he had heard that name somewhere before.

"Which part of East Germany are you from?" he asked.

"I live in Berlin."

"I thought it was hard for East Germans to come into the West."

"Not when they go to a scientific conference." He leaned toward Sidney. "Actually, I'm here because of you." Seeing Sidney's surprise, he explained, "I saw your name on the list of delegates and asked my superiors to make me a delegate too." He stood up ceremoniously and introduced himself: "I'm Dr. Hans Furchmuller, your cousin Hugo's brother-in-law."

Conversation at the table had stopped. A young French doctor spontaneously raised his glass.

"Let's drink to this family meeting!" He saw Sidney's embarrassed expression and asked, "Did I say something wrong?"

"No," Sidney replied, "but Hugo Halter and his wife were murdered several years ago in Israel."

"By terrorists?" Rabbi Lewinson asked.

"Yes."

Suddenly, there was a terrible silence. Dessert was served but no one dared touch it. The first to speak again, finally, was Hans Furchmuller.

"Did you ever meet my sister?"

"No."

"But you did know Hugo?"

"Yes, but not very well. Even so, his death affected me greatly."

Furchmuller looked at Sidney and nodded thoughtfully. Then he said abruptly, as if he had just had a sudden illumination, "If you're not too tired from your trip, we can go to a bar to have a beer and talk about Hugo together."

And so it came about that in a noisy, rancid-smelling old café in the old part of the city, Sidney learned some things about his cousin that he had not known before.

Dr. Hans Furchmuller first talked about himself. He was the oldest of four children. In 1941 he was drafted and sent to the eastern front. His brother Peter was killed in Yugoslavia and his other brother, Wilfrid, was now a pharmacist in Kiel. Near the end of the war, Hans was wounded in Berlin. There he was given medical treatment and met the woman he married. He wasn't very happy about living under a Communist regime; he wasn't too unhappy either. As the head of a hospital, he naturally had a privileged position. The members of his family came to visit him, one after another. And so just before Christmas in 1959 he saw his sister Sigrid and her husband. He had a good first impression of Hugo, and liked and respected him from the start. He admired his culture and his intense concern for peace: in spite of misunderstanding and hatred, Hugo had been able to establish excellent relations with both the Israelis and the Arabs, and he had the great merit of having been able to go beyond the boundaries of his race, his people and his memory. Furchmuller wasted no time: he quickly introduced his new friend to a man named Wolfgang Knopff, who at that time worked for the HVA, an East German intelligence service, and was probably a secret agent. Knopff took an interest in Hugo. He appreciated his efforts, encouraged him to continue, and one day told him about the presence in Frankfurt of Israel Beer, an important adviser to Ben-Gurion and "a man of great ability." He advised Hugo to approach Beer and put him in contact with his Arab friends. Hugo evidently took his advice; he negotiated with Beer. Two years later, Furchmuller was greatly surprised when he learned from the newspapers that Beer had been arrested in Israel on a charge of spying for the Soviet Union.

What a strange story! Sidney thought. *What a god-awful mess!*

For the rest of the evening, Furchmuller went on developing the same themes, filling in details in his portraits of Hugo, Beer and Sigrid. Was he naive or crafty? Was he informing Sidney or deceiving him, putting him on the right track or a wrong one? What exactly did he want to know? Why had he introduced Hugo to Knopff? Why, ten years afterward, had he now wanted to meet him, Sidney? Did he want to know how the police investigation stood, what the police and the family had discovered? Did Hugo's death have a more complicated background than Sidney had so far imagined?

Those questions tormented him all night. At dawn, when he had hastily eaten breakfast, he decided to call Benjamin Ben-Eliezer in Israel.

Ben-Eliezer seemed less troubled by the story than Sidney had expected. He questioned Furchmuller's dates but confirmed what Furchmuller had said about Ben-Gurion's adviser Israel Beer, who had been arrested one day before Hugo and Sigrid were killed. But he insisted that, with the information he now had, he could make no connection between their murder and Beer's treason. Unless . . .

"Unless . . . I may have an idea," he said. "How long will you be in Frankfurt?"

"Only a couple of days. I'm flying back to New York on the sixth."

"In that case, I'll call you in New York."

Sidney left Germany on September 6, as planned. He bought some presents and magazines at the airport. After takeoff, comfortably settled into his seat in Ambassador class, he drank a glass of champagne and began looking through *Time* and *Newsweek*. He was distracted from his reading by two men hurrying toward first class. He heard shouts, and then a short, dark man seated two rows in front of him stood up and pointed a big pistol at the passengers.

"Don't move!" he ordered loudly.

From behind him, in economy class, children were crying. Sounds of fighting came from first class, a hysterical scream from somewhere else. One man protested, another cursed furiously; the first was hit on the head with a pistol butt, the second was threatened. The plane suddenly nosed down. A few packages fell to the floor and the loudspeaker began crackling.

"Attention, ladies and gentlemen. Please fasten your seat belts." The voice spoke calmly, in correct English. "This is your new captain. The Popular Front for the Liberation of Palestine, which has taken command of this TWA flight, asks all passengers to obey the following instructions."

The plane leveled off. Sidney looked at the Pakistani couple sitting next to him. They seemed afraid to move or even to breathe.

"Remain seated and keep calm," the voice continued. "For your own safety, put your hands on your heads. Make no move that might endanger your life or the lives of the other passengers."

NEW YORK, SEPTEMBER 1970

Early in September I went to New York again. In Hugo's notebook, beside the word "taxi" under the letter T, I had seen the name of Benny Mendelson, with his phone number. I had called him from Paris to ask him to meet my Air France flight.

I was impatient to meet him, to pick up that new lead, even though I feared I would be disappointed again. And I was also eager to be back in New York, the only city in the world where the present is already the past and the past is so obsolete that it's relegated to museum neighborhoods that seem dedicated to preserving the memory of the city: the Washington Square of Henry James, Edith Wharton and John Dos Passos, with its red brick buildings and good-natured effervescence; Greenwich Village, with its streets that still have names, a beginning, an end, and houses imported from the Old World; Chelsea; Little Italy, with its sidewalk cafés and cappuccinos; the Lower East Side, with its synagogues and *shmate* stores; Chinatown, for Asia's orphans; Soho, for those who confuse Puccini's Bohemia with the artistic life. . . . And then, of course, there's the *other* city, the one that keeps climbing higher and higher into the sky, constantly pushing it back, tearing its clouds, piercing its blue, giving humanity more and more light, more and more freedom, but also more and more anxiety. And, struggling against that anxiety, trying to lighten its weight, are all those little churches and synagogues that seem embedded in the icy, gleaming masses of the skyscrapers — strange urban collages, foreign bodies in a city that gives the feeling of having been built without them, even against them. Imagine the Loire in the Grand Canyon, or the Place de la Concorde in the Negev desert! New York, the supreme artifice. . . . And what if New York were the modern Babylon? What if it were about to succeed where the Biblical city failed? The luck, the genius of New York is having been able and willing to cast all the world's accents into the mold of a single language.

Yes, New York. . . . I landed at about noon. The weather was beautiful. The cab driver, a fat, bald man, was there, holding up a sign with my name on it.

As soon as we headed away from the airport, he started the conversation by asking with a strong Yiddish accent, "Where are you from?"

"Paris."

"And before?"

I laughed and told him about Warsaw, Poland, Argentina and the rest. He said he knew Russia and that his parents were from Odessa. Then he turned his unshaven face toward me a little and said musingly, "So your name is Halter. . . . I used to know a Halter. He worked on *Forward*."

"Hugo Halter, yes, I know. He was my cousin. What can you tell me about him?"

Showing no particular surprise that I was aware he had known my cousin, he began talking about him.

"I often drove my cab for people from *Forward*. They used to call me for all kinds of little errands. I'd park just across the street from the building. It's a Chinese temple now. Things go fast in this town. Anyway, that's how I met your cousin: he used to ride in my cab. He was a nice, considerate man, but his wife . . . oh, his wife! You know how it is, people in a cab don't pay attention to the driver. They talk, they let themselves go, they argue, they quarrel. And I won't even mention the things they do sometimes, when they think nobody can see them. But that's not what I . . . your cousin's wife had a German accent like Henry Kissinger's. She dominated your cousin and I'm sure he did exactly what she wanted. I'm never wrong about things like that, you know what I mean? When you've questioned as many people as I have, you turn into a little Sigmund. You know who I'm talking about, don't you? Sure you do. He was one of ours, right? To me, there are two kinds of adult males: men and husbands. Your cousin was a husband, a one-hundred-percent husband."

"Do you remember what they used to talk about?"

"Of course not! It was a long time ago. All I remember is how they acted, and the way they talked." He turned toward me again. "You didn't know them?"

"Hardly at all."

"Then I'm sorry I can't give you any more details. They're both dead, aren't they? I guessed right, didn't I? Like I told you, I'm a little Sigmund! Well, here we are. That'll be fifteen-fifty, please."

23

ISRAEL

Arieh

SEPTEMBER 1970

Arieh had hardly said a word since coming back to the kibbutz. When his friends questioned him about his stay in Argentina, he answered with monosyllables, grunts and evasive grimaces. Ever since Anna Maria had calmly informed him that she no longer loved him, he had felt that words themselves were bearers of treachery and deceit, and he had withdrawn his trust from language as if he had quarreled with a friend.

"Maybe we should take him to the hospital at Qiryat Shemona and have him examined by a specialist," his mother suggested from time to time.

But Mordecai only laughed.

"Come on, Sarah, have you already forgotten what love is like? Arieh doesn't need a doctor, he needs a girl."

"Mordecai!"

"Don't get angry, Sarah. In this case, the old platitude is true: it takes time, that's all. Time is the key. You know: 'A time to kill, and a time to heal. . . . A time to love, and a time to hate.'"

"That's from the Bible, Mordecai."

"I know. The Bible is life."

"What do you mean, 'The Bible is life'? Have you become religious now?"

"You don't understand, darling. The Bible isn't religion, the Bible is —"

"Maybe I don't understand, but I do know one thing: Arieh is suffering and we have to help him. How do you suggest we do it?"

But poor Mordecai didn't have much to suggest. No miraculous remedy. He couldn't think of anything better than to take Arieh to Tel Aviv to meet "the cousin from Paris." I was the most "exotic" of their cousins, the one with the most memories and political plans that might be fascinating. And above all I had the advantage of being well acquainted with Anna Maria, Argentina, and terrorists.

But unfortunately Mordecai said nothing about those subjects while he and Arieh were visiting me in Tel Aviv, and I was so wrapped up in myself, my strategies and my dreams that I didn't take the time or the trouble to pay attention to Arieh.

When they had left me and begun the drive back to the kibbutz, Arieh's silence continued and became almost hostile.

Mordecai took the seaside road, by way of Haifa and Acre. Near a gas station on the outskirts of Acre, several male and female soldiers were hitchhiking.

"Shall we pick up one of them?" Mordecai asked his son, who, sulkier than ever, didn't deign to answer.

He stopped abruptly, making his tires screech, and one of the young women ran to the car.

"Get in," he said. "If you're going to Qiryat Shemona, Providence sent us to you."

Her name was Judith. Judith Ben-Aharon. Her parents had come from Yemen just after Israel's declaration of independence, at the time of Operation Magic Carpet. "I bare you on eagles' wings, and brought you unto myself," said the Almighty, and Judith said, "My family was brought to the Holy Land on the wings of Israeli planes."

Mordecai observed that strange prophetess in the rearview mirror. He found her strikingly pretty, with her dark braided hair, dark eyes and suntanned face, and with her breasts clearly outlined beneath her uniform.

"In a week," he said, "Arieh will also be in uniform."

"Really?"

"Yes, really," Arieh muttered without looking at her.

At Nahariya, Mordecai took the road to Sasa. There they finally saw Mount Meron, on their right. The sun, which had been painfully bright and seemed for a time to have become motionless in the sky, began its rapid descent behind Mount Hermon, leaving blood-red stains on its snowy peak.

"It's beautiful," Judith said. "I've never seen Hermon from close up."

Mordecai smiled at her, more and more attracted to her. Arieh looked up and saw her eyes in the rearview mirror; but, suddenly remembering Anna Maria's face, he looked away and grunted again.

As Judith was getting out of the car Mordecai said, "Come and see us at Kibbutz Dafneh," on the off chance that she might actually do it.

But she scarcely heard him. After one last glance at the son, who stubbornly kept his eyes lowered, she distractedly waved to the father and walked off toward Qiryat Shemona.

A week later, the great day came. Arieh was still as sad and silent as ever, still mulling over the same memories and regrets, but now it was time for him to leave for the army.

The Ford again, with Mordecai behind the wheel and Arieh beside him. The sunny road, the clouds of dust behind them, the hitchhiking soldiers casually signaling to them. Then halfway, near the village of Tel Kedesh, traffic became a little heavier than it should have been at that place. What was happening? A traffic jam? An accident? Something even more serious and unusual?

"Something's wrong," Mordecai said with the "instinct for disaster" that he liked to describe as characteristic of pioneers.

He had scarcely finished his sentence when he heard car horns and police sirens only a short distance away. Then the radio music they had been listening to for an hour was suddenly interrupted:

"At ten minutes before noon today, three bazooka shells struck an Eged bus carrying schoolchildren on the road from Tel Kedesh to Baram, near the Lebanese border. Seven children were killed and twenty-one wounded. The bus driver, Rami Yarkoni, of Safad, and the teacher, Deborah Ben-Aharon, of Qiryat Shemona, died of their injuries."

A few hundred yards farther on, there was a roadblock and the police were diverting traffic toward Ramot Naftali. Mordecai followed the stream of cars. But as soon as he could, he turned right, took the Tel Kedesh road in the other direction and, without having intended or expected it, found himself approaching the damaged bus. Ambulances, police cars, a crowd of parents in tears, cries and moans from curious onlookers and witnesses of the tragedy.

"Keep moving! Keep moving!" shouted a policeman on the verge of hysteria.

"I can't," Mordecai said. "The road is blocked."

"Then wait. . . . No, keep moving. . . . All right, stay there. We'll clear the road. But right now, there's nothing to do but wait and keep your mouth shut!"

Mordecai and Arieh got out of the car and walked toward the wreckage of the bus.

"Anna Maria's friends," Arieh muttered.

"What did you say?" Mordecai asked.

He took off his glasses and, with the back of his hand, wiped away the tears that were blurring his eyes.

"I said it was Anna Maria's friends," Arieh repeated.

"What are you talking about?"

"The bastards who did that. The terrorists." And, abruptly: "Look, Papa, there's Judith!"

The young Yemenite was there, lost in the crowd, like a beautiful dark bird with broken wings, motionless in a gesture of despair. Arieh went up to her and took her by the shoulders. She turned around, surprised. And their eyes met, as they had done several days earlier in the rearview mirror of the old Ford. This time, Arieh didn't look away.

On his first Shabbat after going into the army, Arieh unexpectedly came back to the kibbutz. His parents were at home. His father was reading in an old cane-bottomed rocking chair and his mother was giving Dina, his little sister, her dinner.

"What's the matter?" she exclaimed when she saw him.

"Everything's all right, Mama, don't worry. I needed to see Papa."

"You could have called."

"Yes, but it's something personal. . . . I had to see Papa and talk to him man-to-man."

"All right, I'm leaving," Sarah said resentfully. Then she smiled brightly. "You're talking now! Listen to him, Mordecai, he's talking again!"

She took little Dina by the hand and, with a false look of irritation, left the two men alone together.

"Well?" Mordecai said.

"I have something to ask you."

"I'm listening."

"Could I work with Benjamin?"

"Work with Benjamin?" Mordecai echoed, surprised.

"Yes, your friend Benjamin. He belongs to the Mossad, doesn't he?"

"Yes, more or less."

"Well, I'd like to work with him," Arieh said firmly. And he continued while Mordecai stared at him, even more surprised: "Soldiers and policemen can't prevent the kind of attacks that killed your cousin Hugo and Judith's mother. Against terrorists, other means have to be used. The ones fighting us aren't based only in Lebanon; they're also in Europe, and Argentina. They're young people, like me. I know them."

Mordecai had never seen his son in such a state. He had never seen that harsh, almost vicious glow in his eyes. What, and whom, was he thinking about? Why that tone of reproach, almost of hatred? And where had he gotten the strange thirst for revenge that Mordecai sensed in his words?

"Do you know Anna Maria is a terrorist, Papa?" Arieh went on. "Do you know her friends plant bombs? I can see you didn't know! Most terrorists are like that. Some of them really believe in what they're doing. That's why they're dangerous." He took his father by the arm, as if he had forgotten his presence and now suddenly remembered it. "You'll talk to Benjamin, won't you? I think I'll be good at fighting those bastards."

Mordecai did as Arieh asked. And on September 6, 1970, Arieh was ordered to come to the defense ministry in Tel Aviv. A soldier met him at the reception desk and asked him to follow him. Benjamin Ben-Eliezer's cramped office was on the fourth floor, at the end of a long hall. Several telephones on the desk, a big fan on the ceiling. Benjamin was wearing his usual gray suit and big horn-rimmed glasses. He invited Arieh to sit down and asked him to tell what he knew about the activities of Anna Maria and her friends. When Arieh had finished, Benjamin stood up.

"You're now in the offices of the Aman, the army intelligence service. Your father has told me that you'd like to work for an intelligence service. It's not impossible, but you'll have to finish your first year of military service. Do you speak Arabic?"

"Yes."

"Do you speak it well?"

"I think so."

A phone rang. Benjamin excused himself and picked it up. Another one rang; he picked it up too and asked the caller to wait. He held a phone to each ear, and within twenty seconds everything was said.

"Come with me, Arieh. We're going to the telex room. Two planes have just been hijacked by the Palestinians. One from El Al, the other TWA."

24

BEIRUT

Black September

SEPTEMBER 1970

In early September 1970, Hidar was again staying in Beirut. This time he was alone. He had finally promised to marry Olga. He had done it sincerely, with his eyes wide open, knowing perfectly well that once his decision became known it would be criticized by both the Soviets and the Arabs. But, for the moment, Olga wasn't there. He was facing his anxieties alone.

What worried him most was Operation Jordan. He had defended its principle in Moscow and he now felt responsible for its success. After being rejected several times, it was finally going to be carried out. To follow it more closely, he had moved into a studio apartment above the apartment that Wadi Hadad had fitted out on the fourth floor of the Kataraji Building. An undertaking as important as Operation Jordan couldn't be seriously monitored from headquarters on the Mazraa hill, with reporters and fedayeen constantly coming and going. Wadi Hadad had already been in Jordan for a week, traveling back and forth between Amman and the Wahdat camp. Ghassan Kanafani and Bassam Abu Sharif made sure there was always someone on duty in the fourth-floor apartment.

Yes, Hidar was worried. Operation Ben-Gurion had fallen

through: the men who were slated to go to Buenos Aires from Copenhagen had been caught by the police as they were packing weapons in the home of a young Arab painter. And two months ago Hadad himself had miraculously escaped death when a shell, fired by persons unknown, devastated his living room and bedroom and wounded his wife and son. Hidar was actually glad that the attempt to kill Ben-Gurion had failed, but he wasn't at all glad that the men who were going to carry it out had been discovered so quickly, or that Hadad's apartment had been attacked when its address was supposedly known only to his closest friends. It showed that the Israelis were perfectly informed, or even had infiltrated the leadership of the Front. He knew he wasn't the only one who had drawn that conclusion. And he knew that eventually it would sow mistrust among them all, and cause scores to be settled with bloodshed.

On September 6, D-Day, he was in the apartment on the fourth floor of the Kataraji Building. It was furnished with a teak table, a few chairs and a couch. On the table were three black telephones, with their tangle of wires, and on the windowsill, hidden by a blind, was the telex. The atmosphere was tense. It was a hot day. The big fan did nothing but flutter the papers lying next to the phones. Sweat had made dark spots come out on Habash's silk shirt. Kanafani nervously mopped his forehead. No one said anything.

At 2:05, at last, the telex began humming, and a phone rang almost at the same time. Kanafani answered it.

"Good news!" he cried. "Samirah and Patrick have hijacked the El Al plane!"

Hidar tried to smile, but his face was so tense with anxiety that he could manage only a faint grimace. Like everyone else, he began waiting for what would come next.

2:12. The telex and a phone both came to life at once. A fedayee took the dispatch from the telex. It reported, from Frankfurt, the hijacking of a Boeing 707 belonging to the American airline TWA, carrying a hundred and forty-five passengers to New York.

2:27. Success! The Swissair DC-8, bound from Zurich to New York, had also been hijacked. For the first time, Hidar and his friends expressed their joy. They stood up and almost danced. Bassam Abu Sharif opened a bottle of champagne. Habash hugged Kanafani. Embraces alternated with congratulations.

But at 3:03 the phones all rang at once. Kanafani picked up one of them.

"What? No . . . no, that's impossible."

It was obvious that he didn't understand what he was hearing, or rather that he *refused* to understand it. When Hidar went over to him, he was pale and seemed about to faint.

"The El Al plane just landed in London," he said simply.

Habash gave a start.

"London? That can't be right!"

Kanafani made a helpless gesture.

"Patrick was wounded by the Zionist guards. Samirah was disarmed. They're both in the hands of Scotland Yard." He looked over the dispatches that were now coming out of the telex at an increasingly rapid rate. "If the others succeed, it will still be a victory."

"They *must* succeed!" Habash said grimly.

Hidar took one of the dispatches from Kanafani.

"The Swissair and TWA planes just made contact with the control tower in Beirut."

"What about the other dispatches?" Habash asked.

"They say the same thing. The planes are evidently going to Baghdad."

There was silence in the room. Each man seemed to be holding his breath. To kill time, Bassam Abu Sharif began making coffee. Tension was at its height when one of the telephones rang.

"It must be Amsterdam," Kanafani said.

"Yes, of course," Hidar said as he picked up the receiver, "I'd almost forgotten about Amsterdam."

A faraway voice — from Amsterdam, as expected — announced the hijacking of a Pan Am jumbo jet flying from Amsterdam to New York.

Habash's broad face brightened. He took Hidar by the shoulders.

"We're succeeding, Hidar! We're going to shake up the world and force it to take account of Palestine! This will be our Six-Day War!"

It was beginning to get dark. The coffee had cooled, but Bassam Abu Sharif served it anyway. The room was filled with a feeling, if not of euphoria, at least of optimism and enthusiasm.

At 8:50, Hadad called from Amman to announce that the TWA plane had landed at "the airport of the Revolution," where the Swissair plane had already landed earlier.

"But the jumbo jet can't land there. The runway is too short."

"Have it land in Amman," Habash advised.

"That's impossible. We're in control of the city, but the king's armored units control the airport. I'll call again at midnight."

And he did call then, but it wasn't until two hours later that a member of the Front in Cairo called to say that the jumbo jet had landed at 1:21 at the Cairo airport and that the fedayeen had blown it up, after taking out all the passengers and crew.

"There! We've won the first round!" Hidar said. "Tomorrow, the whole world will have its eyes on us."

"First let's see how they react to our ultimatum," Habash said. "We have to demand that Samirah be released immediately." Then, as though he wanted to prove his serenity: "And now, I advise you all to get some sleep. Tomorrow's going to be a long day."

The next morning, when Hidar went down to the fourth-floor apartment, he was given a message from Habash asking him to come to headquarters.

Intense excitement reigned there. The building and the courtyard were full of elated fedayeen. The newspapers were favorable to the hijackings; nearly all of them felt that the hostage-takers were attracting attention by the only means available to them, and they all published the Front's communiqué in a prominent place. The words "Palestine" and "Palestinians" had never been printed so often before.

Hidar made his way through the reporters, photographers, television crews and armed fedayeen. He kicked a cable aside, jostled one cameraman and nearly fought with another. After going through a room where Kanafani was answering questions on Japanese television, he came to Habash's office, which was guarded by two fedayeen armed with Kalashnikov assault rifles.

Habash was sitting opposite a swarthy, prematurely graying young man with a mustache. Standing behind the young man, Bassam Abu Sharif introduced him to Hidar:

"This is an Argentinian comrade, one of the leaders of the famous Montoneros."

The young man stood up.

"I'm Julio Feldman."

"I'm very glad to meet you," Hidar said in English, shaking the hand that had been held out to him.

"I was telling Dr. Habash," Feldman said, "that the Palestinians have just given the world a great lesson. The world was calmly sleeping on a bed of injustices, and you've awakened it."

"Julio Feldman is a great poet," Habash said with a hint of mockery in his voice. "His organization is ready to help us." He took Hidar by the arm and drew him over to the window. "I've read the passenger list of the TWA plane we hijacked. Bassam will give it to you. You may have a surprise when you see it."

"A surprise?"

"Yes, but keep a grip on yourself when you discover it: don't let emotion make you vulnerable. I'll call you from Amman. Meanwhile, call Moscow to find out their reaction."

Embraces, goodbyes, false declarations of friendship. When Habash left the room, Hidar went to Bassam Abu Sharif, who was still talking with the Argentinian, and asked him for the passenger list of the TWA plane that had been hijacked to Jordan. Hidar realized what Habash had meant when he saw one name on the list: Sidney Halter.

25

JORDAN

In the Zarqa Desert

SEPTEMBER 1970

It was hot. The air was still. No breeze, not even a draft, came through the wide-open doors of the plane. Looking out of a window that the rays of the morning sun took for a mirror, Sidney saw nothing but an expanse of yellow sand. Now and then a few armed men came into view, as though on a stage in a theater, and quickly disappeared into the wings. In front of him, a woman with hairpins hanging pitifully from her disheveled hair was trying to calm a baby who had been crying for more than an hour. The pilot, Captain Carroll Woods, a man in his fifties with a slightly rounded back, walked down the aisle for the third time without saying a word, as if he thought his presence alone would reassure the passengers.

Beside Sidney, Rabbi Jonathan David, of Brooklyn, calmly took a prayer shawl from a gray cloth bag, put it on his head and murmured, "How excellent is thy lovingkindness, O God! therefore the children of men put their trust under the shadow of thy wings." Then, with measured movements, he took out his phylacteries, wrapped them around his left forearm, turned toward Jerusalem, which wasn't far away, and began saying the *shaharith,* the morning prayer.

A burst of submachine-gun fire interrupted him and made Sidney jump. The baby on the seat in front of them shrieked loudly. Sidney looked through the window: in the distance, against the blue background of the sky, several dark tanks with Jordanian insignia were taking up combat positions.

Rabbi Jonathan David continued: "Thou who art appeased by mercy and swayed by prayer, let thyself be appeased and swayed by an unhappy generation, for there is no help."

Sidney looked at him with envy and admiration. The rabbi was apparently immune to anxiety and self-pity. Like Sidney's uncle Abraham in the Warsaw ghetto? Yes, exactly. He too had felt protected. That had not kept him from dying, but at least it had kept him from being afraid. And Sidney, to his own surprise, covered his head with a handkerchief and joined his voice to the rabbi's:

"Hear, O Israel, the Lord our God, the Lord is One."

He thought back on the night before, when the plane had landed roughly on the runway of an unknown airport lighted by car headlights. He remembered the three armed men who came into the passenger compartment. One of them, young and smiling, with a khaki shirt open over his suntanned chest, told the passengers in correct English that the plane was now in the hands of the Popular Front for the Liberation of Palestine. He promised that they would be well treated, but added that they would not be released until Britain, West Germany, Switzerland and Israel freed the Palestinian fighters held in their prisons.

The night had been especially cold. Sidney had taken a sweater from his bag, put it on and put his jacket on over it. Then, still shivering, he had put on his striped flannel pajama coat.

"Did you do it on purpose?" Rabbi David asked when he had put away his prayer shawl and phylacteries.

"Did I do what on purpose?"

"Your pajama coat . . ." The rabbi saw that Sidney didn't understand. "With your tired, unshaven face and your striped pajama coat, you look like a prisoner in a concentration camp." He nodded sadly. "But you may be right. What's happening to us has the same basis as what happened to our parents' generation in Europe thirty years ago."

As Sidney remembered all that, he was struck by the absurdity of the situation. He, Sidney Halter, a perfectly ordinary doctor, Marjory's husband and Richard and Marilyn's father, was trapped there in the middle of a desert, as if he were in a movie or a novel. Till now, he had thought such things happened only to other people. But no, this one was happening to *him,* and the truth was that he could still hardly believe it.

Now that the night was over and the sun had risen, the heat was already stifling. Sidney was in his shirtsleeves, and he was thirsty.

"Can you give me some water?" he asked a passing stewardess.

"I'll bring you a glass, but we have to use water sparingly. We don't know how long we'll be here, and in a desert . . ."

After drinking his glass of water, Sidney felt drowsy. His mind was still clear enough for him to reflect on the phenomenal human capacity for adaptation. Once again he thought of his uncle Abraham in the Warsaw ghetto, and for some reason he again saw poor Hugo at the time of their last meeting, when he had come to New York to try to talk him into cosigning the three-hundred-thousand-dollar loan. Finally he dozed off.

He was awakened by the loudspeaker. At first it was hard for him to remember where he was. Several fedayeen were standing in the front of the plane. The young Palestinian he already knew was reading names of passengers into the microphone.

"What's happening?" Sidney asked Rabbi David.

"The terrorist is reading the names of passengers who will be taken to Amman."

"Will they be released?"

"He hasn't said."

When the Palestinian had finished reading off the names and nationalities of the passengers concerned, loud tumult filled the fuselage. The passengers whose names had been read assembled their baggage. Some of them were worried about their destination. Those who were staying began hurriedly writing messages to their families in the hope that those who were leaving would be able to have them delivered. Children cried, folding tables clattered, and Sidney thought once more about the Warsaw ghetto. Troubled by that disproportionate comparison, he wrote a note to his family and asked a young woman who was among the "liberated" passengers to mail it in Amman.

A stream of passengers slowly flowed out of the plane. Those left behind sat in dazed silence. Through the window, Sidney saw several trucks loaded with men, women and children leave the runway and move toward the Jordanian tanks. He watched them till nothing was left of them but a thick cloud of dust. When he turned his head, Rabbi David was praying again:

"Help us, O Lord. May the King grant our prayer on the day when we invoke His name."

A woman approached. She was short, her gray hair was pinned back, and her glasses, attached by a red cord, dangled over her big breasts.

"I'm Sarah Malka," she said, "from North Bergen, New Jersey."

"Glad to know you," replied the rabbi's wife.

"Have you noticed that nearly all the passengers left behind are Jewish?"

"No," said the rabbi.

"Well, they are," said Sarah Malka, nervously toying with the big green ring she wore on her left little finger. "I've gone through the plane. A few rows behind you, there's Mrs. Beeber, from Brooklyn, and Rabbi Drillman and Benjamin Finstin, from Whitestone, New York, and . . ."

"But I'm not Jewish!" protested a young woman in a miniskirt. "If they're keeping only Jews here, they'll have to let me go!"

Rabbi David tried to calm her.

"Look, I'm sure you're not the only Gentile on the plane. Walk around and ask."

Sidney smiled. Then he stood up to stretch his legs. The heat was becoming more and more stifling as the sun seared the duralumin of the fuselage. Only at the end of the day, when darkness fell, would the temperature become more or less bearable.

The next morning, the situation was unchanged, except that the bathrooms were dirtier and there was almost no water left. But the worst of it was the uncertainty, the lack of information, the anxiety. The men were absorbed in gloomy thoughts. More and more of the women were cracking and having fits of nerves. The captain gave them sedatives. The crew tried to soothe them, but in vain. Hour by hour, the waiting became heavier and more intolerable.

At about eleven o'clock there was another visit from the

fedayeen. The one who spoke English had a second list of names. He read them off in a monotone, as he had done the first time. Sidney's name was among them. He obediently stood up without knowing what lay in store for him, and he asked only one question:

"Shall we bring our baggage?"

"No, leave it here."

He felt a tingling in his throat and the skin below his whiskers seemed to contract. But he prepared to go with the Palestinians. When he came to the door, he was struck in the face by such bright sunlight that he closed his eyes and stumbled on the first step.

He stood on the runway with about fifteen other passengers, including a black-bearded man with a skullcap on his head who waited resignedly to see what would happen next. Sidney was surprised to see a Swiss plane in front of the TWA plane. Both were guarded by something like a hundred armed fedayeen. A short distance away, a dozen machine-gun nests were lined up, along with several jeeps armed with heavy submachine guns, and an ambulance of the Palestinian Red Crescent.

The atmosphere was tense. The fedayeen — one of whom wore the insigne of Swissair on his uniform jacket — kept their fingers on the triggers of their guns. The little group of passengers seemed overwhelmed by the shadow of the Boeing 707. Sidney was sweating heavily.

"Are they going to shoot us?" asked the young woman in a miniskirt.

It wasn't till some time later — a time that seemed to Sidney as long as a walk across the desert — that a young Palestinian woman came up to the group.

"Reporters are going to interview you," she said. "But I want to make this very clear: no personal messages, no speeches, no proclamations. Remember that the lives of all the passengers depend on each of you."

She signaled to the fedayeen to move away from the planes. They followed her along the dirt runway, which was crackled from the heat. Sidney noticed that the captain of his plane wore the insigne of the Popular Front for the Liberation of Palestine pinned to his dirty, wrinkled white shirt. Then he saw the bare feet of one of the TWA stewardesses and remembered a sentence from the

Talmud that his father had often quoted: "When men do not respect the Law, they eat each other alive."

A few minutes later, the reporters arrived. The fedayeen placed them at a good distance from the little group of passengers. It was an odd press conference! Both the reporters and the passengers had to use loudspeakers to make themselves heard.

"How are you doing?" a reporter asked.

The chief steward of the Swissair DC-8 answered in English with a strong German Swiss accent:

"Our guards are very nice. They're doing everything they can for us. But sanitary conditions in the aircraft are unacceptable. The toilets can no longer be used. We have food, but we no longer have anything to drink."

No photographs, no untimely interventions; just that torrid sun, that growing headache, that persistent impression of nightmare and horror. Sidney felt so bad that he didn't really mind at all when it was time to go back into the plane. But as he was about to climb the steps a Palestinian in his forties, wearing a khaki uniform, with bald temples and a black mustache, called out to him:

"Are you Sidney Halter?"

"Yes."

"How much baggage do you have?"

"Only one bag."

"Get it and come back. I'm taking you to Amman."

26

BEIRUT

Sidney's Disappearance

SEPTEMBER 1970

Ever since teletypewriters had churned out the first dispatches announcing to the world the simultaneous hijackings of the El Al, TWA and Swissair planes, Hidar Assadi had been on the alert. Operation Jordan was his operation, yet he had no control over it and could not change its course. He had written the play, but now he was watching it as a spectator while it unfolded without him. In a way, he was a hostage of the hostages in the Zarqa desert, and so he kept going after information, hurrying back and forth between the headquarters on the Mazraa hill and the apartment in the Katarji Building.

At 11:30 in the morning of September 9, he learned that a BOAC DC-10, flying between Bahrain and London, had been hijacked. That hijacking had been carried out with his consent: since the British refused to release Samirah and there were no British citizens among the Zarqa hostages, the Palestinians needed to give themselves a bargaining chip. But things didn't happen as quickly as Hidar had wanted and expected. Negotiations for the release of the hostages in exchange for Palestinian prisoners being held in Switzerland, Britain, Germany and Israel were dragging on, and as for the military offensive launched against the King of Jordan, it seemed to have bogged down.

The time that Moscow had allowed for completing the operation was running out, and Hidar was fretting helplessly in Beirut. "Whatever you do, don't go to Jordan," his contact in the Soviet embassy had told him. "A man linked to Moscow mustn't be seen with the Palestinians in Zarqa or in the camps near Amman." And so here he was in Beirut, desperately inactive and anxious.

He was awakened by a phone call from Moscow. It was Olga. Her call staggered him: except for a few highly placed Soviet officials, no one was supposed to know his number in Beirut. Olga coyly admitted she had gotten it from her brother Sasha. It was incomprehensible that Sasha had revealed a secret phone number, even to his own sister — unless he wanted to harm him. That hypothesis was confirmed by the news that Olga announced to him: Rachel Lerner, having been told by her daughter that her American cousin Sidney was an eye specialist and used treatments for glaucoma that were almost unknown in the Soviet Union, had tried to call him in New York and ask his advice, and had learned of his abduction.

"His abduction?" Hidar exclaimed. "I know he was on one of the planes commandeered by the Palestinian resistance, but . . ."

"Not anymore."

"What did you say?"

Olga raised her voice.

"I said, 'Not anymore.' Sidney *was* on the TWA plane hijacked by terrorists, but he's not on it now."

"Please be more precise," Hidar said impatiently.

"I'm telling you what my mother told me. Sidney gave a letter to a woman who was one of the TWA passengers released by the Palestinians, and she called his wife from Amman."

"What did the letter say?"

"Don't shout, Hidar, I can hear you very well. I don't know what the letter said, but it seems that all the passengers have been released now — except for the Jewish ones."

"So Sidney is still with the Jewish ones?"

"No, that's just it. A terrorist leader came to the plane and took him away, right after the press conference organized by the Palestinians. And he hasn't been seen since then."

Hidar was greatly displeased by this turn of events, first because he didn't like the idea of discrimination against the Jewish hostages, and also because, even though he had no special liking for him, Sidney's disappearance bothered him. It worried him, in fact, because he couldn't help thinking that it was aimed against him, just as he had been the indirect target of Hugo's murder. He remembered Kamal Jumblatt's remark: "When a man can't protect a friend, he loses some of his influence; when he can't avenge him, he loses his friends." And for the hundredth time he wondered about the mysterious hatred that a leader of the Front seemed to have for him.

He took a shower, got dressed and went down to the fourth-floor apartment. Ghassan Kanafani was already there. One of the fedayeen assigned to the telex brought them coffee and Kanafani handed Hidar the dispatches. The first one reported that Iraq was making efforts with the Front to obtain the release of the passengers on the hijacked plane. The second one reported a statement by President Nixon, in which he solemnly promised to obtain the release of all the hostages, without regard to nationality, race or religion.

"What idiots they are!" Hidar growled.

"Who?" Kanafani asked.

"Our friends. They were supposed to set up a media event that would come off cleanly and without hitches, and win the world's sympathy. Instead of that, they've created arguments against themselves and handed them to Nixon on a silver platter — arguments that will go over very well in the media. Now it's easy for Nixon to accuse them of anti-Semitism."

"I'm sure they couldn't have done otherwise," Kanafani said quietly, without taking his eyes off Hidar. "Israel is sensitive only to threats against Jews. And Israel is where most of our imprisoned comrades are being held."

Hidar scowled angrily.

"What are you talking about? You know as well as I do that the purpose of that operation wasn't to free our comrades, but to win over international public opinion and take power in Jordan."

"But what about our comrades?"

"If we achieve those two aims, we'll automatically gain their release."

Hidar nervously took a few steps in the room, limping on his

sidewalk. Shouts from other drivers, insults, then his name, called out by a woman's voice. He saw Leila Chehab get out of the little car and run toward him.

"You scared me," he said by way of greeting.

"I'm sorry," Leila answered, "but I was hoping to find you here. I've been looking for you everywhere. I had to see you."

Her voice was a little unsteady. She was wearing a thin white silk dress that molded her body perfectly and Hidar couldn't help finding her desirable.

"Sidney . . . ," she said. "Have you heard about Sidney? Remember?" she asked as if she weren't sure he understood. "Sidney, my American friend. The doctor. Your Russian friend's cousin. You met him here, at La Grotte aux Pigeons."

"Yes, yes, I remember. He was on the TWA —"

"No," Leila interrupted. "I mean, yes, he was on the TWA plane, but I heard on the radio that he'd been abducted by unknown men. There's been no news of him for two days. He's not with the hostages anymore." She waited for an answer, then went on, "I've been looking and looking for you. You're the only one who can help me. You have to find him! You hear me? You have to find him!"

"Why me?" Hidar asked, suddenly calm.

Just then a car stopped nearby. A Chevrolet. Two couples got out of it, laughing. They looked at Hidar and Leila for a moment, said something inaudible and went into the café.

"Because you know him," Leila said. "Because you work with the Front. Because you represent the Soviets."

Hidar turned pale and pulled his arm away from her grip.

"What are you talking about?"

"My husband told me . . ." She looked at Hidar with tears in her big, dark eyes and added softly, "My husband is very well informed."

He hesitated a second, then said with a forced smile, "I'll take care of it."

"Please do!"

27

TEL AVIV

Arieh in the Upheaval

SEPTEMBER 1970

Arieh felt that he was living the most important days of his life. From the time when the first dispatches had come through, he had become Benjamin's shadow. Caught up in the whirlwind of events, receiving telex messages and having them taken to Moshe Dayan and Yigal Allon, Benjamin didn't notice, or pretended not to notice, the young man's presence beside him.

It was late in the evening, after they had received a report from the Israeli security agent who had overpowered the Palestinian terrorist on the El Al plane, when he turned to Arieh and asked, "How will you get back to the base, at this time of night?"

The fact was that Arieh hadn't thought about it.

"All right," Benjamin said, "I'll notify your superiors that you're staying in Tel Aviv, then we'll get something to eat. You must be starving."

They separated, then met a short time later in a little restaurant near the House of Journalists on Lessin Street, where Benjamin obviously felt at home. Arieh noticed that he had put on his tie and carefully combed his hair, and that he again looked like a model government official accompanying a relative who had come from a faraway kibbutz.

"Why are you looking at me like that?" Benjamin asked.

"Because you've changed so much. A little while ago, in the ministry, I saw you without a tie or a jacket, and you were very busy, but now . . ."

"Yes, I know. When I work, I sometimes forget myself a little." Benjamin took off his glasses and wiped them. "My father escaped from Germany and Nazism in 1935. He crossed several borders illegally and took more than five months to reach Palestine. But when he arrived in Haifa he was wearing a suit — which he had washed and pressed himself while he was on the ship — and a tie. 'You must always avoid letting yourself go,' he used to say, 'out of respect for others.'"

Even at that late hour, the little restaurant was overflowing with people. On the Formica bar, a fan was running, for no reason. Arab music came from a radio. A dark-haired young waitress gracefully slipped between tables, carrying plates.

"You like her?" Benjamin asked, obviously ill at ease in that kind of conversation but wanting to be sociable with his friend's son.

"No," Arieh answered, "but she reminds me of Judith."

He told about his meeting with the young Yemenite and how they had exchanged a look, only a look, on the day when the bus was attacked.

"That's why I wanted to work with you," he concluded.

Benjamin smiled but made no comment.

When they had finished their meal he said, "I asked Myriam, my secretary, to reserve a room for you in a hotel near here, on Ibn Gvirol Street. I have to go back to the office. The world goes on turning. . . ."

And so Arieh worked with Benjamin Ben-Eliezer and followed events in Jordan. He was kept informed hour by hour, minute by minute, of what was happening in Zarqa, in the camps around Amman and in Amman itself. Was this how he had imagined intelligence work? Yes and no. Much of what he saw around him was like what took place in ordinary business offices, but he learned so many things and heard such amazing news! As he carried dispatches from one room to another and sometimes lingered to listen to conversations, he found out things that were never reported in the media; for example, that Yigal Allon had just had a long meeting with King Hussein in Aqaba, but that Dayan didn't regard the little king as the best person to talk to.

Myriam, Benjamin's secretary, a tall woman in her forties with black hair drawn back in a chignon and big, green, almond-shaped eyes, was amused by Arieh's enthusiasm.

"I thought," she said, "that young people nowadays weren't interested in anything but rock music and partying."

On the morning of September 12 the dispatches reported that the Palestinians had released many of the hostages and destroyed the three hijacked planes. They now held only the fifty-six Jewish hostages.

"They've made their first mistake since the beginning of the operation," Benjamin said when he learned the news. And, seeing Arieh's surprise, he continued, "The Palestinians planned a media campaign and a military offensive. The media campaign was supposed to win the world's sympathy, and it was essential to the success of the military offensive against Hussein. But if they make the world see them as racists by discriminating against people on the basis of race or religion, then . . ."

As though to convince him better, Benjamin sent Arieh to the data-processing department on the third floor, to get the names of the fifty-six Jews held by the Palestinians in Jordan.

When Arieh brought him the list, Benjamin quickly read it. But instead of being glad and repeating that the Palestinians had made a mistake and that it was a stroke of good luck for Israel, he turned pale and exclaimed, "Damn them! What have they done with Sidney?"

"Sidney?"

"Yes, your uncle, Sidney Halter."

"What does he have to do with the hijacking?"

"He was one of the TWA passengers and his name isn't on the list of passengers held by the Palestinians."

Benjamin picked up the phone, dialed a number, and gave a few brief orders that Arieh didn't understand. Then he sat down again and said, "Let's wait for more news."

"Benjamin . . . did you know about Sidney from the beginning?"

"Yes."

"How?"

"We had a list of the passengers on the hijacked planes."

"Then why didn't you tell me?"

"Why should I have told you?"

"He's my uncle!" Arieh protested heatedly. Then, embarrassed by his anger: "The Arabs say, 'He who has one drop of your blood will always be interested in you.'"

The two men sat in silence. To pass the time, Benjamin wiped his glasses, as he often did, and Arieh watched the fan stirring the air in his office. When the phone rang, they both jumped at once. Benjamin picked it up and listened for a moment.

"My God! Sidney has been abducted by Wadi Hadad!" he said to Arieh.

"Why?"

"That's a good question!"

Arieh stood up.

"May I tell my father about it?"

"Wait two days," Benjamin answered after a brief hesitation.

Two days later, the situation had changed drastically: the Palestinians had occupied Irbid and King Hussein had left Amman.

The Israeli army intelligence service was turned into a beehive. In the halls, Arieh passed Generals Sharon and Bar-Lev, religious ministers, noncommissioned officers and privates. Benjamin went from meeting to meeting and from briefing to briefing. But hours and days passed without bringing any news of Sidney.

The American government had officially shown concern. The International Red Cross had addressed a plea to Palestinian headquarters. The media had become involved. A picture of Sidney was shown every day on television. Even his family, in the person of Mordecai, had joined in. Mordecai had talked to Arieh several times. Marjory, frantic with anxiety, had called him from New York. And when he arrived in Tel Aviv late in the morning of September 16, shaken and almost in a state of shock, it took all of Benjamin's eloquence to convince him that things would turn out all right, that Sidney wasn't far away, and that his abduction was directed against someone else, through him. Who was that someone else?

Hidar Assadi, the Soviets' unofficial emissary to the Palestinian organizations. And — who could say? — maybe Sidney's abduction was linked to Hugo Halter's murder.

On September 17 the pace of events quickened. King Hussein, feeling threatened by the Palestinians' offensive inside his borders and the Syrians' offensive outside them, called on the Americans for help. Israeli intelligence intercepted his conversation with Henry Kissinger. Kissinger immediately contacted Yitzhak Rabin, the Israeli ambassador in Washington. Rabin then arranged a telephone conference between Kissinger and Golda Meir, the Israeli prime minister, who at that time happened to be staying at the Hilton in New York. Kissinger wanted a promise that Israel would intervene to save the King of Jordan. Meir asked for twenty-four hours to think it over, and notified Jerusalem.

"It's real psychological warfare," Benjamin remarked as he looked through the dispatches.

"To frighten the Palestinians?" Arieh asked.

"No. To impress the Soviets."

"Any news about Sidney?"

"No, nothing yet. But we've learned that Hidar Assadi is now staying in Beirut. He just met the second secretary of the Soviet embassy, who's none other than the head of Soviet intelligence in the Middle East." Benjamin took off his glasses. "I have a feeling that when Wadi Hadad abducted Sidney, he made a second mistake."

28

BUENOS AIRES

A Terrorist's Misgivings

SEPTEMBER 1970

Anna Maria and Mario left the city by way of the northern highway. He drove and she sat close beside him, finding it hard to restrain her excitement. She liked to leave Buenos Aires, confront the pampas and set off along that endless road. She liked the cracked, bumpy pavement with waves of sand across it that made the car swerve. Today the cracks were full of rainwater and the road was very slippery. But her happiness was the same. And her heart was incredibly light as she faced the hundreds of miles that separated her from Belén de Escobar, where the meeting was to be held. "An important meeting," Mario had said. She knew that, of course, and she wouldn't have missed this trip for anything in the world.

She had been totally involved in clandestine work ever since Arieh left. She had spent a month in a training camp near Córdoba, and she now knew how to handle every kind of weapon that the guerrillas received from the Warsaw Pact countries. She could distinguish the Kalashnikov AK-47 rifle from the slightly altered AKM model. She knew how to take apart and reassemble the Hungarian submachine gun with a folding metal stock, but she preferred its Czech version, the VZ-58, which was much lighter, with its fiberglass stock. She had even learned to throw grenades, and her instructor had taught her to use V-40s, Dutch fragmentation grenades that were lighter and "handier" for a woman. She had taken part in minor operations. And in spite of her comrades' opposition, she nearly always walked around armed with an Egyptian nine-millimeter pistol called the TO-Kagypt. "They won't take me alive," she kept repeating, like a child delighted at having said something shocking.

Six miles outside of Buenos Aires, she and Mario came up against a roadblock. Policemen were stopping cars in two lines and Mario had to pull up behind a big Chevrolet whose license number showed that it was from Mendoza.

"Where are you going?" a policeman asked.

"To Rosario."

"Let's see your papers."

The policeman, a tall, husky man with a very young face, examined Mario's identity card, then Anna Maria's. He showed them to his companion, who was short, chubby-cheeked and also very young, and handed them back, evidently with regret.

"Why are you stopping cars?" Anna Maria asked.

The two policemen looked at each other. It was the tall one who answered.

"Tourists aren't the only ones who travel this road, señorita. Unfortunately we also have bandits and terrorists in Argentina."

"Have you ever arrested any of them here?"

"Yes, it happens. You can go now."

"*Gracias.*"

Mario drove past the big Chevrolet, whose driver was emptying its trunk, and headed off down the road again. They drove for a time in silence, between pastures enclosed by barbed-wire fences.

"What made you question that cop?" Mario finally said accusingly. "Do you think you're a reporter?"

Anna Maria laughed. A little too loudly.

"There's nothing to laugh about!" he protested. "What if they'd searched the car and found the leaflets, and your pistol? Imagine their faces if they'd come up with your pistol!" He was furious. He glanced at his watch. "The meeting will have started by now. Julio must be telling about his trip to Beirut."

For several days the Montoneros had been waiting for Julio Feldman's return. They wanted to know, to understand. . . . The simultaneous hijacking of four planes by the Palestinians had been cheered enthusiastically, and their taking of Irbid and Zarqa had set off an explosion of joy. The Palestinians were taking part in the common struggle against imperialism and they had set a magnificent example for all the world's struggling peoples. Anna Maria had tried to state a few reservations. When she learned that the Jewish passengers had been segregated from the non-Jewish ones, she expressed doubts about the revolutionary qualities of the Palestinian comrades. "It's easier to criticize in Buenos Aires than to fight in Amman," she was told. She made no reply.

And now she was on the road to Belén de Escobar.

She and Mario reached the meeting place at nightfall. It had stopped raining. A star was shining through a gap in the clouds. Mario parked the car in front of a kind of English country house. They both got out, relieved at finally being able to stretch their legs.

"Thank goodness! Here you are at last!"

Anna Maria immediately recognized the little man hurrying forward to meet them.

"Roberto!" she said in the tone of someone seeing a childhood friend for the first time in years.

"We were starting to worry," Roberto said, out of breath. "With all those police roadblocks, you never know what may happen."

Walking rapidly, he led them between carefully tended lawns to the front steps of the house.

"What a beautiful house!" Mario exclaimed.

"Yes, it's a real mansion. It belongs to one of our comrades' parents."

An impressive bronze door; a long hall with engravings of horses on the whole length of its walls; a big room with flowered wallpaper, proudly displayed portraits of ancestors; a fire burning in a white stone fireplace. If it hadn't been for the score of young people gathered there — some sitting in lustrous leather armchairs or on dark wooden chairs, others standing, holding drinks — it would have been easy to believe that this really was a venerable mansion belonging to equally venerable people in possession of an inheritance that stretched back into the misty depths of time.

Julio greeted the newcomers.

"Ah, there you are! We've been waiting for you." He turned to the others. "We're all here now. We can begin."

For more than an hour he talked about Beirut, his discussions with Habash, Kanafani and Abu Sharif, their enthusiasm and intelligence, their internationalism.

"For the Front," he said, "the struggle against Israel is only the first step toward the Arab socialist revolution."

"And what will they do with the Israelis?" Anna Maria asked.

"The Israelis will have their place in a Middle Eastern socialist federation."

"As Israelis?"

"As a religious minority."

"Religious!" Roberto cried in his high-pitched voice. "What will they do with nonreligious Jews, for God's sake?"

Julio was beginning to lose patience.

"I don't see why you always have to judge things in relation to the Jews. The world doesn't begin and end with them!"

"That's true," Roberto agreed, "but from the way they're treated you can often judge other things: the humanism of a movement, for example."

Mario leaped to his feet, pushed his hair back with one hand and demanded, "Who's talking about humanism?"

"Then what *are* we talking about?" Anna Maria asked quietly.

She disliked everything that had been said so far. The more she thought about it, the less she believed in a revolution that involved kidnapping innocent men and women.

"What are you saying?" Mario asked her.

"Nothing. I was just wondering how many Jews there were in the hijacked planes."

"About sixty," Julio answered.

"All Zionists?"

"All Zionists!"

There was a movement in the room. A tall, thin young woman, with red hair tied in a ponytail, said gruffly, "What does it matter?"

Anna Maria's dark eyes became larger and harder.

"What does it matter, Juanita? Human life doesn't matter? Then why are you struggling? To populate the world with corpses?"

Julio raised his arms and gesticulated broadly.

"C'mon, everyone. Let's keep our cool."

Anna Maria had no desire to: she shouted, sobbed, angrily assailed her comrades, then sulked.

The next day, when she learned that her own cousin was among those sixty supposed Zionists, she again lost control. It took a lot of patience and effort to calm her down.

"You shouldn't let yourself get into such a state," Roberto told her, taking her in his arms. "You know very well that we depend on the Palestinians for logistics."

"So our conscience is only a matter of logistics?"

"To hell with theory! I agree with you, but we're here to make a revolution in Argentina, not to talk about Israel and the Palestinians. We're planning something big. Very big. And we need you."

PARIS, SEPTEMBER 1970

The hijackings by the Palestinians had been on the front pages of the French newspapers for a week before we learned that our American cousin was among the hostages. My mother heard it from a Yiddish poet, a friend of Sidney's father in Winnipeg, who was passing through Paris. The next day she called Mordecai at Kibbutz Dafneh, who confirmed it. She was furious at this latest outrage visited upon a relative thirty years after the family had been uprooted, martyrized and nearly wiped out.

"So you see the kind of thing your Palestinians do!" she said to me. "And you want to make peace with them?"

I hardly knew Sidney. I had met him only three times in Beirut, and his plight hadn't affected me any more deeply than that of the other Jewish hostages. But I realized one consequence of the hijackings: I could no longer hold out any hope for the Israeli-Egyptian meeting that Golda Meir had asked me to bring about.

And my mother's anger was contagious. That tall, red-haired man was, after all, my cousin. He and I shared the same history and the same memory, and we both recognized ourselves in the same photographs of bearded Jews at the end of the last century. Furthermore, I could see no cause or struggle in the world that justified taking hostages. And to me, the fact that those hostages were Jews, that they were still being attacked a generation after the Holocaust, made the crime even more outrageous.

Today, as I write these lines, my closest relatives are no longer alive: my parents, my aunt Regina, my cousins Mordecai and Sidney, the Lerners. Yet my attachment to their memory grows stronger as time goes by. I sometimes see them with cousin Hugo, so distinct from each other, but all drawing their memory from the same source as did my father, his father's father, and so on. And a wave of nostalgia carries me away from my story. The further I go in this family story, the more my desire for ancestors increases, and the more that desire increases, the farther its object moves away. Soon there will be an endless desert between it and me.

But let's not get ahead of ourselves. For the moment, we're still in September 1970, during the events in Jordan, and without news of Sidney. It happened that Vladimir Volossatov, the third secretary of the Soviet embassy in Paris, called me at that time. We had been in touch with each other for several years. He was interested in the Middle East and spoke Arabic. We had met now and then: I had to get information on Soviet policy from him, he to question me about Israel and its leaders. This time, I was glad to be able to talk with him about Sidney.

Volossatov said that Sidney's disappearance was "distressing." He suggested that we meet again later, "to talk about all this after we've slept on it." In his language, that meant "after I've had a chance to get more information."

We met the next day in the Café Cluny, at the corner of Boulevard Saint-Germain and Boulevard Saint-Michel, on the second floor.

"I have news for you," he said in his rough accent as soon as he saw me. "Your cousin is alive. He's in the hands of Wadi Hadad."

He sat back comfortably on the bench, facing me, and added in Russian, as though talking to himself, "Wadi Hadad — what an idiot!" Then, seeing my surprise: "That's my personal opinion. What matters is for your cousin to be released."

"Will he be?"

"Yes, soon."

"By Hadad?"

"No, by Al Fatah."

"Al Fatah? But doesn't the Soviet Union support the Popular Front?"

"That's going to change," he said decisively.

He ordered a Scotch. When the waiter brought it, and a glass of hot milk for me, Volossatov leaned toward me and said, "Your family is consistent: they're always involved in Middle Eastern affairs."

"It's been going on for centuries."

"No, I'm talking about now. First there was your cousin Hugo, then you, and now your cousin Sidney."

I was disconcerted to hear him say Hugo's name.

"Did you know Hugo?"

Volossatov's bony face brightened in a smile.

"I met him several times, at international peace conferences."

"You never told me about it."

He emptied his glass of Scotch in one swallow, as if it were a glass of vodka, and, with no further prompting, gave me a description of Hugo that matched my memory of him fairly well. Then he spoke of the Soviet Union's desire for peace and said that "Jewish idealism" was misunderstood in his country. Finally, without transition, he confided that his wife, Vera, was half Jewish.

"On her father's side," he said, and added almost apologetically, "he thought it didn't matter."

"For Hitler, it mattered."

"That's true. He was deported by the Nazis."

We were silent for a moment. A ray of sunlight swept across the red imitation-leather bench and made Volossatov close his eyes.

"That sun feels good," he said.

"Why do you think Hugo was killed?" I asked bluntly.

He shrugged.

"It may have happened by chance. Terrorists don't always choose their victims. Or maybe enemies . . ."

"Did he have any?"

"Everyone has some. Don't you?" He rubbed his eyes, still bothered by the sunlight even though it had begun to disappear; then he glanced at his watch. "I'm already late. We'll have to meet again. I'd

like you to tell me about Golda Meir and her relations with Dayan."
He stood up, put his broad hand on my shoulder and said, "In any
case, you should know that the Soviet Union was not involved in
your cousin Hugo's death in any way."

And, leaving me taken aback by that statement, he walked out
of the café.

29

JORDAN

Like a Dog . . .

SEPTEMBER 1970

The car was rolling along in a cloud of dust. The wipers creaked as they vainly tried to clear the windshield. The man who had come to take Sidney away from the plane now sat next to him, dozing. The driver gripped the steering wheel and the man beside him gripped a submachine gun. Sidney could see nothing of the driver except the back of a fat neck with tufts of black hair on it. Of the other man in the front seat, he saw a very young profile, a short nose, a budding mustache and a determined chin. They passed a convoy of trucks pulling tank carriers, then a Land Rover packed with soldiers.

Sidney found the situation absurd. Fate had put him on a plane that was going to be hijacked, and now these strangers were taking him God knew where.

Did they know about his abduction in New York? He thought of Marjory, Richard and Marilyn. He also thought of his father and Leila. Did Leila know what had happened to him? If so, how was she reacting? He couldn't understand why the Palestinians were interested in him, particularly in him. Because of Hugo? As soon as that idea came into his mind, it seemed ridiculous to him. Was he going to puff himself up with importance and put himself on the same level as his prestigious cousin?

How he wished he could ask questions, talk with his kidnappers, explain to them, understand them! But the man beside him was snoring quietly and the young one didn't seem at all friendly.

Sidney thought of Marjory again. There had never been any real closeness between them. Richard was moving away from him as he grew up, becoming something of a stranger to him. As for Marilyn, she was still too little — but here in Jordan she suddenly seemed very close to him.

It was hot. The bodies in the car gave off an acrid heat. The car rocked back and forth. The sun had turned purple. Finally Sidney saw a road sign indicating that Amman was near, and then he saw the runways of the airport outside the Jordanian capital.

A whitewashed stone building on a steep hillside in a suburb of Amman. The spacious room where he was being questioned was at the end of a long hall. An old radio and a few family photographs on a dark teak dresser still recalled the former owners. An elegant young man sat behind a table covered with a red and white checkered oilcloth on which there was a bottle containing only a cigarette butt. Three armed fedayeen occupied the room: two guarding the door and one standing in front of the window, through which the calls of muezzins could be faintly heard.

The fedayeen had emptied Sidney's pockets. Everything they had taken from him was spread out on a green plastic tray on the table: a few dollars and his watch, pen, passport, address book and credit cards.

"Do you have relatives in Israel?" the young man asked in perfect English.

"Yes," Sidney acknowledged.

"And friends?"

"Yes."

The young man nodded as if that answer were a confession of a crime and motioned the two fedayeen standing by the door to take the prisoner away.

Sidney was locked in a room about six feet square, a windowless storeroom at the other end of the hall. He sat down on the cot that took up half the space and looked up at the solitary light bulb hanging at the end of a wire.

He thought of K. in the film version of Kafka's *The Trial* that he had seen. He mustn't lose his mental balance, or his hope. He stood up and examined the walls and the door. They were smooth all over, like a pebble, without a crack anywhere. He sat down again, disheartened. Who could find him there? He thought of things that had happened to him since Hugo's death; of his meeting with Mordecai and Benjamin Ben-Eliezer; of his affair with Leila. . . . It was true that you went farthest when you didn't know where you were going. If only he had a pencil and a piece of paper! He had noticed that there was no phone in the building.

He needed to go to the bathroom. He had to pound on the door a long time before it opened. A bearded man pointed a large-caliber pistol at him.

"I have to go to the bathroom."

"Come," the bearded man said, and showed him the way.

The bathroom was opposite the stairs, between the room where the fedayeen had questioned him and the one in which he had been imprisoned. The rusty bathtub hadn't been used in a long time. Daylight came in through a crack between two of the cinder blocks with which the window had been closed off.

"Hurry," the bearded man ordered.

He slammed the door.

Sidney walked around the room without finding anything he could use to write a message. He noticed an empty medicine cabinet above the basin, opened it and looked carefully inside: yes, a razor blade. Time was pressing. He made up his mind. He cut the palm of his hand with the razor blade, took a piece of straw that ants had carried under the bathtub and, using it as a pen dipped in his blood, wrote on a piece of the cardboard toilet-paper container, "Please help me. My name is Sidney Halter. I am being held hostage on the third floor of this building." He also wrote his phone number in New York, and after thinking for a moment he added Leila's in Beirut. He barely had time to slip the cardboard through the crack before his jailer suddenly pushed open the door.

"You're finished? Then let's go."

*　　*　　*

Every day, soon after a modest lunch of soup and pita bread, the bearded man took him to the room at the other end of the hall, where he stood in front of the elegant, polite young man who slowly and deliberately asked him the same questions, to which he always gave the same answers. The young man then shook his head disapprovingly and had Sidney taken back to the storeroom.

A little past five o'clock in the afternoon of the fourth or fifth day, Sidney heard rifle shots through the walls of his cell, followed by the sound of artillery fire and exploding shells. He automatically raised his arms to protect himself and burst into nervous laughter. He didn't know against whom he had to protect himself, but he did it anyway. Sitting on the edge of the cot, he began counting the explosions. Then he thought of Jerry Cohen, the anesthesiologist; it was because of him that he had gone to Beirut. How strange it was, how absurd! Only a little while ago he had been grateful to Jerry for giving him a chance to discover the wonders of Beirut. And now, this mess. . . . It must be the end of Shabbat, he thought, and so he began reciting the Psalm: "He that dwelleth in the secret place of the most High shall abide under the shadow of the Almighty. . . ." But, to his great shame, he couldn't remember what came next. He began counting the explosions again, tried to guess who was attacking whom, and why, and finally fell asleep, exhausted.

The next morning, the bearded man came at dawn to take him to his daily questioning. Sidney saw a gaping hole in the wall of the bathroom. *A shell hole,* he thought. *Yes, that was right: a shell hole.* And all at once he remembered the end of the prayer for closing Shabbat: "The Lord is my rock, and my fortress, and my deliverer; my God, my strength, in whom I will trust. . . ."

"What are you saying?" the bearded man asked.

"I'm praying."

Despite the roar of heavy artillery punctuated by the crackle of automatic weapons, and all those repeated shocks that jolted the building and rattled the windowpanes, the elegant young man remained impassive.

"What's happening?" Sidney asked.

"Fighting has been going on for four days," the young man answered.

From the next room, Sidney heard a radio broadcasting a

speech in Arabic. Seeing that he was listening to it, the young man said, "King Hussein."

"What's he saying?"

"I don't know. I don't care what he says or doesn't say."

"But your men are dying. . . ."

"We like to die, you know," the young man said. Then, abruptly, he again became the one who asked questions. "Your Israeli brother has a son, doesn't he?"

"Yes."

"Is his name Arieh, and does he work with Benjamin Ben-Eliezer in army intelligence?"

Sidney was scarcely able to hide his surprise.

"I know Benjamin Ben-Eliezer, but I don't know where he works. As for my nephew, he's in the army now, doing his military service."

"You don't know anything about their activities?"

"No."

The young man slowly stood up and walked toward Sidney with a springy step. He was slender, and shorter than the American.

"And what were you doing in Beirut with Hidar Assadi?"

"Hidar who?"

Sidney had really forgotten his cousin Olga's lover.

"Are you making fun of me?"

"What do you mean?"

A slap made Sidney's head turn. He nearly retaliated, but restrained himself in time. He knew it would be suicidal, and so he replaced his anger with pity. His body seemed to contract; he lowered his eyes and bent his back. Thinking that he was gathering his strength to attack, the fedayeen standing beside the door rushed at him, brutally grabbed him and knocked him unconscious.

He woke up in his cell, lying on the cot. His head ached and all his muscles were sore. His jaw seemed heavy and massive. *Pity,* he thought. *I felt pity for those men. I acted like my ancestors in Polish villages before the war: when a nobleman hit them with his riding crop, they reacted only with passive contempt. They really felt contempt, and they felt enormously superior to those brutes who had to use violence to assert themselves. It's strange to repeat my ancestors' thoughts, behavior and reactions like that.*

He sat up on the cot, not without difficulty. His back was bent, his knees felt wobbly and he was shaking as if he had a fever. He thought of the futility of life, whose meaning no one understood, and the even greater futility of death, whose significance was forbidden to the living. *Will anyone find my message? Will anyone come to help me? If only I could say, "Lord, have mercy on me!" I'd feel so much better. But who could I make that prayer to, since I almost never set foot in a synagogue?* For the first time it occurred to him that maybe Richard wasn't entirely wrong in turning back to religion.

He thought of his father, his wife, his children. The first night he had spent with Leila. Hidar Assadi's face, so small and strange. And above all, the sight of Park Avenue under an infinite sky. . . . He had involuntarily clenched his right hand. He sank back down onto the cot and lay there a long time, looking up at the light bulb above him.

Suddenly the artillery fire began again. Sirens howled, machine guns stuttered. Shots close by, almost just outside the wall. Shouts. All at once, like a drowning man clutching a life preserver, he regained hope. Maybe someone had found his message. He laboriously stood up and stepped toward the door. His head still hurt. He heard shouting in Arabic, shots, more shouting.

Suddenly the door was violently thrown open, knocking him down onto the cot. When he stood up again, he saw two bloody bodies on the threshold. Hope: the door was open. He stepped over the motionless bodies, went to the stairs and, not seeing anyone, started down them. He was already on the ground floor when he heard someone above him calling to him in English.

"Stop, sir! Don't run away! We've come to save you!"

And another voice, a little younger: "Wait, sir! Wait! We're coming!"

Overjoyed, Sidney looked in the direction of the voices and didn't see two fedayeen, one of whom was his bearded guard, coming up behind him.

"Look out!" someone warned him from the top of the stairs.

"Dog of a Jew!" the bearded man shouted, coming toward him with a pistol in his hand.

Sidney started back up the stairs but one of the two men grabbed his ankle. He fell, arms outstretched. The fedayeen attacked him. He heard a burst of submachine-gun fire and, almost at the same time, felt violent pain in his hip.

"Dog of a Jew!" the bearded man repeated.

Sidney's eyes had already grown dull. He seemed to hear a kind of distant murmur. For the last time, he pictured Marjory and the children in his mind. Hugo, too. Then his body relaxed; he made a little gesture of indifference and said, "Like a dog . . ."

30

BEIRUT

The Turnabout

SEPTEMBER 1970

Hidar's appointment with his contact at the embassy was moved forward several days. In Amman, things were not happening according to plan. A hundred Syrian tanks, Soviet-made T-55s, had penetrated into Jordan, but had stopped at Irbid while King Hussein launched a lightning attack against the Palestinians massed around his capital.

The message from the embassy arrived on Friday, September 18, at ten in the morning. It set the meeting for two o'clock that afternoon. Hidar was nervous. He felt an unpleasant tingling in the pit of his stomach, as he always did when his intuition told him that something troublesome was about to happen. He would have liked to call someone, just to exchange a few words. But who? What friend? He had no friends in Beirut. He decided to go out.

Beirut was not a city that seemed to invite solitary strolling. In Hamar or at the Bab-Edress intersection, you quickly ran into street porters, beggars and tireless speechmakers who crowded the sidewalks. The pavement was packed with cars, and the noise of their horns was deafening. As usual when he felt a little lost, Hidar wished Olga were with him.

A little after one o'clock — that is, nearly an hour early — he went to La Grotte aux Pigeons. The sun was at its highest and the heat was sweltering. Near the railing that overlooked the sea, a guide was recounting the history of the city to a group of French tourists. The café wasn't crowded and he easily found a table in the shade. He ordered an arrack, sipped it slowly, emptied his mind of everything that might depress him and listened to the guide.

"Beirut's origins go back to the beginning of seafaring. Its name comes from *berot,* which means 'well' in Phoenician Canaanite, and it was called that because of its abundant water resources."

A blond lady, no longer young but still pretty, was hurriedly writing in a little yellow notebook. She felt Hidar's eyes smiling at her and went on writing while the guide continued his lecture.

"The scribes who wrote the letters discovered at Tell al-Amarna, a city founded by the poet-pharaoh Akhenaton and his wife Nefertiti, sometimes replaced the name of Berot with the cross-shaped ideogram meaning 'well.'"

The blond lady stopped writing and looked back at Hidar. A smile, a wink, a silent understanding, a subtle invitation . . . she blushed. He deliberately turned his more flattering profile toward her. Absorbed in his little game, he didn't notice the partly bald false tourist in a tan jacket who sat down at the next table.

"Are you enjoying yourself?"

Hidar started.

"Go on looking at the tourists," the man advised him. "With that kind of guide, you always learn something."

But the little group was already moving on. Hidar heard the guide say that in ancient times Beirut could be compared with Athens and Alexandria, and that in the fifth century B.C. it had a law school where teaching was done in a systematic manner. Then he again felt anxiety invading him.

"I talked with Chebrikov on the phone," the Russian said. "An agreement with the Americans has been concluded. Everything must be stopped. Immediately."

"Everything?"

"Yes, everything. It's an order."

Hidar watched a gull dive into the water and found it beautiful. He felt as if it were pulling him down with it, into the depths of the sea. Then for some reason he suddenly had a mental image of Olga's milky-white breasts offered to his desire.

"Make contact with Al Fatah," the Russian went on. "You have a few friends there. Tell them to see to it that the war is stopped and the hostages are released."

"We're changing our alliance?"

"Yes. You can promise them whatever seems necessary. We'll honor all your promises. The Palestinians must also realize that you have power."

The Russian, who till now had been talking to Hidar without looking at him, as though talking to no one in particular, turned his head toward him and scrutinized him a long time through his two blue slits.

"You're lucky," he finally said.

"Lucky? Why?"

"In my country, they feel that you're responsible for the failure of the operation."

"But it hasn't failed. We —"

The Russian silenced Hidar with a gesture and gave his order to the waiter who had just arrived: "Mint tea, please." He turned back to Hidar. "The operation has lasted too long."

"The Syrians are at Irbid."

"They're going to leave."

"The Iraqis . . ."

"They won't move." The Russian was silent till the waiter, who had just brought his mint tea, had left. "Uncle Sam demands the immediate release of the Jewish doctor." He took a few sips of tea. "You were right, however, about Kamal Jumblatt. When he became the interior minister, he legalized the party. In my country, they say we have you to thank for that." He emptied his cup and stood up without waiting for any objections or comments that Hidar might want to make. "Good luck. From now on, everything is in your hands."

He put money on the table and walked away without looking back.

A few minutes later, Hidar did the same. He lingered briefly in front of the café to contemplate Beirut and its accumulation of white, ochre and gray buildings. Then, shrugging his shoulders as though to drive away an annoying idea, he hailed a taxi and left.

Where was he to begin? The hypnotic rhythm of an Arab song on the radio kept him from thinking clearly. It was hot and damp, and siesta time. The taxi rolled along a tropical street with no one strolling on the sidewalks. The whitish brightness of the hot pavement was broken only by the shadows of porters. *The first thing I have to do,* he thought, *is to move, to get beyond the Front's reach.*

Even before doing that, however, he went to the fourth-floor apartment in the Kataraji Building and looked over the dispatches. Then he went up to his little apartment, packed his suitcase and looked around to make sure he hadn't forgotten anything, amazed at his own calm. Only after he had called the Hotel St. George to reserve a room did he call Al Fatah. When he was told that Abu Iyad wasn't there, he left a message asking him to call him at the St. George. Finally he went downstairs and left the building.

He met with Abu Iyad that same day, and with Arafat, who was back from Amman, the next day. Arafat quickly understood Hidar's proposal. He knew that if he didn't regain control of operations in Jordan, he would lose leadership of the PLO forever. It wasn't "his" war, he told Hidar. And so, since Hidar seemed willing to give up . . .

Hidar notified the embassy that evening. The next day, the Iraqi forces stationed in Jordan transferred heavy armament to the Al Fatah commandos reinforced by several thousand Palestinians from Syria. And on the afternoon of Tuesday, September 22, Hidar received a visit from Ghassan Kanafani. They sat on the hotel terrace overlooking the sea, at an iron table painted white, as in some Paris bistros.

"Has Moscow switched alliances?" the Palestinian asked without preliminaries, putting a news-agency dispatch on the table.

Hidar was reasonably sure he knew what was in the dispatch, but reading it would give him a little more time before starting his conversation with Kanafani. The headline told him that the combined efforts of Washington and Moscow had restored King Hussein's position. *Things are going faster than I expected,* he thought.

"What about the hostages? Tell me about the hostages!" he said, following the principle that the best defense is an attack.

"Al Fatah has released some of them, and the Front has transferred others to the north."

"Where's the American doctor?"

Kanafani seemed embarrassed.

"Have you seen what's happening in Amman?" he asked. "It's a dead city. A large part of its population has been killed, and many of the survivors are close to death. The destruction is so great that it seems as if no house or building has been spared. So, with all that, one hostage more or less . . ." His face quivered briefly. His high forehead was covered with sweat and his big dark eyes stared at the sea. He abruptly turned his head toward Hidar. "I talked with Wadi on the phone. He called me from the Jordan Hotel, which overlooks the city. From there he could see many columns of black smoke rising into the sky, and other fires could be seen in the direction of Jebel Hussein and Wahdad, where there are Palestinian refugee camps. The number of casualties isn't known, but Wadi says that thousands have been killed and wounded. He —"

"Words, words, words!" Hidar interrupted irritably. "You talk like those writers whose books are full of remorse. The trouble with them is that they've never killed anyone. It's true that war is terrible. Didn't you know that?"

Kanafani slumped slightly forward. His back was bent, as if he were overwhelmed by the weight of the situation.

"A revolutionary isn't a murderer," he said in an undertone. "He's a man who kills, yes, but he kills to save life." He suddenly sat up straight and gave Hidar an accusing look. "Did you know that Al Fatah was going to negotiate with Hussein?"

"Yes. To save what could still be saved. To save life, as you've said. And also to free the hostages. . . . And speaking of hostages, you still haven't told me about the American doctor."

Kanafani looked back at the sea and said without seeming to acknowledge Hidar's presence, as if he were talking to the gulls, "He was killed."

"Killed?" Hidar leaped to his feet. His face and eyes had become strikingly hard. "Do you mean you killed him?"

"No, no. Wadi Hadad was holding him in a suburb of Amman to question him about his relations with one of the heads of Israeli military intelligence —"

"And with me, right?"

Kanafani didn't answer.

"With me?" Hidar repeated, taking him by the arm. "Say it, you bastard! Come on, say it!"

"The whole thing was stupid. A combat group from Al Fatah tried to free him. There was a misunderstanding, and an exchange of fire. Your American tried to run away. Someone shot. He was killed."

"But killing someone isn't a mistake that can be corrected, like dialing a wrong number!"

Kanafani freed his arm from Hidar's grip and stood up. His refined face — the face of a poet who had strayed into politics — was also hard, and extraordinarily tired.

"Don't forget," he said, "that you're the one who wanted that operation."

"Yes, but it was only meant to remind the world of the Palestinian tragedy. The hostages were supposed to be released immediately."

Two couples sitting farther on had turned their heads to listen, and waiters were watching the scene with curiosity through the glass that separated the terrace from the lobby of the hotel. Kanafani became aware of this attention and sat down again.

"To hell with your scruples," he said under his breath. "No one has ever understood your weakness for that family of Jews."

Hidar was deeply distressed by the news of Sidney's death. He had no special liking for the bearded, red-haired American, and yet . . . was it because Sidney was Hugo's cousin? Was it because he, Hidar, couldn't get Hugo out of his memory? Was it because he saw Sidney's death as an omen of something else? Whatever the reason, he spent the rest of the day walking around Beirut, between the harbor and the beaches of Khalde, along the Corniche. He was afraid to go back to the hotel, to be alone listening to the news. *I'm human, too human,* he thought. *Someone who wants to heal the world should be able to heal his conscience.*

He went into a café and ordered an arrack. Seeing a telephone on the bar, he moved toward it like a sleepwalker, not really knowing whom he wanted to call. He remembered Leila. Should he tell her the news? He called her. To his surprise, she already knew. But he was glad to talk with her, and she seemed glad he had called. They agreed to meet that night on the terrace of the Hotel St. George.

Night had come and Leila was there. Her face was drawn but she was still beautiful. So was the night. The bay was incredibly luminous. Everything in the air around them invited them to let themselves go. What was this feeling overwhelming him? Why this sudden need to kiss her warm eyelids? He was amazed to realize that he desired her, and that, in spite of her grief, she too felt an almost irrepressible desire for him. The sea was there, close by, with the lulling sound of its waves. She moaned softly, with her head on his shoulder. Her tearful, deeply moving face was pale against the blue-black of the sky. He gently ran his fingers across it.

He heard tires crunching on gravel and, soon afterward, a familiar voice speaking his name. He drew back from Leila and looked around. The headwaiter was coming toward him, followed by a massive figure.

"Mr. Assadi," the headwaiter said, stepping aside with conspicuous servility to reveal a fat man with thin lips, half-closed eyes and a long, pimply nose.

The man held out his white, ringed hand toward Leila and, in a metallic voice, said matter-of-factly in French, "I've come to get my wife."

□

PARIS, OCTOBER 1970

My mother wept. And, I don't know why, it irritated me. Maybe I
knew that when we weep for a death, we weep for ourselves. Maybe
I sensed a prophecy of her own death behind those incongruous
tears. In any case, she wept. And she mourned for Sidney as if he
had been someone close to her. She even wrote a poem that began,
I remember, "Take my tears and my reprobation, O my God."

Vladimir Volossatov called me one last time. He had already
been upset by my cousin's disappearance, he said, and now he was
saddened by his death.

"It was a terrible misunderstanding," he told me in his inimit-
able Russian accent. "A combat group from Al Fatah tried to free
your cousin. He misunderstood and ran away. Fate! Yes, my friend,
fate!" But he had also come to say goodbye, because he was going
back to Moscow, for good. "Yes, my dear friend, everything must
come to an end. I must leave Paris. It's so sad. . . ." Then, just before
he hung up, he said something that still haunts me. I couldn't make
up my mind whether he said it out of self-interest, thoughtlessness
or kindness: "By the way, I've made inquiries about your other
cousin — Hugo. To find the reason for his death, you'll have to look

in the direction of Israel Beer. Tell that to your Israeli friends. They'll understand."

That revelation took me so aback that I immediately called Benjamin Ben-Eliezer.

"That's odd," he said when I had told him of my conversation. "Israel Beer, Ben-Gurion's former adviser, was actually a Soviet spy. Your cousin Sidney also talked to me about him after meeting Sigrid's brother, Dr. Furchmuller, in Frankfurt. Strange ... and now your friend Volossatov. Soviet intelligence ... very strange indeed ..."

He promised to check into it further and keep me posted. Then he put Mordecai's son Arieh on the phone. Arieh was obviously proud to show me that he was working with Benjamin.

"Hello, Marek. So I understand that you've discovered some new link between Hugo and Sidney? I hope I'm not speaking out of turn. . . ." Then, suddenly changing his tone, he said: "I hope you're coming to Israel soon. My father and I will be happy to see you again."

31

ISRAEL

Arieh's Investigation

OCTOBER 1970

The sun lingered a moment on the mountain tops. Then, as though languid or even exhausted, it fell into the plain somewhere and Kibbutz Dafneh was abruptly submerged in darkness. A mechanism quickly started the main generator, as it did every evening. Lights went on, first along the streets, then around the sheds and storage buildings and at the top of the water tower, and finally in the houses. Knowing that the time had come, the members of the kibbutz headed for the dining hall.

"You should have put on a sweater," Sarah told Arieh. "It's not like Tel Aviv here. We're in the north. It's good you came back for the holidays. This year we've built a huge *sukkah*. The children love being in it. Your sister Dina doesn't want to eat anywhere else. Shall we go there?"

"No," he answered with an affectionate smile, "I'd rather we went to the dining hall. I have to talk to Papa."

Intrigued, Mordecai looked at his son, but in the semidarkness he could see him only as a silhouette. And the whole family filed into the dining hall, with its good smell of cucumbers, fried food and coffee.

The kibbutzniks greeted the prodigal son warmly. They told him how good he looked in his uniform, how healthy. They questioned him about life in the army, and they looked at him strangely, as if he were already a hero.

"What's new on the kibbutz?" he asked his father when they were finally alone together, sitting at one of the tables.

"Not much. A few infiltrations by fedayeen from across the border. A few animals killed, but no people. We also bought a new tractor. And some babies have been born. That's about all. But what about you? Do you have a problem? You said you wanted to talk to me."

"Yes, but not here."

After dinner, Arieh put on a thick sweater, his father put on a sheepskin jacket and they both went out to sit on lawn chairs in front of their wooden house. Far off in the darkness, clusters of lights showed the locations of villages on both sides of the border. Mordecai gazed silently at his son. He felt a little intimidated by him — perhaps because he was seeing him for the first time as an adult. Then, consciously choosing a banality to open the conversation, he said:

"So you're spending your army time working with Benjamin?"

"That's right. I closely followed those airplane hijackings, and then Sidney's kidnapping."

"So you know something about it?"

Arieh continued as if he hadn't heard.

"Our French cousin called us. I mean, he called Benjamin. And I talked to him too. He said a Russian diplomat had told him to look in Israel Beer's direction to find the reason for Hugo's murder."

"Wait," Mordecai said, "not so fast. Why are you talking about Hugo when I asked you about Sidney?"

"Because we're all convinced that if we can discover the reason for one of those two deaths, we may also be able to clear up the mystery of the other." Arieh leaned toward his father, and in his eyes, his expression and his bearing there was a gravity that Mordecai had never seen in him before. "Did you know Israel Beer?"

"I met him once. At a Labour Party convention. It was . . . I think it was in 1959."

"What was he like?"

"He had a big black mustache and a loud laugh, and I remember that his face was slightly Oriental-looking."

"Do you think he really was a traitor?"

"Who knows? He wrote a book while he was in prison, in which he said he was convinced that Israel's security depended on creating closer ties with the socialist camp."

"But that's a far cry from handing over documents to the socialist camp!"

"He always claimed he exercised his own censorship on the information he delivered. Why are you interested in him?"

"Because of his relations with Hugo."

"With Hugo?"

"Yes. Did he talk to you about that?"

"No, not really. I know they knew each other. Hugo wanted an appointment with Ben-Gurion. The first time, he had to meet with Israel Beer instead."

"There's a file on Beer in our records," Arieh said, "but Benjamin won't let me look through it. I think he really doesn't trust me. He feels I'm too young."

They heard the cry of a bird of prey from close by, and the dogs began howling.

"What's that?" Arieh asked, suddenly on the alert.

"Nothing, nothing," Mordecai reassured him. Then, after a silence during which he looked up at the stars: "You know that tomorrow is Simkhat Torah, don't you?"

"Are you becoming religious, Papa?"

"No, only nostalgic. I remember, in Winnipeg . . . it was a beautiful holiday. We took all the Scrolls of the Law out of their cabinets. We danced, the children were given all kinds of sweets. . . ."

Another long silence. The tranquillity of the darkness, the warmth of that renewed nearness, the father and son sitting side by side in communion with the night.

"Did you call the widow?" Arieh finally asked.

"The widow?"

"Uncle Sidney's widow, Marjory."

"Yes. She's waiting for his body to be returned. The Red Cross is taking care of it. Richard wants him to be buried in Jerusalem."

"Like Hugo."

"Yes, strangely enough, like Hugo."

Before Mordecai could say anything more, the quiet of the night was shattered by the barking of dogs, followed by loud cries from the poultry yard. Then there were rapid footsteps on the gravel.

"Who's there?" he asked in a voice muffled by anxiety, his ears straining to pick up every sound and all his muscles tense.

"Jacob Oren. Get your guns and hurry to the water tower. A group of fedayeen have been spotted. They're coming toward the kibbutz."

All lights went off at once, except for a searchlight probing the environs from the top of the water tower.

"Do you have a gun?" Mordecai whispered to his son as they ran toward the house, bending forward.

"Yes, a submachine gun. I put it in the cabinet."

A few moments later they were both armed and running toward the water tower. They passed other men heading for their assigned stations. No one spoke or called out. The barking of the dogs drowned out the sound of footsteps. It was like an admirably choreographed ballet that had been endlessly rehearsed and was now being performed with perfect precision.

When they reached the water tower, they found four other people there.

"We're all here now," said Jacob Oren, a short, powerfully built man, and Mordecai couldn't help noticing that the situation had transformed his bearing, his tone and even the sound of his voice. "Come on, follow me!" he continued with the unsuspected authority of the peasant soldier.

The six men went past a shed, and, just as they reached the low surrounding wall topped by barbed wire, they heard shots. A siren, a burst of gunfire from above the wall, another burst. Arieh shot without thinking. Once, twice. And they heard a cry from close up, a horrible cry, somewhere between a roar and a whine. Then the dogs redoubled their barking.

"I think I hit someone," Arieh said in a toneless voice.

"We'll go and see," Mordecai said.

"No," Jacob Oren ordered. "Don't move. It's too risky."

The shooting moved farther away. Arieh saw a meteor streak across the sky and relaxed. The streetlights went on while two helicopters droned past overhead.

"They got here in a hurry," Oren remarked. He watched the

218

running lights of the helicopters fading into the distance. "Now we can go and see."

Near the wall, in the direction of Arieh's shots, they found a Soviet-made submachine gun and a bloody Arab headdress. Where was the man, the shadow? Gone, vanished.

At dawn the next morning the search was resumed, without result. The commander of the nearby garrison, who had come to the kibbutz, concluded that the fedayee was wounded and had used his headdress to wipe his wound, and that his companions had carried him away.

Arieh was inwardly glad it had turned out that way. It was the first time he had ever shot at a man, and while he was proud that his courage hadn't failed him and he hadn't missed his target, he wasn't sorry that the Palestinian had been able to get away. If the situation had been reversed, would the Palestinian have had the same qualms? Or would he have been like those who attacked the bus, and taken pleasure in blowing Arieh's brains out? Maybe so. But to Arieh the thought of killing a man was intolerable.

As soon as he was back in Tel Aviv after the holidays, Arieh asked to speak to Benjamin.

"I'd like to take charge of the file on Hidar Assadi."

Benjamin looked at him with amusement.

"Don't you think someone else is already in charge of it? We didn't wait for you to come here before we —"

"I think I can do better."

"'The presumptuous man becomes a raisin before being a ripe grape.'"

And while Arieh took on the stubborn expression of someone determined not to leave without getting satisfaction, Benjamin added, as though regretfully, "Be that as it may, you know what Talleyrand said: 'We believe only in those who believe in themselves.'"

"Who's Talleyrand?"

"You see, you still have a lot to learn! Talleyrand was a French diplomat who, by means of his intelligence and scheming, was able to stay in power all through the Revolution, the Empire, the Restoration and the reign of Louis-Philippe. Let's say he had a prodigious ability to . . . look ahead."

Benjamin was about to say something more when the phone rang. "Hello. How are you?" A few moments of polite chitchat that seemed out of character for him, then he pressed the receiver against his thigh and firmly asked Arieh to leave.

"Have you been thrown out, poor little lamb?" Myriam asked, laughing, when she saw Arieh come out of the office with a resentful look on his face. "That's how it is here: when things become too secret, the children are sent away."

"In a year or two, those secrets will be mine," the "child" answered, half mocking and half serious.

"No one is ever really in possession of a secret," Myriam said knowingly.

After lunch, Arieh went back to Benjamin's office and found a short man with long arms and thick, graying hair. Benjamin introduced him:

"This is Zvika. He'll bring you up to date on Hidar Assadi's activities. He'll also show you the file on Israel Beer. From now on, you're authorized to know about top secret matters." Seeing Arieh stare at him in bewilderment, he asked, "Didn't you tell me you wanted to take charge of the file on Assadi? Well, I've thought it over and I've decided to let you do it, in a year or so. When the time comes, Zvika will hand over the case to you completely." He cut short Arieh's effusive thanks: "I'll leave you with him now. Good luck."

Zvika Amihay, known as "the Bulgarian" because of his native country, was a reserved man. He was also feared. He had survived a Nazi concentration camp and come to Israel only a few days after its proclamation of independence.

He went down to the third floor with Arieh, disappeared behind a metal door and came out a few minutes later with two file folders. Without a word, without the slightest explanation or comment, he led his young colleague into a very small office and put the folders down on a table.

"I'll come to get them at six o'clock. Six o'clock sharp. You have three hours to study them. We'll talk about them afterward."

The office was damp, and empty except for a trestle table, a chair, and a map of Israel on the wall. And now for the dossier on the famous Israel Beer. Arieh's heart was pounding, his hands were moist and his fingers trembled. Where should he begin? The memorandum slips? The statements of witnesses? The trial records? The various "deductions," more and more refined, that had accumulated through the years? Beer always claimed he had been a student at the officers' school in Wiener Neustadt, Austria, yet here was a statement by the head of the clandestine training center for the special forces of the Haganah, who remembered his surprise in 1938 when he received the "legendary" Israel Beer and discovered that he knew almost nothing about how to use weapons. And here was a statement by Jan Mishka, who had served in the International Brigades, where Beer was supposed to have spent two years: he wrote that after a one-hour conversation in Paris, in the presence of the military attaché of the Israeli embassy, he was nearly certain that he had never met Beer before.

Arieh was so fascinated by what he read, and so troubled by those contradictions, that he forgot about the passing of time. When he finally looked at his watch it was already twenty to six and he had only twenty minutes to go through the Assadi dossier. He quickly opened the folder. Photocopies fell out of it and scattered over the floor. As he was picking them up, he noticed several sheets of paper covered with names and phone numbers and held together with a big paper clip. Looking at them more closely, he saw that they were nothing less than a photocopy of Hugo's address book. His father's name was there, and Sidney's address and phone number in New York, and Salomon's in Paris, and so many others. . . . Under the letter H, beside a crossed-out name that might have been Hidberg or Hilberg, was Hidar's name, followed by a figure that was not a phone number: it was the figure 300,000.

Three hundred thousand . . . did it mean three hundred thousand dollars? And did it refer to the loan that Hugo had tried to get from an American bank and unsuccessfully asked Sidney to cosign?

Arieh was suddenly sure he had discovered something important. He was so excited that, forgetting Zvika and the dossiers, he opened the door to go and tell Benjamin the news. And in the doorway he found himself face to face with Zvika.

32

MOSCOW

The Taking of the Kremlin

FEBRUARY 1971

Aron Lerner learned of Sidney's death from *Pravda.* In a long article praising the Soviet Union's outstanding contributions to the quest for peace in the Arab-Israeli conflict, there was a passing reference to the death of an American doctor, Sidney Halter, who had been abducted by "a group of extremists acting to further the interests of Israeli imperialism." Aron had never laid eyes on his wife's cousin Sidney, but he had the confused but insistent feeling that he had lost a close relative. "A man dies as many times as he loses a member of his family." That was one of the best maxims of Publius Valerius Publicola, that founder of the Roman Republic to whom Aron had just devoted one of his lectures at the university.

As for Rachel, her reaction was both simple and strange.

"Six million and two killed," she said after reading the article that Aron had shown her.

For her, there was no doubt: her cousins Hugo and Sidney had been killed because they were Jews, and so their names had been added to the martyrology of the Holocaust. A year earlier, Aron would have protested. He would have tried to demonstrate to his wife that what she had said was appallingly absurd. But now he wasn't so sure. . . . He had seen the anti-Semitic cartoons in *Ogoniok* and the *Moscow News,* he had heard the calls for the destruction of Israel put forward by "Palestinian comrades" who had been invited to speak at the university and were warmly applauded by the audience, and he had to admit that the political murder of a Jew was seldom a matter of chance, that it nearly always resulted to some extent from a policy of extermination.

The truth is that Sidney's death probably moved Aron a little further away from his son Sasha, whom he had already been seeing only rarely since their quarrel over the Six-Day War, and brought him closer to the little "Zionist group" that his wife had been meeting with for the last three years. It included a journalist named Zaredsky, a stern but courteous former army officer who displayed three rows of ribbons and medals each year on the anniversary of the victory in World War II. There was also an engineer named Levin, a gentle, unobtrusive man; and a professor of Russian literature named Slepak, who knew Pushkin by heart. Each member of the group had asked for permission to emigrate to Israel. In retaliation, they had all been fired from their jobs, and since then they had been living as best they could by means of "unofficial" work. Levin drove a taxi. Zaredsky did small bricklaying jobs. The least resourceful kept going with the help of friends and relatives. Aron found them all idealistic and touching — and so much more interesting than his colleagues at the university! So much freer! So much more human, too! Would he follow their example? No, of course not. He hadn't yet reached that point. In spite of everything, the Soviet Union was still his country. But as time went by, he was more and more fascinated and haunted by the situation of those men and women.

Two or three days after the article in *Pravda,* Hidar Assadi returned to Moscow. They were shocked by how changed he was. His curly hair had turned gray. He walked a little more heavily than before. His left arm was in a cast and, to Aron and Rachel's great surprise, this time he had no stories to tell, no events to comment on. But, strangest of all, he had become more considerate. He took an interest in their lives and their health, and he brought little gifts every day when he came to their apartment.

One night he announced that he was going to marry Olga. This time Rachel and Aron weren't surprised: for a long time they had been prepared for that news — and resigned to it. Good losers, they even decided to "do things right" and take advantage of the New Year's holiday on January 1 to celebrate the wedding.

They invited Rachel's "Zionist" friends and Aron's colleagues at the university. Hidar invited the leaders of the Committee for Solidarity with the Peoples of Africa and Asia, and several Arab ambassadors. As for Olga, she limited herself to members of the pediatrics department in the hospital where she worked. It was an incongruous, explosive mixture of people.

When the evening of the celebration came, Rachel didn't know which way to turn. She was in the kitchen, the living room, Aron's study, the bedroom — in short, wherever there were guests, and there were guests everywhere. To some, she offered cookies that she had made herself; to others, vodka and kvass; with still others, she put on her most urbane manner and initiated conversations. And with everyone she stayed alert and kept a close watch on encounters that might go badly.

For a time everything went well. A friend of Olga's had brought an accordion. Zaredsky, a refusenik, played a World War II song, and Chebrikov, a KGB man, sang it, to Hidar's great joy. Just then Sasha came in with a journalist from *Literary Russia,* Matvey Fedorovich Egorov, who seemed already drunk.

"We've been at a going-away party for a friend," Sasha explained. "He's going to be our consul in Bucharest." He looked around him. "What's this? Mama has invited her whole gang of cosmopolitans."

Aron heard him, looked daggers at him and went over to him.

"This is your sister's wedding, Sasha," he said under his breath. "Don't forget it. Especially since —"

He was interrupted by laughter and applause behind him. He looked around. Inside a circle of guests joyfully clapping their hands, he saw Levin, the old engineer who was now a cab driver, doing a Cossack dance around Olga.

"Why, it's the Jew Levin!" said Egorov, Sasha's friend.

The laughter stopped instantly. There were a few embarrassed coughs and snickers, then total silence while Levin stepped forward.

"Yes, I'm a Jew," he said to Egorov. "And you?"

"I'm a Russian!" Egorov proclaimed, proudly pounding his fist against his chest.

"You're not a Russian," Levin replied calmly. "You're nothing but shit. Under the czars, you'd have been in the Union of the Archangel Michael, and taken part in pogroms. In 1917, the Bolsheviks would have shot you."

"Stop, please stop!" Rachel begged, feeling that something disastrous was about to happen.

But Egorov didn't listen to her.

"The Bolsheviks would have shot *me,* a Communist?"

"Yes, you and everyone like you. You're not a real Communist. If you have a Party card in your pocket, you got it either by luck or by special favor. The Nazi Party is the one you should have joined."

"Shut up, you dirty kike!" Egorov shouted, livid with rage.

And while Rachel and Olga tried to separate them, Aron gripped Sasha by the arm.

"Take that garbage out of here, right now!"

Sasha looked at his father as if he had never seen him before and then, without a word, took Egorov by the shoulders and led him toward the door.

The next morning, Aron announced to Rachel that he had made up his mind to apply for an exit visa. To Israel. She was so surprised that she didn't know what to say.

Only half an hour later, when Aron came into the kitchen — which was still full of dirty dishes, empty bottles and cigarette butts — to help her make breakfast, did she ask timidly: "Are you serious?"

He nodded. She looked at him with tears running down her cheeks and kissed him.

The winter of 1970–71 was turning out to be difficult. January was cold and windy. The lines of people in front of stores grew longer and longer. After applying for a visa to Israel, Aron daily expected to be dismissed from the university. His new friends had begun coming to see him in the apartment on Kazakov Street, and they often stayed far into the night, discussing literature or politics.

One evening in February, when several of them were gathered

in the apartment, drinking tea and joking, the doorbell rang. Aron went to answer it, already walking with the resignation of a future prisoner. But it was Levin. He nodded a silent greeting and, after a quick look at Aron's study to make sure it was empty, motioned him into it. As soon as they were safely inside, he closed the door and bolted it.

He took a sheet of paper from the desk and began writing feverishly without taking time to sit down: "I came here in my taxi and I'm sure I wasn't followed. This is urgent and very important. At 11 o'clock tomorrow morning we're going to occupy the reception room of the Presidium of the Supreme Soviet of the USSR." He glanced at Aron's astounded face and went on writing: "One by one, without attracting attention, we'll go into the building, which is on Red Square, and then we'll announce a hunger strike. We won't leave till the president sees us. Our goal is freedom to emigrate to Israel."

He put down his pen and looked at Aron steadily. Aron smiled, a little skeptically. Levin took another sheet of paper and continued writing: "I understand your reaction. Nothing like this has ever happened before in the entire history of the USSR. It will be the first strike of its kind, but maybe not the last. We're sure to be arrested. Sentences will be stiff, at least ten years. But that's better than staying here, waiting. Our arrest will stir up a storm all over the world. Will you join us?"

Aron saw Levin look at him again. He felt as if he were living a dream, and he was panic-stricken. Things were moving too fast. Why him? There were tens of thousands of other Jews who wanted to emigrate to Israel! Ten years in the gulag was a lot more serious than staying in Moscow without work. But could he refuse? He looked at Levin. Clearly he was neither a lunatic nor a hero. Just an engineer who had become a cab driver. And Aron thought that Homer had been wrong to say: "There is nothing on earth weaker than man." With a hand he had trouble controlling, he picked up Levin's pen and wrote, "Who's coming with us?"

Levin smiled and wrote down some names, those of Aron's new friends, honest and upright men.

"Good," Aron wrote, amazed at his own decision. "When?"

"Tomorrow at 11," Levin wrote. "Take the subway and get off at the Lenin Library station. Then walk to our meeting place."

Aron nodded. Levin gave him a friendly pat on the shoulder,

struck a match, set fire to the sheets of paper and put them down on the ashtray. When they had burned completely, he reduced their ashes to dust with his thumb. Then, moving quietly to avoid being heard by the guests, he left as he had come, without a word.

When Aron went back into the living room, he signaled Rachel not to ask any questions. Only when their friends had left did he take a pen and a pad of paper and sum up the situation, in writing, as clearly as possible. Rachel read and reread what he had written and, like him, didn't take time to think.

"I'll come with you," she wrote.

That night Aron slept badly. He had nightmares and woke up several times. At about four in the morning he thought he heard someone open the front door. He got up, saw that the door was still bolted and went into his study. There he looked through the disorderly pile of books on his desk, read a poem by Ion of Chios and a page of Aeschylus and lingered over a scene in Sophocles's *Antigone*: "I know I can; it was inevitable. . . . If I perish before my time, I look on death as a blessing. When someone lives in the midst of affliction, how can he fail to benefit from dying?" And for the first time in his life he wondered if Ecclesiastes, which says almost the same thing, might not be closer to him.

The entrance of the reception room of the Presidium of the Supreme Soviet of the USSR was impressive: square, massive, decorated with gilded moldings. The heavy oak doors had enormous brass handles. In front of those doors, policemen in black coats, their faces reddened by the cold, seemed doomed to endless guard duty. Outside it was snowing and there was already a crowd despite the early hour. Aron and Rachel were there. They met Slepak, the professor of Russian literature, who nodded to Aron and took Rachel by the arm.

"No, not both of you," he whispered. "One person per family. No use all of us going to prison."

Aron kissed Rachel and asked her to go home. Then, instinctively closing his eyes as if he were jumping into the void, he went inside.

He stepped into a big room made mostly of marble, lined with black leather benches. At the far end was a half-wall with little windows in it. Bureaucrats' heads could be seen through the windows. A line had already formed on the left. Dozens of disabled people on crutches, women with small children, old people and badly dressed peasants were observing each other and quietly telling each other their troubles. On the right, along the opposite wall, were the Jews.

Aron rapidly counted them. There were twenty-two of them, twenty men and two women. Among them were Levin and Zaredsky. Also Ivanov, a half-Jew; he had decided to join the others out of respect for his mother, who had died after being deported by the Nazis. And then there was Slepak. He left the group, went to one of the windows and handed a sheet of paper to the man behind it. The man read and reread the paper. His face showed immense astonishment. He said something to Slepak and read the paper once again, as if its meaning escaped him. Finally he picked up the phone while Slepak came back to his companions, smiling.

"I said," he told them, "that we're going to stay here till we talk with President Podgorny."

Tension in the room was extreme. Hardly anyone was talking now, or even moving. The dumbfounded bureaucrats watched the Jews through the glass of their windows. A man in civilian clothes, but with military bearing, stared at Aron from under his fur hat and then, seeing that he too was being observed, pretended unconcern. Another man wearing the same kind of fur hat quickly snapped a few pictures.

All at once, for some mysterious reason, life resumed: the crowd pressed forward again, the lines in front of the windows became as long as they had been before, the twenty-two Jews regrouped to the right of the windows and, in the midst of general indifference, the little ballet of misery regained its rhythm and went on as if nothing had happened.

Hours went by. Darkness fell. Aron was getting hungry, but mainly he was very tired. The room was beginning to empty now.

Soon there was almost no one left but the policemen and the Jews. A sickly-looking functionary came forward, making sure that his footsteps resounded on the marble floor, as in the theater. And without looking at anyone, speaking as though to himself, but loudly enough for the twenty-two Jews to hear, he said, "It is now closing time. Please leave the room." Seeing that no one moved — neither the Jews nor the policemen — he added, "The cleaning squad may begin work."

Five women in blue smocks, with scarves on their heads, came in. Indifferent to what was happening in the reception room of the Presidium of the Supreme Soviet, they put down their buckets, splashed water on the floor and, without even looking up, set to work methodically and mechanically.

Fascinated, Aron watched the five women pushing dirty water in front of them with their scrubbing cloths. When the water reached the place where he was sitting, he raised his feet. His companions did the same. The five women came back with the buckets, sopped up the dirty water and left without so much as a glance at the twenty-two Jews sitting along the wall with their feet in the air.

Everything had happened as in a play by Sophocles. The main characters had come onstage one by one, in front of the same set, along with the chorus, the messengers and the silent characters. And, as though to confirm Aron's impression, a silent functionary emerged from the wings, went to the windows and lowered the blinds. The big baroque chandeliers suddenly shone with all their tragic brightness.

A short, dark man wearing a black suit and tie came into the room, accompanied by two men who respectfully walked behind him. *One of the main actors,* Aron thought. The man stopped in front of the twenty-two Jews, stared at them one after another with his slanting Tartar eyes and introduced himself:

"I'm Tuchin, Deputy Chancellor of the Office of the President of the Presidium of the Supreme Soviet of the USSR, Nikolai Viktorovich Podgorny." And, imperiously, "I demand that you leave immediately."

"We're staying," Levin said.

The Jews all began talking at once.

"We won't leave till we've been given the right to emigrate to Israel!"

"You can arrest us if you want to!"

"We're not leaving!"

Tuchin seemed surprised and almost amused by the little group's unreasonable attitude. He raised his hand and asked for silence.

"Do you realize what you're doing? You're occupying a government building. Our laws take a dim view of such things. Do you understand? If you're arrested, your sentences will be very severe."

He looked significantly at the compact mass of policemen blocking the exits. "I'll allow you to leave without incident now. This is your last chance. Soviet law is merciless to its enemies."

"We're not enemies," Aron said. "We're Soviet citizens, like you, but we demand respect for our rights."

This time Tuchin seemed annoyed. He made a brusque gesture with his left hand, as though he were brushing away a fly, and said, "The court will decide whether you're enemies or friends. As far as I'm concerned, there's no more to be said."

He turned on his heel and ordered that the lights be turned off.

"Now they're going to arrest us," said one of the Jews.

"They can just take us out of here by force," a second voice said in the darkness.

"We'll get at least a year," a third one remarked.

"If we only get a year, we'll be lucky," the second one replied. "I think it will be more like ten years. They'll throw the book at us to discourage everyone else."

"Well, at least they won't shoot us!" said one of the women.

"They'll do whatever they want," Levin said.

"No, it's not like it was under Stalin," Slepak said. "We'll get ten years in a camp. That's enough, believe me."

There was a silence. The Jews moved closer together. They felt the heavy presence of the police in the darkness.

"Jews, I have a transistor radio," Levin said after a time.

"Can you get foreign stations?" Aron asked.

"I'll try."

They heard static, fragments of music, words in foreign languages, a series of voices, music again, and finally a faraway voice speaking in Russian:

"Our correspondents report . . . Moscow . . . a group of Jews who . . . right to emigrate to Israel . . . this morning occupied the building of . . . Soviet . . . hunger strike. . . . The building is now surrounded by policemen and soldiers. The whole world . . . attention . . . the unfolding of that desperate struggle. The twenty-two men and women represent hundreds of thousands . . . Soviet Jews . . . in vain . . . for years . . . win respect for their . . . we have learned from well-informed sources . . ."

Jamming drowned out the voice completely.

230

"They know!" cried Slepak. "We're not alone!"

"I'm not afraid anymore," Zaredsky said.

"*Shema Yisrael,*" Levin murmured.

A woman began weeping. Carried away with sudden excitement, Aron recited, "'Among so many wonders in the world, the greatest wonder is man.'"

"Professor Lerner," said a young voice close beside him.

"Yes?"

"This is Volodia. I'm one of your students."

"Volodia who?"

"Blumstein."

"Ah, yes, Volodia Blumstein. I didn't recognize your voice," Aron said, trying to find the young man's hand in the darkness.

"I was behind Professor Zaredsky. I was afraid to approach you, but . . ."

"Yes, Volodia?"

"I remember when I and a few other Jewish students talked with you after class one day. You told us you were against Zionism. Yet now . . ."

"It's true, I've changed," Aron said simply.

And he talked about Hugo, Sidney, Sophocles and Ecclesiastes. He talked a long time, a very long time. The little group listened to him in silence. "'If the clouds be full of rain,'" he recited, "'they empty themselves upon the earth; and if the tree fall toward the south, or toward the north, in the place where the tree falleth, there it shall be.'"

Just then the chandeliers went on. The sudden light startled the hunger strikers. Aron blinked his eyes and looked at his watch: it was five in the morning. The Kremlin chimes immediately confirmed it.

"Look!" Levin said.

In the middle of the empty room stood Tuchin, with his two guards. Policemen stood vigilantly in front of the doors and windows.

"Listen to me," Tuchin said triumphantly. "I've been told to give you this message . . ." He paused, as though better to savor the effect of his words, and announced, "Your request is granted."

Aron was breathless with surprise. Slepak looked at Levin incredulously. Levin stepped forward.

"Are you saying that we can emigrate to Israel?"

"Wait, wait." Tuchin gestured. "High authorities have ordered the creation of a government committee to take charge of emigration to Israel. And all twenty-two of you are invited to the first meeting of that committee."

"And we'll be allowed to go to Israel?" Volodia asked.

"I think so," Tuchin answered hesitantly. "Go home now. On the first of March, come back for the meeting of the committee."

"What about all the others who want to emigrate to Israel?" Slepak asked.

"The committee will be there to hear them."

Levin took another step toward Tuchin.

"How do we know you're not trying to put something over on us?"

Tuchin seemed surprised by this question. He looked around him, as though trying to find support for what he had said. His eyes lingered briefly on the mass of policemen in front of the doors. He abruptly turned to Levin.

"The proof that you can trust me is that you're not going to be arrested. And furthermore you have the word of the President of the Presidium of the Supreme Soviet of the USSR, Nikolai Viktorovich Podgorny."

"Well, Jews," Ivanov asked, "shall we trust his word?"

Tuchin gestured toward the exit. The mass of policemen opened. Aron led the way out of the room.

33

MOSCOW

The Great Return

MAY 1971

Aron Lerner and his friends were surprised by a victory that seemed too quick and easy. Did the authorities' sudden liberality hide some sort of trick? Was there going to be a new wave of persecution? When the little group of refuseniks left the building in the glare of police spotlights and the camera flashes of foreign newspaper photographers, they gave increased courage to Soviet Jews as a whole, but what lay behind that apparent indulgence on the part of the government? Shouldn't it arouse more wariness than joy?

The committee promised by Tushin met on March 1. The twenty-two Jews were invited to attend and things happened more or less properly. The committee members questioned them about their wish to leave the Soviet Union. They answered. Each side clearly made an effort to understand the other. Gevchenko, the committee chairman, concluded the meeting by promising visas in the spring and wishing a good trip to those who would receive them.

But things quickly took a turn for the worse. The Soviet press launched a big campaign for the preservation of Russian culture and values. There were cartoons in *Pravda* and *Izvestia* showing the enemies of socialism, the "cosmopolitans," as "Jews" with long noses and pointed beards. Some cartoonists, afraid they might not be understood, even added a very explicit Star of David to their caricatures. And it was in that alarmingly deteriorating climate that a meeting of professors and assistants was held at the university in late April. Aron attended it, not without a certain apprehension.

It was by no means the first meeting of its kind, and Aron was used to hearing Party leaders rail against "cosmopolitans" and ask the professors to exercise greater vigilance. But this time it was said that Ivan Vasilyevich Evgenin, general secretary of the Party section in the history department, was going to deliver a particularly violent diatribe against "enemies of the people who have succeeded in infiltrating the university and sowing seeds of discord."

As it turned out, Comrade Evgenin's speech was even more ignoble than anyone had feared. He missed nothing: he dragged in all the worst stereotypes and all the most vicious slanders, and finally, when he was out of arguments and almost out of breath, he took a piece of lined paper from his pocket and read off the names of Jewish professors and assistants. He then asked them to sit on a long wooden bench to the right of the audience. They hesitated and looked at each other, but a long habit of obedience — most of them were members of the Communist Party — won out: after wavering a few seconds, they did as they were asked. Only Aron spoke up:

"I'd like to know why Comrade Ivan Vasilyevich Evgenin wants us to sit on that bench. Are we going to be on trial? If so, I ask to be tried by the judicial system of my country. In that case, I'll at least be told what crime I'm accused of."

The other Jews, who hadn't yet reached the bench, stopped indecisively. Evgenin's round, babyish face turned crimson.

"We're not in a courtroom," he said, "we're in a university lecture room. And we're here to discuss teaching methods."

"Then let's discuss them," Aron said. "What complaint do you have against our teaching methods?"

"They're bad."

Aron was thoughtful for a moment. He realized that Evgenin was drunk and would probably sink to the lowest depths of infamy. Not wanting to show a lack of solidarity with the other Jews, he joined them on the bench. Then the performance began. One by one, the "good" Communists went up to the rostrum. They were honorable men and women, professors of high merit. For years he had known them, associated with them and liked them. None of them said the word "Jew," but, as though seized with madness, each of them came forward to denounce those "Zionists," those "people without a real country," those "vagabonds without passports" and, worse, those "bad teachers." Fedor Rabinovich was reproached for having placed too much stress on Lenin's peasant policy and his reforms within the framework of the New Economic Policy, and not enough on the congress of Asian and African peoples held in Baku in 1922. Tenquiz Abuladze was criticized for having referred to Mayakovski's suicide in his course on contemporary Soviet poetry. One of Aron Lerner's lectures on Plato was exhumed, in which he had raised the question of whether, in asserting that a perfect social system existed, Plato had opened the door to a horde of false messiahs.

Aron, who had restrained himself till now, rose to his feet.

"Getting information from informers is contemptible," he said, "but if you consider it worthy of you, at least report the information completely."

"Professor Lerner does not have the floor," Evgenin said.

"I've been at this university longer than you have. I'll talk as long as I feel it's in the interest of truth."

Tension in the room had abruptly risen. Several murmuring voices could be heard. And Vasily Slepakov stood up, trembling.

"I object, Comrade Evgenin! I think we should listen to Professor Lerner. He may have something to say in his own defense."

"Comrade Slepakov," said the Stalinist, his face growing redder and puffier, "I've already pointed out that we're not in a courtroom. There's neither an accused nor an accuser here. But our country is assailed by anti-Soviet ideologies. And, as Comrade Brezhnev said at the last plenum of our Party, the universities must be in the forefront of the struggle against deviationism."

Aron was about to answer again, but Fedor Rabinovich, a little man whose thinning hair seemed determined to look as wretched as his scraggly beard, spoke up before he could open his mouth.

"Comrade Evgenin is not completely wrong," he said in a peculiar voice that sounded as if it were coming from a loudspeaker. "We may have been careless now and then. Sometimes we get carried away when we're talking to our students. But that doesn't justify accusing us of deviationism!"

Aron couldn't believe his ears. He looked at Rabinovich. Should he shake him? Remind him of his human dignity? But another Jewish professor, Boris Zelataien, had already begun his self-criticism while Evgenin listened delightedly. Then came a third one, and a fourth. . . . Finally it was Tenquiz Abuladze's turn to speak. He quickly stood up, dropped his glasses, hastily picked them up and began rummaging through his pockets. Smiles, mocking remarks, embarrassed looks. Abuladze waved his passport in the direction of the rostrum.

"Comrades!" he cried out in a voice choked with emotion. "Comrades! I'm a Georgian!"

This time there was laughter in the room, along with exclamations and outright joking. The men sitting on the rostrum exchanged rapidly scribbled notes. Evgenin was increasingly pleased by the turn of events. He leaned forward.

"Of course, Comrade Abuladze, of course. Please come here and let me see . . ."

Abuladze stepped toward the rostrum, repeating like an automaton, "Yes, yes, I'm a Georgian, a Georgian. My passport proves it."

Evgenin frowned and attentively examined poor Abuladze's passport.

"Hm, hm," he muttered, turning it in all directions as though to make sure it wasn't false. Finally he handed it to his comrades on the rostrum. The others held their breath. When the passport had been passed around the table and back to Evgenin, he returned it to Abuladze.

"Yes, it's true," he said in a falsely authoritarian tone. "You may go back to your original seat."

Clutching his passport, Abuladze hurried away, stumbled, nearly fell, and resumed his seat in the last row amid a new outburst of laughter and banter.

Then Slepakov stood up and quietly walked toward the rostrum. The audience fell silent. They all knew and respected Slepakov. He was an eminent professor, one of the oldest Party members at the university, and his latest book, *The Causes of the Second World War,* had won him the congratulations of the President of the Supreme Soviet. When he reached the foot of the rostrum and turned to face the audience, they held their breath.

"My dear colleagues," he began.

"Comrade Slepakov does not have the floor," Evgenin interrupted in a voice that had lost its self-assurance.

Slepakov didn't even look at him.

"We're in the room where I usually give my lectures," he went on, "so I'm speaking to you as a professor of contemporary history — the history that's sometimes made in front of us, or with us." He paused for dramatic effect, wiped his lips with a handkerchief and put it back into the inside pocket of his jacket. "Allow me to hope that what we've seen and heard here in the last hour will never be recorded in a history book, because our children, the Soviet citizens of tomorrow, would be ashamed of it, and we ourselves, as we grow older . . ." He passed his fingers through his white hair. "I'm an old Communist," he continued, his voice faltering with emotion, "and I want to remain a Communist. So I ask you, my dear comrades, to stop this masquerade immediately!"

Evgenin stood up as though driven by a spring and pointed an accusing finger at Slepakov.

"What right . . . what right do you . . ." he spluttered, obviously choking with rage.

Slepakov haughtily ignored him.

"All those in favor of ending this meeting now, raise your hands."

A murmur ran through the room, then there was a beginning of tumult that arose in the last row, swept across the room and stopped at the bench occupied by the Jews. Aron raised his hand. Two professors of ancient Slavic civilization, sitting in the last row, raised theirs. Others did the same, and still others, until all the participants in that strange meeting (except for Abuladze, the Georgian) had their hands raised.

All at once, silence returned. There was something menacing about that forest of upraised hands in front of the rostrum. Evgenin stood looking at them, incredulously.

"Comrades, how can you . . . all of you . . . how can you give your backing to enemies of the Soviet Union?" He quivered, he *trembled* with indignation. "Well, since you've all asked me to end this meeting, I'm ending it, as of now. It will be resumed in a few days. You'll be notified."

He came down from the rostrum and walked, rather unsteadily, out of the room.

When he was gone, the professors looked at each other in amazement. How could they have done that? How had they dared? Was the sky going to fall on their heads? Could they possibly be forgiven for such a rebellion? They felt both embarrassment and pride, and their boldness was succeeded by a kind of vague uneasiness.

"Thank you, Vasily," Aron said to Slepakov, going over to him. "You've illustrated Publius Valerius Publicola's famous maxim that it's better to trust courage than luck."

But he was the only one to approach Slepakov, the only one who dared to congratulate the rebel. Slepakov, obviously exhausted, smiled sadly without answering. Aron pressed his hand.

"Goodbye, Vasily. You acted as a friend."

"No," Slepakov said, "I tried to act as a man."

The next evening, when Olga came to have dinner with her parents in their apartment on Kazakov Street, she already knew what had happened at the meeting.

"So, Papa, that drunkard Evgenin tried to send you to the gallows!"

"Why do you call him a drunkard?"

"Because everyone knows he drinks like a fish."

"I wish you'd talk about something besides that meeting," Rachel grumbled, coming in from the kitchen. "Why don't you tell us where Hidar is, for example?"

"He had a meeting of the Solidarity Committee," Olga answered, "but he promised not to be very late." She turned to her father. "On the way here I met Sakharov, the academician. He complained about not having heard from you. I told him about the meeting at the university. He was outraged, and promised me that he'd make his feelings known."

Despite the passing of time, Olga hadn't changed much. She had the same big eyes and shapely figure, and the same "regal bearing" that had captivated Hidar before their marriage. Her blond hair had dulled a little, but that only allowed her to say "I'm getting old" with the exquisite coquettishness of women who know they are doing nothing of the sort. She hadn't changed in other ways, either. She was still the same high-spirited young woman. Only the other evening, Viktor Alexandrovich Chebrikov, whose influence in

Moscow continued to grow, had complimented Hidar on having such a gracious and attractive wife. At official meetings she sometimes made irreverent remarks about the Soviet bureaucracy, but, coming from a beautiful blond, that blasphemy prompted laughter, indulgence and even applause. And the fact was that if it hadn't been for her gnawing anxiety about her parents and the possibility of their going to Israel, she would have been the happiest of Muscovites. She still worked at the hospital. But she was looking forward to her next trip to Beirut, which Hidar had promised her, and she had good memories of her first one, two years earlier.

"'My beloved is white and ruddy, the chiefest among ten thousand. His head is as the most fine gold, his locks are bushy, and black as a raven.'"

"What are you saying?" Rachel asked in surprise, having heard her murmuring something.

"Nothing, I was just reciting the Song of Solomon."

"In English?"

"Yes. I learned it from an English Bible that I found in a hotel."

"You must learn Hebrew, Olga. It's the language of our ancestors."

"Yes, I know. . . . To me, the Song of Solomon is the language of love, whether I say it in English or Yiddish or anything else, and whenever I say it . . ."

Olga didn't finish her sentence, because the doorbell rang at this point. It was her beloved himself. His locks were less bushy, less black now, but she still kissed him as ardently as ever.

"So, Aron Lazarevich," he said, gently pushing Olga away, "you had a close call! Stalin's ghost is still with us!"

"You already know?" Aron asked, surprised.

"When it comes to gossip, Moscow is like a little village. But tell me exactly what really happened."

Aron shrugged his thin shoulders.

"Slepakov acted very well."

"Don't be too modest, Aron Lazarevich. From what I've heard, you acted pretty well too."

"I had nothing to lose. With Slepakov it was different. . . . But let's eat now."

At the table, the conversation resumed.

"The soup is delicious," Hidar said. "I talked about that meeting with Chebrikov, and he said he considered Evgenin's conduct inexcusable. What do you think of that, Aron Lazarevich?"

"I'm glad to hear it!"

"So was I. And do you know what else Chebrikov said?"

"No, tell me."

"He ordered an investigation, and guess what he discovered."

"Come on, Hidar, stop keeping us in suspense," Olga said, toying with his hair.

Hidar finished his soup, wiped his lips with the back of his hand and said in a low voice, looking at the others one by one, "What Chebrikov discovered is that the initiator of that vile meeting was none other than Sasha Lerner."

"Sasha!" Rachel exclaimed, dropping her spoon.

"Are you sure?" Aron asked, suddenly looking bewildered.

Hidar nodded.

"But why would he have done such a thing?"

"Maybe to keep you from going to Israel. Maybe also to protect himself. And who knows if he might not have done it to prove that he had nothing to do with his parents' efforts to leave the country? Yes, who knows? 'A man's truth is first of all what he hides.'"

Hidar had no need to say anything more. And Aron had no need to ask any more questions. The meal ended in gloomy silence, broken briefly now and then by falsely playful remarks and forced jokes.

That night, Rachel and Aron had trouble sleeping. They got up one after the other, Aron to read his Bible, Rachel to write again to her cousin in Argentina — a letter her cousin would never receive. At dawn, Aron shaved closely, took a shower, got dressed and left quietly, being careful not to wake up Rachel — who pretended to be fast asleep while she lovingly watched him from under her slightly open eyelids.

The chimes of the Tower of the Savior in the Kremlin had just struck six o'clock. The day promised to be misty but not cold, and the air smelled of springtime. Aron walked along Chkalov Street, which was already animated even at that early hour. The Komskaya subway station was spewing out sleepy people onto the sidewalk. After narrowly missing being hit by an official Ziss car, he went to

Taganskaya Square, where trucks were making their morning deliveries to a few stores. At exactly seven o'clock he came to the foot of a dark seven-story building on Mayakovski Street. He looked up. At some of the windows, curtains were being opened and faces were appearing. Aron crossed the street and leaned against a tree, knowing that from there he could watch the front door of the building.

He soon saw Sonia, Sasha's wife, with their two children, Natasha and Boris. Then a moment later Sasha himself came out, stood at the top of the steps and looked up and down the street as if he were waiting for a car. Aron told himself it had been a long time since he last saw his son. He noticed that his back was a little bent and that he looked older. He was too far away to see his face clearly, but, since he wasn't wearing a hat, he saw that his forehead had lengthened and his blond hair had thinned out. "'O my son Absalom,'" he recited, "'my son, my son Absalom! would God I had died for thee.'" And he crossed the street.

Sasha did not see his father till he was already at the foot of the steps. He tensed, stepped back and held out the hand that wasn't holding his briefcase, as though to protect himself. Without showing the slightest emotion, Aron slowly climbed the steps with his eyes fixed on his son's troubled face.

"What . . . what do you want?" Sasha asked in an unsteady voice.

"Nothing," Aron answered calmly. "I just wanted to tell you hello."

And before Sasha could react, he took him in his arms and kissed him.

34

BUENOS AIRES

Argentina, Argentina

AUGUST 1971

It was only by chance that Doña Regina learned of Sidney's death. Nearly a year had gone by. It was Sunday, an unusually warm and humid August day. Like most of the people in that working-class neighborhood along San Martín Avenue, Doña Regina and Don Israel were sitting on their front steps, enjoying the breeze from the sea. A tango by Gardel was coming from a radio that one of the neighbors had put down on the sidewalk. Doña Regina read an article on Black September in *Freiheit,* the Communist monthly in Yiddish, in which the author accused the CIA of having manipulated Palestinian killers to discredit the Arab revolution in the eyes of the American public.

"One less Halter," she said as her only comment.

"The Angel of Death kills and then leaves sanctified," remarked Don Israel, who always tried to think of something intelligent to say in such circumstances.

"Your angel has taken on some strange appearances in the last thirty years," she answered with a deep sigh.

She went back to her reading. But then, out of the corner of her eye, she saw her husband stand up, stretch and pull up his trousers.

"Where are you going?" she asked.

"Who said I was going anywhere?"

"I know you," she told him with her most exasperated expression, "and I know you're going somewhere."

Don Israel's toothless mouth froze in a forced smile.

"Well, you guessed right. I'm going to my game of dominoes."

He tugged at his suspenders two or three times, as if he were waiting for a reaction, and stood in front of her for several long moments. Then, still getting no reaction from her, he repeated, "I'm going to my game of dominoes."

Since his august wife clearly intended to ignore him and seemed absorbed in her paper, he shrugged and walked sadly away.

The truth is that Doña Regina was worried that day. She was waiting for a visit from Martín, her older son, without really expecting it very much. Miguel, the younger one, had stopped coming altogether. And there was that wretched husband of hers; she couldn't talk with him about anything, and he preferred to go off and drown his sorrows in a game of dominoes. And especially there was Anna Maria's future, which constantly preyed on her mind. Her granddaughter had now dropped out of school. She kept disappearing without saying where she was going. A month earlier, a big, swarthy policeman had come to see Doña Regina and courteously but firmly questioned her for an hour about her granddaughter's friends and movements, without giving her a reason for that sudden interest.

She sensed that Anna Maria was involved in "something fishy" but she was a long way from even suspecting how dangerous her activities were, or how deeply committed she was to them.

That very Sunday, for example, while she sat in front of her door on San Martín Avenue mulling over her sorrows and memories, the poor woman would have died on the spot if she had had any inkling of what her exquisite granddaughter was doing.

Anna Maria's organization was working militantly for the return of Perón. Mario and Julio had even gone to meet the old leader in Spain. But now the killing of sixteen guerrilla fighters imprisoned at the Trelew naval air base had stirred up passion again and the leaders of the movement had decided to carry out reprisals. Those men were dogs, they said, and should be treated as dogs. They had therefore decreed a punitive expedition to Tres Lomos. Why Tres Lomos? Because there was a torture center there, disguised as an army institute for advanced studies, and they had decided to execute the head of it, a man named Miguel Pelado. Julio had managed to get a photograph of him.

There were five of them in Mario's old Packard that morning. Julio was driving. Beside him sat Luisa, a young woman Anna Maria didn't know. Luisa had been introduced to her as an experienced terrorist and Julio had wanted to bring her along because, he said, the presence of two women would ward off any suspicion that the police might have. Anna Maria sat between Mario and Roberto, and she felt almost the same as when she had gone on her first country outings with her first boyfriends.

The car rolled steadily along, like an ordinary car on a weekend drive. It was a beautiful day, with a big sun shining in a cloudless sky. Anna Maria loved the pampas. As always, she enjoyed being in that boundless, borderless space that was neither fluid like the sea nor shifting like a desert, but solid and good like the earth. Driving across the pampas was an adventure in the midst of eternity. The road kept drawing the traveler onward, like the sirens' singing. And Anna Maria, who was on her way with her comrades to execute Miguel Pelado, couldn't help being lulled by poetic, melancholy thoughts.

At one point, while she was lost in her reverie, the car swerved abruptly and she nearly slipped off the seat: Julio had just missed a truck that was slowing down to leave the road and head for the Río Salado.

"Be careful!" Mario cried out. "You're liable to kill us before we can kill that son of a bitch!"

Anna Maria heard herself say, "Don't talk like that, Mario."

"Why not?" he asked in surprise, pushing back his hair.

"Because we're already going to kill the poor man — we don't have to insult him too."

"What do you mean, 'poor man'? When you shoot a torturer, aren't you glad?"

"No, not really. Mainly I'm sorry there are torturers to shoot."

The conversation went on for several minutes in that vein. They passed an ochre village with an admirable baroque church rising above it. They went through a muddy stream that ran across the road, over a half-destroyed bridge, and then along a dusty road that Julio described as a shortcut. Roberto and Luisa sang:

> *Since he left, I live sadly.*
> *Friendly little road, I too am leaving.*
> *Since he left, he has not come back.*
> *I want to follow his footsteps; little road, farewell.*

At nightfall they finally reached Tres Lomos, a muddy village with which Roberto was somewhat familiar because he had come there the week before to do the necessary scouting. At the end of the day, Miguel Pelado, the torturer, was in the habit of walking across the public square, in the middle of which was a fountain, on his way to the church. When she looked at that church, a colonial-style building, Anna Maria thought it could serve as the setting for a good movie.

"From now on, no mistakes," said Luisa, who had kept quiet till now.

She reached under the seat, took out a semiautomatic pistol and checked to make sure it was loaded. Like a professional.

"Park the car next to that laundry van," Roberto said to Julio. "I put it there last week. It will hide us a little. Two cars beside each other are almost a parking lot. . . . Keep going. There. Now, park parallel to the road that leads to the church. There. Now, back up a little so you can start off as soon as we've done our job. Keep away from that puddle. Good. Yes, by God, that's very good! Now, open the windows on the side toward the church, and don't attract any attention."

Roberto took a Czech VZ-58 submachine gun from under the seat and, from the same place, Anna Maria took out her Egyptian nine-millimeter pistol.

"Be sure not to miss him," Luisa said because someone had to say something.

"Will he be alone?" Anna Maria asked.

"No," Roberto said, "but you're not alone either."

Then there was silence against a background of sounds made by the village as it got ready for the night. A cart drawn by a sickly-looking donkey lingered in front of the church a long time.

"I hope it will get out of there in time," Roberto grumbled, but said nothing more.

Time passed at a snail's pace, heavy with anxiety. So this was what an assassination was like, Anna Maria thought. Was it the same even with the Palestinians? No heroes, no heroism. More precision than daring, more planning than courage. Acting more like a conscientious accountant than like a guerrilla fighter. Sitting for hours in an old parked car, constantly gripped by fear and shivering with cold. And what was the purpose of all that? To kill some poor guy whose only ambition was to torture his fellow men. For whom? For Juan Perón. He would probably come back to Argentina before long, and she believed he was the only one who could establish social peace and bring a little justice back into the country's life.

When she had reached this point in her thoughts, they were interrupted by Roberto.

"Get ready, comrades! Here they come!"

She saw a short, rather fat man in a black uniform walking unsteadily toward the church with his four bodyguards behind him.

"Goddamn it!" Roberto exclaimed. "The cart!"

The cart had moved. With its wheels creaking, it had placed itself between the Packard and the man in the black uniform. Luckily, though, Miguel Pelado came back into the field of fire after a few more steps, then stopped near the fountain to pat a child on the head.

"Ready?" Roberto asked in a voice choked with emotion. Since no one answered and the others all seemed hypnotized by the sight of Pelado patting that child on the head, he repeated frantically, "Ready? What the hell's the matter with you? Are you ready?"

But by now Pelado had started walking again, this time slowly and majestically, like a dignitary at a royal court. When he had nearly reached the church he suddenly turned around and seemed to look into the car. With no further preliminaries, Roberto called out his order:

"Fire!"

The five young people all fired at the same time. Pelado turned toward the Packard with a look of astonishment on his face. They watched him gradually sink to the ground, as in a slow-motion film. They saw two of his bodyguards fall almost at the same time, but more rapidly, more heavily, as if they were in another film. Then the third one tumbled into a puddle, splashing water on the road. Anna Maria shot again and again. The fourth bodyguard was still on his feet, but swaying. The poor men hadn't had time to take out their guns. Soldiers came running down the steps of a green wooden building opposite the church. Roberto gave the order to leave. Julio turned the ignition key; the engine started immediately, and the car sped off along the road.

NEW YORK, SEPTEMBER 1971

It was a beautiful Sunday in September. For once, the weather fore-cast had been right: this year, New York was enjoying an Indian summer. My cab driver, a Soviet Jew working for an Israeli Jew, both of whom had settled in the United States only recently, unhurriedly took me through the almost deserted city, crossed the Brooklyn Bridge and drove along the Eastern Parkway, which I have always loved, with its broad pavement bordered on both sides by grass and trees. Low cement buildings in English or Dutch style, out of keep-ing with the width of the street, displayed their strange signs: Kingdom Hall of Jehovah's Witnesses, Calvary Evangelistic, Univer-sal Temple Church, The Church of God and Prosperity. Finally we came to number 770, where there was a crowd of men in long black coats and broad-brimmed black hats who seemed to have come out of my farthest memories.

"You should have told me you were going to see the Lubavicher Rebbe," the driver said reproachfully.

The Lubavicher Rebbe was — and still is — an authority in the United States. Political figures and television and film stars, Jewish and non-Jewish, sometimes waited months for a meeting with him.

I was lucky enough to have a friend, a close associate of the Lubavicher Rebbe in Los Angeles, who put in a good word for me, and so I was able to get an appointment on rather short notice. The name of the Brooklyn Lubavicher Rebbe was not in the famous black notebook, but I remembered Hugo's story about a religious retreat in Brooklyn just before the war, and something told me I might be able to gather new information there. Simple curiosity may also have had something to do with it. And I knew about the experience of Sidney's son Richard. . . .

Almost as soon as I got out of the cab, a young man took hold of my sleeve.

"Ah, here you are! I saw your picture in the paper. I'm Mendel Fogelman, a friend of your cousin Richard. I was asked to meet you." His tone became more formal: "The Rebbe is expecting you."

"And what about all these people?"

Fogelman threw up his arms.

"All Jews need the Rebbe."

"To settle disputes?"

"No. Disputes between people are arbitrated by rabbinical tribunals. The Rebbe deals only with problems between people and the Almighty, blessed be He."

"I thought Jews didn't need an intermediary to speak to God."

Fogelman gestured impatiently, as if I had asked him an absurd question.

"The Rebbe receives visitors on Sunday morning at eleven," he told me, avoiding comment on what I had said. "His sextons give each visitor a dollar, but you'll be received before . . ." Picking up some signal from the guards in front of the door, he said to me in Yiddish, the official language of the Lubavichers, "We're ready. Follow me." He began making his way through the crowd, calling out, still in Yiddish, "Rebbe's guest! Step aside, please! Rebbe's guest!"

The crowd opened and we soon reached the front steps. Fogelman knocked on the door. It was opened by an ageless bearded man with dangling earlocks.

"This is the Rebbe's guest," Fogelman repeated once again.

We went into a vestibule where several Jews were swaying to the rhythm of a prayer. I took a skullcap from my pocket and put it on. At the end of the vestibule, on the left, was a staircase on which two children were playing with a doll. On the right was a small room with drawn curtains. In it a little white-bearded man sat motionless.

"Good morning, Rebbe," I said as I walked toward him.

"Good morning," he answered in a melodious voice. He raised his forefinger, which was like a pale line in the semidarkness. "You didn't send me your book."

There was nothing reproachful in his tone; he was simply noting a fact.

"I didn't think it would interest you, Rebbe."

"You could have sent it to me in French," he said abruptly, in French. "I know your country."

He fell silent, as if the subject were already exhausted. Then he asked, in Yiddish again, "Do you know the *Habad*?"

"Yes. My grandfather Abraham was a Hasid."

"Why do you say 'was'?"

"Because he died in the uprising of the Warsaw ghetto."

"And you're here. . . ."

"Yes, but I'm not a Hasid."

"Now I understand why you say 'was.'"

Having exhausted the second subject, he fell silent again. I was the one who brought up the subject that meant most to me.

Yes, he remembered Hugo: a tall, blond young man who had come from Poland with rage in his heart and visited his predecessor, Rabbi Joseph Isaac Schneerson, one day in the fall of 1940, just a few months after he himself had arrived in the United States. He had been strongly impressed by Hugo, no doubt about that. He had naturally sympathized with his despair and his anguished appeals on behalf of the Jews in Europe. Had he seen him again after the war? Yes, sometimes. Hugo wasn't a mystic, no, not at all, but there was something demanding about him; he was driven by a kind of thirst, and he had a strong sense of loyalty.

The Rebbe ran his slender fingers through his beard, nodded his head and added in a lower voice, "Your cousin was like a David who had suffered like a Job." Then, after a silence that I nearly interpreted as a dismissal: "I'm going to tell you something I'm sure you don't know. . . . It's a secret, a great secret, but I think the time has come. . . . After all, it happened so long ago. . . . Would you like to know a very great secret?"

"Yes, of course, Rebbe."

"Well, here it is. I know how disturbing it will be to the Jew that you are. Did you know that Hugo had a child?"

"A child?"

"Yes. He had a son. The mother died in childbirth. But the son was born. Rabbi Schneerson followed the whole thing closely. He had the boy circumcised, and found a nurse for him. And he put him in school at the age of four. Then there was destiny."

"Destiny?"

"What else could it be called? One day when the boy was crossing a street, a car . . . As it is written, 'Weep softly for the dead, for they have found rest.'" Tears welled up in the Rebbe's eyes. "It happened after the war, but your cousin didn't hear about it immediately. He was still in a hospital. He'd met a German woman who evidently saved his life. You knew that, didn't you? When he was well again, he came to get his son. And then . . ."

The Rebbe put his thin hand over his eyes, as though he wanted to escape from an unbearable vision, and murmured, "But he who is about to perish, does he not reach out his hand? He who is afflicted, does he not cry out for help?" He uncovered his eyes and said simply, "Job." Then he continued in a weary voice, "We tried to help him. That child, you understand, was his flesh and blood. He'd hardly known him, hardly seen him. The war, you understand, that time of disruptions and obsessions. . . . But the boy was his flesh and blood. And it happened just when he thought he could put down his burden awhile and catch his breath. He'd paid his tribute to heroism, you understand, he'd served the cause and the glory of his people. And it was just when he thought he'd finally won the right to enjoy that son, to love him — it was just then that he died. You see? Wasn't it destiny? With the help of the Almighty, blessed be He, your cousin regained his balance. But I think he married the daughter of a Nazi general to exorcise the hatred gnawing at him, and that he took up his pilgrim's staff again and went to the Middle East to quell the rebellion raging inside him."

The Rebbe fell silent, then suddenly smiled, stood up and stepped toward the door: the audience was over. It had lasted only seven minutes, but when I went back into the vestibule the Rebbe's sextons were already waiting for visitors.

Mendel Fogelman led me outside by way of a hall with a wash

basin in it. When we were on the sidewalk, he looked at me intently with his green eyes and said, "The Rebbe remembers all faces and all miseries. He's the righteous man among the righteous."

He went on talking but I wasn't listening: the Rebbe's story had deeply troubled me.

35

ISRAEL

Yom Kippur 1973

SEPTEMBER 1973

For the Rosh Hashana holidays, Arieh had chosen to go back to the kibbutz. In the bus climbing the eucalyptus-shaded hills of Upper Galilee, he suddenly thought of Anna Maria. Why hadn't he ever written to her? After all, she was his cousin. If it hadn't been for her, his stay in Buenos Aires would have been unbearable. Benjamin Ben-Eliezer had questioned him about her activities several times, and about relations between the Montoneros and the Palestinians. Arieh knew very little about those things and he now regretted the little he had reported. It was sure to be detrimental to his pretty cousin.

In the dossier on Hugo, which had been assigned to him, there were still many unanswered questions. But the dossier on Hidar Assadi, which he had also inherited, was beginning to be cleared up. An interesting man, Hidar! Arieh was becoming attached to him. He wished he could follow him closely for a few months, understand his behavior, maybe meet him. Not that Hidar had wanted Hugo and Sidney to die, but Arieh was convinced that he was involuntarily responsible for their deaths. If so, how did he feel when he was with Olga, cousin of the two murdered men? She was said to be more and more strongly attached to her family's memories. It was hard for him to imagine Hidar accommodating himself to that attachment.

Arieh had become acquainted with the Lerners. They had finally obtained their visa. One day, with Levin, Zaredsky, Blumstein, Slepak and others, they had been summoned to the Office of Visas and Registrations and received by an official of the interior ministry. And one evening a month later they had found themselves at the Sheremetievo airport, about to leave for Israel.

When they arrived in Tel Aviv they were assailed by reporters and photographers, then almost abducted by representatives of the foreign ministry. The Jewish Agency provided them with an apartment in Jerusalem and Aron had recently begun teaching a course on ancient Greek civilization at the Hebrew University.

Arieh was a little surprised when he met them. This was not how he had imagined refuseniks. In spite of their specifically Soviet behavior, they immediately felt at home in Israel. They recognized every place and remembered every event. It was as if every Jew had the topography and images of the Holy Land engraved in his memory from birth.

Mordecai had invited them to the kibbutz for the holidays. Judith, who had finished her military service and was now a student at the Technium in Haifa, would also be there. Arieh was looking forward to seeing her. In the three years they had known each other, they had never made love, but they were always happy and deeply moved to be together again. He had a girlfriend, Shoshana, in Tel Aviv. She was a pretty young woman with dark hair, white skin and hips a little too wide. She worked as a nurse at the Bellisson hospital in Petach Tikva and had a little studio apartment near the hospital where they often saw each other. They made love abundantly, without passion but with friendly tenderness. He told her about Judith and she read him the letters she received from her fiancé, Amos, a young surgeon who had gone off to work for a year in a hospital in San Francisco.

And now Arieh was coming home for Rosh Hashana. The bus station was several hundred yards from the kibbutz and he was glad to walk that distance because he needed to stretch his legs after the bus ride. And he was eager to breathe deeply in the high-altitude air. Night was falling and a dry wind was blowing, bringing a smell of burned manure and freshly cut grass. Dogs were barking in the Arab camp in the valley. A close-set row of prickly pears hid the fence of the kibbutz.

Arieh's parents were waiting for him. Dina, his little sister, threw her arms around his neck. The Lerners had already arrived and Mordecai had taken them to the guest house, between the water tower and the fishpond. Judith had left a message. She would come the next day; she wanted to spend the evening of New Year's Day with her father in Qiryat Shemona. Was Arieh disappointed? He would have liked her to be there. And even though his parents seemed overjoyed, he felt real sadness. *Well, it can't be helped,* he thought while he and his parents were walking toward the dining hall.

On the way, they stopped at the guest house to take the Lerners with them. Arieh expressed surprise at their perfect knowledge of Hebrew. Rachel laughed and replied that it was "catacombs Hebrew" that she had learned "underground."

The whole family went into the attractive dining hall, with its white tablecloths, walls and curtains. From table to table, people were wishing each other, "*Leshana tova tikatev vete hatahem.*" Mordecai poured the wine and said the Kiddush. Then everyone ate a slice of apple dipped in honey and said, "May this beginning year be sweet and pleasant for us." They drank to peace, and finally the meal was served.

The Muscovite cousins seemed to be filled with wonder. Arieh found them agreeable and intelligent, but he didn't know what to say to them. Should he ask about the lives of Jews in the Soviet Union? He had nothing more to learn on that subject: the press had given countless descriptions of Soviet Jews' problems and struggles. The truth was that he no longer had the slightest curiosity about them.

Rachel wept when the kibbutzniks began singing at the end of the meal. Mordecai smiled, wiped his glasses, leaned toward her and recited softly, "'Thus saith the Lord; Refrain thy voice from weeping, and thine eyes from tears: for thy work shall be rewarded.'"

Instead of being soothed, Rachel burst into real sobs.

"Is something wrong?" asked Shlomo, the mechanic.

"Our Soviet cousin misses her children," Sarah said.

"Where are they?"

"In Moscow."

"They'll be here," the mechanic said confidently. "Sooner or later, every Jew comes home."

*   *   *

Judith didn't come to Kibbutz Dafneh till the afternoon of the following day. Her satiny skin and big, dark eyes, with glints of blue and violet, had a striking effect on the young men of the kibbutz. They were excited and agitated, they behaved like roosters and peacocks. The young women made tart comments and sly remarks. Arieh was very proud. Judith was his friend, and though she didn't belong to him, she was there because of him. He tried to remember what he had felt when he was with Anna Maria. Had he loved her? Maybe. . . . But he was surprised at how easily the image of one woman could replace the image of another. For the moment, he was absorbed in the divine happiness of seeing Judith again. The trouble was that he still didn't dare to imagine her as his mistress and that he had to give her a room in the guest house, above the Lerners', while he stayed, as usual, with his parents in their wooden house.

After breakfast the next morning, he took Judith for a walk on the road to Tel Dan. It was a beautiful morning. Sunlight filtered through the heavy branches of ancient oaks and the calcareous rocks on the ground reflected it like mirrors, illuminating the thick trunks from below. Judith and Arieh said nothing. They laughed. They were delighted by everything: the shrill chirping of a young bird, an unexpected row of South American plants that had somehow found their way into that nature reserve, a little gray fox that stopped in front of them to observe them with surprise, then vanished into the bushes. They even laughed, like children, when one of them accidentally kicked a stone and sent it rolling down the hill to the Dan spring.

They walked down to the spring, joking and frolicking. After a time they went into the water, clothed at first, then, laughing still more, half naked, and finally completely naked. The sun warmed their wet skin. They had a sense of freedom that neither of them had ever known before and it suddenly made them feel as if they were alone in the world. Modest looks became bolder, then openly insistent. Bodies moved closer together, skin caressed skin. The miracle, always the same but always overwhelming, of two mouths joining. It was there, at the water's edge, that Judith and Arieh made love for the first time. And it was there that he finally recovered from his love for Anna Maria.

Judith decided to stay on the kibbutz till Yom Kippur. To

Arieh's surprise, she became great friends with the Lerners and on some days spent more time with them than she did with him. Rachel told her about Moscow, Judith repeated stories of her father in Yemen, and Aron smiled as he watched those two Jewish women, each giving the other her history, her memory.

Two days before Yom Kippur, Shlomo, the mechanic, went on patrol with a group of Druze border guards and reported that one of them had told of seeing an abnormal concentration of Syrian tanks near the Golan Heights. This was confirmed by Israeli radio that evening, then by television, which also spoke of unusual activity on the Egyptian border.

What did Benjamin Ben-Eliezer think about it? Unfortunately he wasn't there when Arieh tried to call him. As usual, Myriam, Benjamin's secretary, answered Arieh's anxious questions with a friendly laugh.

"Don't worry, darling, they won't fight a war without you."

Maybe it was only an impression caused by his own nervousness, but it seemed to him that she sounded a little worried when she added that Golda Meir had summoned several generals and cabinet ministers to a meeting in her office that day, and that Benjamin would come to work on the morning of Yom Kippur, which was highly unusual.

"You know we live in the land of miracles," she said. "The Eged bus drivers have been conscripted into public service. You never know. . . . Maybe you'll come back to see me soon."

She wished him a happy new year and hung up.

On Yom Kippur, everything stops in Israel. The streets and roads are deserted. Radio and television are silent. And that absence of sound and motion produces a kind of faint anxiety in the country. Maybe that was why the ancients gave the name of *Yomim Noraim* (Terrible Days) to the week between New Year's Day and Yom Kippur. In public, the silence is broken only by prayers in synagogues. Nonbelievers, who are numerous in Israel, respect that day of days and stay home, reading or resting.

Kibbutz Dafneh, like all of Israel, was plunged in the silence and solitude of the night of Yom Kippur. The Lerners sat on lawn chairs in front of Mordecai's house, whose steps were dimly lighted. Aron told once again about the occupation of the Supreme Soviet and the ensuing "trial" at Moscow University. He omitted the part played by Sasha in that affair. But Sasha was his son, and he hadn't waited till Yom Kippur to forgive him. Mordecai and Sarah sat on a bench, listening to the story with polite interest. Arieh and Judith sat on the steps. A light breeze brought a wayward smell of bread to them. God was there, very close. . . .

Suddenly the phone rang. Arieh moved closer to the light bulb and looked at his watch: it was ten o'clock. He went into the house, where a candle was burning in memory of the six million dead, and picked up the receiver cautiously, with remorse and superstition. It was Myriam.

"Yom Kippur's over for you, darling," she said. She laughed as always, but Arieh sensed a slight tension in her voice. "Everyone who works for army intelligence must come back to Tel Aviv immediately."

"Is it war?"

"What war? You're needed here, that's all. Get yourself a ride quickly, or else start walking. It's a long way. Benjamin will be expecting you first thing in the morning."

After putting down the receiver, Arieh stood looking at it for a moment as if he expected an explanation from it. Then he walked away from it like an automaton. A few seconds later he saw his parents, the Lerners and Judith looking at him through the doorway.

"Did you hear?" he asked.

"No," his father answered, rubbing his glasses on his sweater, "but I think I understood . . ."

They heard footsteps on the gravel.

"Who's there?" Mordecai asked.

"Shlomo."

"Where are you going?"

"I'm going to get my Vespa. I have to go back to the Golan."

"On the evening of Yom Kippur?"

"Yes, it seems there's an emergency."

There were other footsteps. The kibbutz was still in darkness and meditative calm, but tension had begun to build. Sounds arose: doors closing, an engine starting.

"Is it always like this?" Aron asked.

"Always? No, this is the first time it's happened on Yom Kippur," Mordecai answered in a choked voice.

"Oh," Aron said quietly, as if he had just asked an indiscreet question. Then he took his wife by the arm and recited, "'Ah, my dear sailors, you who, alone among my friends, are faithful to your duty, see what a roaring storm has been unleashed, and swirls around me still.'"

"Who wrote that?" Mordecai asked.

"Sophocles," Aron replied. He turned to Arieh. "Do you think they'll take me into the army if I go to a recruiting office? I know how to use a gun."

"There are no recruiting offices in Israel," Arieh said a little sententiously. "Every citizen is a soldier and knows exactly where to go in case of mobilization."

"Then there's a mobilization now?"

"No, I don't think so. If there were, the whole kibbutz would have been waked up by now. But I wonder how I'm going to get to Tel Aviv. . . ."

Dogs suddenly began barking in the valley.

"I'll call my father in Qiryat Shemona," Judith said.

Again they heard footsteps on the gravel.

"Who's there?"

"Jacob Oren. Something's happening. Do you know about it?"

"I've been told to go back to Tel Aviv," Arieh said.

"Do you want a ride?"

"In what? Are the buses running?"

"I'm talking about my brother Ivry. He came for the holidays and now he's been ordered to hurry back to Haifa. He has a little Fiat."

"I'll go to Haifa, then, and I'll find some way to keep going from there."

"I'm coming with you," Judith said. "Maybe Ivry can drop me off on the way."

They walked away together and the sound of their footsteps faded in the distance. Aron was still holding Rachel's arm. Without knowing why, she said almost in a whisper, as if she were praying, "*Shalom* [Peace]."

Her wish was lost in the night.

36

ISRAEL

Yom Kippur 1973 (Conclusion)

OCTOBER 1973

Ivry's car sped along the deserted road. That emptiness, that absence of all life, gave the nocturnal landscape a look of unreality, almost of nonexistence. It wasn't by chance that the God of the Bible told man to give names to the animals and plants, Arieh thought; if man didn't look at them, they might not exist.

Ivry was a doctor with the government health service in Haifa. He spoke little and Arieh liked that. A word here and there, a good-bye to Judith when he let her off at Qiryat Shemona, a gruff remark when he turned on the radio and found it hopelessly silent, without even a coded call to mobilization. After that, he said nothing more till they came to Acre. Nothing but the road, and the car on the road. Between Acre and Haifa, many other cars passed them in silence and blinked their headlights at them, as though to show that they shared the same dreadful secret. What secret? War, of course. Till now, Arieh had never fought in a war. His father had, three times, in fact, since World War II: in the War of Independence in 1948, the Suez campaign in 1956, and finally the Six-Day War in 1967. He knew that war was absurd and that it was by no means the finest kind of adventure, but it was still an adventure. Excitement, fear, and perhaps jealousy too, mingled in his mind to form a bewildering mixture.

It was two in the morning when they reached Haifa. The city was asleep. Mount Carmel, not much darker than the sky, was almost invisible. There was vague animation only in the vicinity of the harbor.

"Shall I let you off here?" Ivry asked.

"No, I'd rather go on a little farther, to the Tel Aviv highway. I'll have a better chance of getting a lift there."

"You may have a long wait," Ivry obligingly pointed out.

"Allah is great!" Arieh said with a smile, inwardly pleased with himself for having made that rather daring reply.

He did indeed have a long wait. For hours the road remained dishearteningly empty. Then several cars went by at full speed, without stopping. He was beginning to lose hope when a big Chevrolet pulled off the road and stopped a short distance ahead of him. It was already five in the morning and the horizon was beginning to pale.

"Tel Aviv?" he asked.

"Get in," the driver said simply. Then, when they had started off, "Why are you going to Tel Aviv on the morning of Yom Kippur?"

"You don't know?" Arieh asked with surprise.

"I don't know what?"

"About the war."

"And how do you know about it?"

Arieh suddenly became wary.

"Oh, I just heard some talk about it, vague rumors. . . ."

The driver smiled but said nothing. And he didn't introduce himself till half an hour later, as they were passing a sign indicating Caesarea. He was Yossef Almogi, the minister of labor. He had been waked up at two o'clock at his home in Haifa, and he was now on his way to Tel Aviv for a special cabinet meeting called by Golda Meir.

They came to army intelligence headquarters, which was all lit up.

"Thanks for the ride, sir."

"Goodbye, young man."

Inside the building there was great agitation. Grim-faced officers in their shirtsleeves were jostling each other in the halls, hurriedly exchanging a few words, opening and closing doors. Arieh didn't recognize anyone or anything. If Myriam hadn't been at her desk, he would have wondered what strange place he had wandered into.

"Ah, here you are, darling," she said, not too sarcastically for once. "You took long enough to get here."

Arieh was still trying to think of an answer when the door of Benjamin's office suddenly opened and he saw him come out behind General Eli Zeira, the head of army intelligence. They were followed by General Yitzhak Hofi, commander of the northern region, and General Shmuel Gonen, commander of the southern region. When Benjamin saw his young protégé, he stopped, gave him a sad smile and patted him affectionately on the cheek.

"Who's this?" General Gonen asked, puzzled.

"He's Arieh Halter, the son of one of my best friends. He works here with me."

"Halter?" the general said. He looked at Arieh more closely. "Halter, Halter. . . . Are you related to Hugo Halter, by any chance?"

"He was my cousin. He was . . ."

"I know. It was very sad. I liked him."

Seeing his chance, Arieh seized it before it could slip away.

"Sir, it so happens that I've been investigating my cousin's death. May I question you, whenever it's convenient for you?"

"This is no time for . . ." Gonen began testily. Then he changed his mind. "Well, after all . . . I'll soon be leaving for Beersheba. You can come with me and we'll talk on the way."

Myriam had heard everything. When Gonen and the others had left, she couldn't help saying to Arieh, "You always know which end is up, darling!"

She then told him about the latest developments. Benjamin believed that Israel was about to be attacked, by the Egyptians in the south and the Syrians in the north. Others, including General Zeira, believed that an attack was unlikely and that the Egyptians and Syrians were massing their troops mainly for the purpose of applying psychological pressure. Still others believed that a general mobilization would be politically disastrous because it would make Israel seem to be a warmongering country, as in 1967, and so it would be better to wait and let the Arabs shoot first. And finally there were those, including Moshe Dayan, who advocated a partial mobilization that would have the advantage of compromise: Israel would mobilize a large but defensive force.

Arieh listened to her with great fervor and intensity. Never before had he realized so clearly how precarious Israel's fate was.

At nine-thirty, when Myriam was just finishing her report to Arieh, Benjamin came back to his office, looking more worried than ever, and alone.

"Where's General Gonen?" Arieh asked.

"He left for Beersheba, by plane. Why?"

Seeing Arieh's disappointment, Benjamin took on the look of someone who had just remembered an unpleasant truth and said soothingly, "Don't be upset, you'll have other chances to question Shmuel Gonen about Hugo." Then he turned away from him to talk with a messenger sent by General Zeira to give him the latest information and the most recent photographs of the Golan and the Sinai. War was obviously near. And the mobilization would take place today.

Summoned again by the chief of staff, General Gonen came back to Tel Aviv by car and arrived at half past noon. When Arieh heard about it, he hurried to meet him. Just as Gonen was coming out of the next building with Benjamin, Arieh stepped in front of him.

"You're Hugo Halter's cousin, aren't you?" Gonen said. He opened the door of the car that was waiting for him. "Get in. I may also need young men like you."

Arieh looked at Benjamin, who nodded. And so he left Tel Aviv in the car of one of Israel's foremost military leaders.

Beersheba, the capital of the Negev, was about seventy miles from Tel Aviv. In spite of Yom Kippur, the road was animated: cars, trucks, vans and even a few buses were stopped at intersections to pick up men who had come in haste and were obviously not dressed for war. The mobilization was under way.

"The attack will begin at six o'clock this afternoon," Gonen said.

"What if the enemy should decide to begin it an hour or two early?" Arieh asked.

Gonen's heavy features tensed.

"In that case, God help us!"

Then, plunged in a meditation whose secrets he evidently did not want to share with anyone, he let himself be lulled by the motion of the car. When he turned to Arieh five minutes later, his face no longer showed any sign of tension. It even showed a certain vivacity when he asked him precisely how he was related to Hugo, then said, "Well, as long as we're here, I may as well tell you what I know about him."

He had met Hugo in 1953, exactly twenty years ago, in Ben-Gurion's house. They had hit it off well together and seen each other again several times during Hugo's later visits to Israel. What had he liked about him? His Talmudic side, his ability to translate Biblical elements into modern terms for a better understanding of the present-day world. He reminded him of Justus of Tiberias. His idealism was naive but refreshing. An example of the way he talked and acted? Gonen remembered something that had surprised him at the time. It must have been 1960. They had both been invited to visit Israel Beer, Ben-Gurion's adviser. After leaving his house at the end of the evening, they had walked awhile together, then Hugo had asked him bluntly if he trusted Beer. Gonen saw no justification for the question, but a year later, when Beer was arrested as a spy, it seemed to him that Hugo must have had a premonition. By then, unfortunately, Hugo was already dead. He had been killed a day earlier.

Arieh was eager to know more. Questions and objections were ready to burst from his lips, but the car had already reached the outskirts of Beersheba. There he had a surprise: he remembered a sunbaked clay village built around a camel market held by Bedouins, and now he was in a modern city, as urban-looking as anyone could wish, with broad streets bordered by trees and buildings.

Gonen suddenly seemed to care nothing more about Hugo and the Halters. He became nervous again, almost brutal. He looked at his watch, picked up the phone and asked to be put through to General Mendler at Rifidim, in the Sinai. After two long minutes, the call was completed.

"Albert," Gonen ordered, "leave the rear bases immediately and advance toward the canal. Don't wait for the Egyptians to attack."

"Too late," said the voice at the other end of the line. "They've already attacked. The bombing has begun."

The attack turned out to be a false alarm. The four formations of Egyptian planes that flew over the Israeli installations at Sharm al-Sheikh, at the southern tip of the Sinai, were forced to turn back by the counteroffensive of the patrol craft anchored near the Strait of Tiran. But overall the news was not good. The Bar-Lev Line, along the Suez Canal, was broken through in several places. Eight thousand infantrymen gained a foothold on the Sinai side of the canal. A score of helicopter-borne Egyptian battalions succeeded in landing behind the Israeli outposts near the communications lines, and the Israeli air force, concentrated on the Golan Heights, where the advance of thousands of Syrian tanks threatened the country's vital centers, was not there to dislodge them.

After gathering and collating all available information, General Gonen — with Arieh still close to him — assembled his officers before a map of the Sinai.

"The Egyptians' objectives are clear," he said. "They want to cross the canal and take Sharm al-Sheikh, the Mitla Pass and the Gidi Pass." He indicated those places with a pointer. "They'll try to reach them within twenty-four hours. If they succeed, the road to Israel will be open to them. If not, they'll try to set up a defense line on our side of the canal by installing ground-to-air missiles." He turned to the officers. "We must quickly regain contact with our forts on the canal, the one at Lakekan, on the Great Bitter Lake, and the one at Orkal, in the northern marshes. We must advance our forces to check the Egyptian's advance."

He was unable to finish his exposition because the information received by radio showed a steadily changing situation. One fort that had needed defending a minute ago was now in the hands of the Egyptians. Another, which had been considered lost, was now perfectly secure. Exasperated by all the contradictory reports coming in more and more rapidly, Gonen finally threw down his pointer and said, "I've told you the Egyptians' objectives. We have to see to it that they don't reach them." He spoke to his aide-de-camp: "Get a plane ready, I'm going to the Oum Kheshiba command post. Notify Generals Sharon and Brenne."

And that was how at midnight, after the end of Yom Kippur, Arieh found himself near the Gidi Pass, twenty miles from the canal. He arrived just as the Israeli command post was attacked by helicopter-borne Egyptian commandos. When he got out of the plane, he had to run a hundred yards under fire before he could take shelter behind a sand hill, where a jeep was waiting for him.

The battle was short. The full moon enabled the Israeli artillery to quickly dislodge the sand-colored commandos. A group of veteran soldiers led by General Sharon, who had returned to the Oum Kheshiba command post in accordance with his orders, were able to take the Egyptians from the rear. By three in the morning, the attack had been repelled. General Brenne arrived at dawn, and General Dayan a few minutes past nine o'clock.

"We have to withdraw to the line of the passes," Dayan said. "We can't risk our soldiers' lives."

Gonen didn't agree. Abandoning a large part of the Sinai seemed to him absurd and risky. Arieh followed the discussion as though through a fog. He hadn't slept for two days. Finally he sank into deep sleep and didn't wake up till nightfall, when he learned of the offensive that Gonen had decided to launch on the southern front and heard him say that he was worried because there was no longer any radio communication with the Milano fort.

"All the forts must be evacuated," he said. "*All* of them, you understand? It's the only way we can bombard the canal."

After more unsuccessful efforts to contact the Milano fort by radio, he said to a young blond captain, "Yossi, take a half-track, get two volunteers to go with you and head for the fort. You may meet the men from it somewhere on the road. If not, tell them to evacuate it immediately."

A soldier raised his hand to volunteer. Then Arieh followed suit.

"I'll go too," he said, "with your permission, sir."

Gonen observed him with a stern expression, as if he were trying to guess what was in his mind. Finally he shrugged and said, "All right, go."

Things happened as Gonen had foreseen. The half-track succeeded in slipping between two columns of Egyptian tanks. It skirted Tasa, took the Baluza road and, at dawn, near al-Qantara, came upon the men who had escaped from the Milano fort. About thirty of them were able-bodied and six were wounded. After brief embraces, they put the wounded into the vehicle and decided on the route they would follow. Since the road ahead of them might be cut off, they would try to go through the ghost town of al-Qantara, praying that it was not yet hemmed in by the enemy.

"I know al-Qantara," Yossi said. "If there's any trouble, we'll meet in the Christian cemetery on the edge of town. It's on the map."

Trouble wasn't long in coming. As soon as they entered the town they saw mounds of freshly dug red clay on their left and, when they came a little closer, hundreds of men making an earth wall, looking like a swarm of ants, their arms invisible in the distance as they wielded their shovels. How to avoid them? The only solution was to go behind the clumps of trees on the right, at the entrance to the town. But just as they were moving toward it, they heard a voice call out in Arabic:

"Hey! Who are you?"

"We're Egyptians," Arieh answered, also in Arabic.

There was silence for several seconds.

"You don't have an Egyptian accent."

Then another voice called out, with anxiety and hatred:

"They're Jews! They're Jews!"

A flare rose into the sky. Yossi ordered his men to scatter. Shots were fired. One bullet, then another, whizzed past just above their heads. Arieh ran, looking back now and then like the little gray fox that he and Judith had seen in the Tel Dan nature reserve. *I don't want to die*, he told himself. *I don't want to fall.* Just as he reached a long gray wall that seemed like a haven to him, he looked back one last time while bullets smashed into the stone all around him.

"The cemetery is on the other side," someone said in the darkness.

Arieh gripped a protruding stone in the wall and tried to climb, but slipped and hurt his knee. He tried again, gripping the stone even harder, but again he slipped. No, he was mistaken: he hadn't slipped, but he had two strange burning sensations in his left thigh and felt that he couldn't go on. His leg had become terribly heavy, as if a big, invisible stone were tied to it. *No, I don't want to die*, he repeated to himself as he summoned up his last remaining strength.

He took hold of his leg, lifted it to the top of the cemetery wall and, breathless, feeling a warm liquid sticking to his hands, let himself fall among the graves on the other side.

"Are you all right?" asked Yossi, who had fallen beside him.

"Yes, but I've been hit."

"Hold on, the command post will soon know our position."

"Where's the half-track?"

"Giora was driving it. He managed to get through."

"My leg hurts," Arieh moaned.

"Come here, I'll wrap my belt around it. There . . ."

Arieh stood up, clinging to Yossi. He covered a few hundred yards that way, then half a mile, then a mile. Each step intensified his pain and made his sight a little dimmer, but he went on walking, mechanically. He repeated to himself over and over, *I don't want to die, I don't want to die.* By daybreak he was breathing with difficulty. The blue of the night was mixed, as though on a palette, with the light pink of dawn. He was unsteady on his feet and kept feeling as if he were about to fall. Two of his companions put on their prayer shawls, knelt and said the morning prayer.

All at once he heard a faint, distant noise. A puff of wind blew it away for a moment, but it stubbornly came back and lingered.

"Tanks! Tanks are coming, Yossi!"

Several minutes later, four soldiers came out from behind a sand hill. Then the tanks. Hands waving above the turrets. A miracle! Arieh fainted.

He was operated on at the Bellisson hospital in Petach Tikva, where his friend Shoshana worked as a nurse. Thanks to her, and with her, he followed the course of that strange war, which ended on October 28 with a handshake between an Israeli general and an Egyptian general. Arieh saw that handshake as the beginning of a peace process that, if it was carried through, would mean that the Yom Kippur War had not been entirely useless.

Judith came to visit him. So did his mother. She gave him news of Mordecai, who had been wounded in the al-Kuneitra region and hospitalized in Tiberias. He asked if it was serious.

"No, it's not serious," she answered with a certain uneasiness in her eyes. "Soon we'll all be together again at Dafneh."

On November 2 he finally left the hospital. He still walked with a cane. Benjamin was waiting for him in a car.

"Are we going to stop by the office?" Arieh asked.

"No," Benjamin said. "I'm taking you straight to the kibbutz. Your father is dead."

37

BUENOS AIRES

Anna Maria: Back Underground

MAY 1974

Although Anna Maria tried to say, with Gide, "Family, I hate you," the successive violent deaths of her father's cousins finally began to affect her. Mario and Julio felt that the Yom Kippur War was insignificant, seeing it as nothing but a confrontation between two lackeys of Yankee imperialism. Anna Maria knew some Israelis. She had spent hours with Mordecai, the kibbutznik, and she had loved Arieh, and she didn't care whether they were accomplices or victims of imperialism: the news that one was dead and the other wounded was something she couldn't accept with indifference.

And while her bloody experience with guerrilla warfare had awakened her to the world, it hadn't been conclusive. The fact was that now, in 1974, she no longer really believed in the revolution or that socialist, Communist or "justicial" society in which everyone would be happy, free and equal. Things could change, she knew that. A little light could still be found to brighten the darkness. And maybe her poor struggle, however absurd, desperate and crazy it might have been, would eventually contribute to the happiness of others. For the moment, there was no doubt that it had contributed to Cámpora's victory and Perón's return. The first thing Cámpora had done after being elected was to reestablish diplomatic relations with Cuba, as the Montoneros had demanded. Then he had proclaimed an "ample and generous" amnesty.

As a result of all that, to the great joy of her parents and Doña Regina, Anna Maria had come back home, resumed her studies at the university and begun steadily moving away from a political combat that, paradoxically, now seemed to her both futile and victorious. She was becoming more and more absorbed in her studies and her reading. She devoured Borges, in particular. She was deeply moved to learn that the author of *El Aleph* had said, "One of my countries is Israel, which gave us the Bible." She also read Unamuno, Emerson and Joyce. And, seeing her leaning over her books, Doña Regina told herself that maybe Martín had recovered his daughter at last.

But while leftist terrorism had lost some of its belligerence, rightist terrorism, surging up from military barracks, police stations and slums, was taking over territory that its adversary had left vacant. Militant trade unionists, politicians and intellectuals were being assassinated. Not a day went by without a corpse being found in the murky water of the Río de la Plata. And if people like Anna Maria had abandoned leftist terrorism, they certainly hadn't done it to accept fascist terrorism. Why was Perón letting those fascists do as they pleased? That was what she found hardest to understand when she stopped to think about it in the midst of reading *Ulysses* or *Finnegans Wake*.

"You're being thickheaded!" Mario said to her one evening when they had gone to have dinner at a restaurant on Florida Street in tribute to the good old days of the past. "Perón lets them get away with it because it suits his purposes."

"But Perónism . . ."

"That's over and done with. Perón isn't Perón anymore. He's an old puppet manipulated by fascists. We have to do something. We can't let that scum go on . . ." He lowered his voice. "We need you, Anna Maria." And, after a silence: "*I* need you."

As usual, his long brown hair hid one eye and part of his face. His other dark green eye looked at her insistently, and she couldn't tell which was stronger in that look: militant conviction or his personal feelings for her.

"Will you take a walk with me?" he asked when he had signaled for the check. "Please."

A walk? Yes, why not? It wouldn't commit her to anything. . . . And Mario was so attractive when he looked at her that way, with the eyes of a beguiling killer.

They walked side by side along the dimly lit streets of Palermo. He stroked her hair. She drew away from him. He took her arm. She let him go on holding it. They saw couples kissing in parked cars and heard muffled grunts and moans. The wind carried whiffs of powerful smells. She shivered and suddenly pressed herself against him.

"Are you cold?" he asked.

She didn't answer. When a long car slowly rolled by with music and an odor of expensive tobacco coming from its open windows, she took him firmly in her arms and kissed him square on the mouth.

"I stayed with you a year," she said softly. "We lived underground. We didn't love each other, but we lived for the revolution. It was between Tucumán and Mendoza, remember? There we gradually turned into soldiers. And we didn't know what civilians thought anymore, or even what they wanted." She kissed him again, more greedily than before. "I didn't tell you at the time, but I didn't feel at ease. Why were we killing? Why did we risk getting killed? To be like Che Guevara? He tried to bring revolution to people who didn't even understand what he said to them. He was a white man, so to the Indians he was the prototype of the colonizer, yet he told them he was bringing them an idea of freedom. He disappeared with that idea. . . . Do you understand what I'm saying? Little by little, I became detached. . . . Then one day I left."

"You'll come back."

Anna Maria stopped and tried to see into Mario's eyes in the darkness.

"You don't understand, Mario. I've discovered that I have an interest in this life and I'm tired of trying to change it."

"We're not trying to change it anymore, we're trying to defend it. And then . . ."

He began walking again.

"And then what?" she asked, taking his arm.

He turned toward her.

"And then to hell with it — I love you!"

Anna Maria's arrival two days later was greeted with friendly exclamations. Mario was complimented on having brought her back into the family. There were cheers and lascivious jokes. The conference room of *Noticias,* the Montoneros' daily newspaper, was full of people she didn't know, but there were still a few familiar faces.

"Welcome back," Julio said in a cloud of cigarette smoke. "You've come at the right time: things are moving in the world."

"Oh?"

"What do you mean, 'Oh?'" The former young man, whose mustache was turning gray, grimaced. "In Portugal, the revolution has come. In the United States, things are falling apart. You *do* know about the Watergate scandal, don't you?"

"Don't start an argument," Mario intervened. "We're here to get ready for May Day."

In Buenos Aires, that 1974 May Day celebration promised to be impressive. At six in the morning, sound trucks began driving through the streets, bawling out their message: "Everyone to the Plaza de Mayo!" On the radio, reporters breathlessly described processions coming in from the suburbs: "La Matanza, Lomos de Zamora, Avellaneda, Vincente López, San Martín . . ."

Mario came by for Anna Maria at eight o'clock. On the streets and sidewalks, large groups of people were loudly singing patriotic songs and orchestras were vying with each other in playing poignant tangos.

Anna Maria and Mario let themselves be carried along by the crowd. They saw that military trucks were parked at intersections and that the stores and cafés were closed. And when they tried to take the subway, they found that its entrance was blocked by a metal grille.

"The stupid bastards!" Anna Maria grumbled. "They've closed the subway on the day of a demonstration!"

Caught up in the spirit of the occasion, she began to be really impatient, as she used to be in the good old days.

"We're going to be late," she repeated for the hundredth time.

"*Calla, señorita*," said a tall bearded man carrying a little girl on his shoulders. "Perón won't speak till three o'clock."

"But we have an appointment for one o'clock!" Anna Maria retorted.

"Then you'll be late for it."

"Why aren't we moving forward?" asked a fat lady behind them.

"The goons of the CGT [Confederación General de Trabajo] are searching everyone," the bearded man said with a know-it-all expression. "And they're checking all signs and streamers."

"It's all right for them to search people," said a thin man wearing a suede jacket, "to make sure they're not carrying guns, but signs and streamers . . ."

"The CGT has decided which slogans will be allowed. They don't want the Montoneros to show their own."

Dozens and dozens of demonstrations were mingled in Anna Maria's head. Shouts, streamers, processions, speeches. And that whole business of those who knew, those who hoped, and those (the majority) who followed without knowing or hoping.

As time passed, she began to wonder what she was doing in that crowd. Mario felt that she was tense and drew her closer to him.

"I'm glad you're here." And, seeing her about to answer: "No, please don't say anything."

Not far away, a group of schoolchildren were singing an old Perónist song:

> *Youth are now marching,*
> *Because they must accomplish their mission,*
> *With steady, resolute steps.*
> *Their hearts are ablaze*
> *With the bright flame of Perón.*

Mario and Anna Maria inched forward a little farther. Then he spotted an opening in the crowd and pulled her by the hand, leaving behind the bearded man with the little girl on his shoulders. To their left, a group was chanting, "*Perón, la Patria Socialista.*" In front of them, another group, squeezed together under a sign that said, "*CGT Obras Sanitarias,*" replied with the same chant: "*Perón, la Patria Socialista.*"

Two hulking men wearing CGT armbands searched them from

head to foot before letting them pass. The square was blue and white, like the bright sky. Two gigantic portraits covered the façade of the presidential palace: Perón and Isabel, his third wife. In front of the palace the crowd was dense, like a concrete wall with pebbles and grains of sand scattered through it. At the back of the square it seemed younger and livelier. In between was a space swarming with soldiers and CGT men assigned to keep order.

Mario was transformed, intoxicated as always by the shouting, singing and chanting.

"Wait and see," he whispered in Anna Maria's ear. "We'll try to rejoin our friends."

All at once the crowd began chanting, "Pe-rón! Pe-rón! Pe-rón!" The people behind Anna Maria and Mario were pushing them toward the no-man's-land in the middle of the square and it was impossible for them to resist.

"Shit!" Mario exclaimed.

"Pe-rón! Pe-rón! Pe-rón!"

Several figures suddenly appeared on the balcony. Contrary slogans were mingled. Then the loudspeakers crackled and made louder, uncertain noises. Finally a quavering voice was heard.

"Comrades!"

The crowd moved forward, then back.

"Pe-rón! Pe-rón! Pe-rón!"

Perón raised his arms and the cheering gradually faded into silence. Then the young people behind Anna Maria began shouting.

"*No queremos carnaval, asamblea popular!*" ("We don't want a carnival, we want a people's assembly!")

Perón kept his arms upraised. Like a heavy double door swinging open, the crowd slowly parted to reveal the back of the square, where an enormous white streamer proclaimed in red letters, "The Montoneros are here!"

Beside Anna Maria, a young woman took out a white scarf and wrote the word *Montoneros* on it with a lipstick. As though by magic, thousands of such scarves appeared above the crowd.

"Comrades," said the formidable voice from the loudspeakers, "twenty years ago, on this same balcony, on a beautiful day like this one, I spoke to the workers of Argentina for the first time. I urged you to consolidate your organizations because difficult times were coming."

The people at the front of the square resumed their chant: "Pe-rón! Pe-rón! Pe-rón!" But, behind them, thunderous shouting burst from tens of thousands of throats:

> *What's happening, what's happening?*
> *What's happening, general?*
> *The people's government is full of goons.*
> *We want to get rid of, get rid of*
> *The union bureaucracy.*

"Quiet, you sons of bitches!" cried a hefty woman in front of Anna Maria.

Coca-Cola bottles were flying overhead, catching glints of sunlight as they passed.

"Comrades!" Perón said again, and the loudspeakers, now turned up to their top volume, amplified the quavering of his voice still more. "Comrades, I was right about the times that were coming, and the union organization that was able to hold out all through those twenty years — no matter what those idiots yelling back there may think about it!"

The crowd at the front of the square responded:

"Pe-rón! Pe-rón! Pe-rón!"

The bearded man with the little girl on his shoulders passed in front of Anna Maria and Mario again.

"There's going to be trouble," he said. "I'm leaving, because of my daughter."

The little girl clutched her father's head with both hands. She seemed terrified.

Perón: "I was saying that during those twenty years the union organizations were unshakable. And now a few beardless agitators are claiming to be worth more than the people who struggled all that time!"

The young people went on shouting at the back of the square.

> *What's happening, what's happening?*
> *What's happening, general?*

Another volley of bottles. Mario pushed Anna Maria toward Defense Street, but the CGT roadblock sent them toward the Montoneros. In the first rank, they saw Julio.

Perón: "Comrades!"

The young people: "Come with us, general, come back to Perónism!"

Perón: "Comrades! We met in this same square nine years in a row, and for nine years we all agreed on our struggle to fulfill the aspirations of the Argentinian people. And now, after twenty years, there are those who don't agree with what we've done."

"Stop talking bullshit, Perón! Come back to Perónism!"

"Comrades!"

"Pe-rón! Pe-rón! Pe-rón!"

Helmeted soldiers, with their fingers on the triggers of their guns, took up positions in the no-man's-land, where bottles were now raining down. Mario and Anna Maria were slowly making their way back to the Montoneros. They could no longer see what was happening at the front of the square. A word ran through the crowd of Montoneros, growing louder as it went:

"*Vamos!*"

The crowd wavered a moment, then suddenly broke into motion.

> *All right! All right, general!*
> *Stay with your goons!*
> *The people will go away!*

Anna Maria and Mario found themselves with Julio.

"You see: things are moving!" Julio said, smiling. "Perón has been taken in by the Argentinian fascists and the CIA, but we'll make them pay!" He turned to Anna Maria. "I'm glad you're with us again. We're going back underground."

38

TEL AVIV

Arieh's Investigation (Conclusion)

APRIL 1974

A little black-bordered brochure on Arieh's desk caught his attention. He picked it up. Published by the army general staff, it was simply a list of soldiers killed or missing in the Yom Kippur War.

The phone rang but Arieh ignored it. That brochure interested him too much. It was rough and gray. It reminded him of the stone placed over his father's grave in the little cemetery of the kibbutz in Galilee: light in appearance, yet so heavy to move.

A man equals a stone, he thought. *Or rather, a man equals a letter, an inscription carved into a stone. Like the Law.* Who was it who had told him that the Torah contained six hundred thousand letters, exactly the number of Jews who, according to tradition, arrived in the Land of Canaan? He couldn't remember. He did remember, though, that the Talmud said the Book would lose its sacred character if it lacked a single one of its letters. But why that playing with images, those mental meanderings, as soon as he thought of his father?

Arieh stood up and took a few steps in his office. It was small but he was very proud of it. He sat down again, picked up the photograph of Mordecai on his desk and looked into those kindly, nearsighted eyes magnified by the lenses of his glasses. Then he opened the brochure again. It contained 2,522 names and one of them, under the letter H, was Mordecai's.

It was incredible, all the letters he had received. He had never even suspected that Mordecai had so many friends. And he hadn't known they had so many relatives. He was irritated by the letter that Aron Lerner had sent after attending the funeral. Aron was always generalizing and moralizing, and he seemed determined to drag Zionism into everything. His letter ended with a quotation: "Countless, alas, are the afflictions I endure. When this people around me suffers, my spirit feels helpless against evil. Seeds die in this illustrious land."

"It's from Sophocles," Benjamin said when Arieh showed him the letter.

"Then Sophocles must have been a Zionist too!" Arieh replied with annoyance.

The letter from Richard, Sidney's son, surprised him for another reason. He hadn't known Richard was so religious. His letter was stuffed with quotations from the Talmud and famous rabbis. It was also full of calls for vengeance, like this passage from the Bible: "Pour out thy wrath upon the heathens that have not known thee, and upon the kingdoms that have not called upon thy name."

He had some odd relatives, no doubt about it. One family with all the good and bad qualities of a whole people!

Arieh's sister Dina had just had her twelfth birthday. They hadn't celebrated it because his mother was determined to respect the period of mourning. But he thought she was recovering rapidly. Her peasant common sense helped her to accept death more easily. As for Arieh, he had stopped limping from his wound and was seriously thinking about playing soccer again. He no longer saw Shoshana, whose fiancé had come back from his stay in San Francisco. He now went to see Judith every week in Haifa, unless she came to visit him in Tel Aviv, and he made love only with her. They were even talking about marriage.

When he spoke to Myriam about it, she laughed and said, "Why get married, darling? I feel like getting divorced. Marriage is like a city under siege: the people outside it want to get in, and the people inside it want to get out."

Doña Regina had also sent Arieh a letter, a long letter in Yiddish that Rachel Lerner had translated into Hebrew. His old aunt grieved for Mordecai. "One generation passeth away, and another generation cometh: but the earth abideth for ever," she quoted. Concerning Anna Maria, she said only that she had come back after Perón's election, that she was in good health and as pretty as ever, that she had resumed her studies at the university, but that now she was gone again. *She must have gone back underground,* Arieh thought, *to wage guerrilla warfare and "make revolution."*

The Yom Kippur War had confirmed him in his decision to go on working for army intelligence. It was the only way to combat terrorism and prevent future wars. As for his investigation into Hugo's death, it was making progress. He felt, in fact, that he had discovered an important piece of the puzzle. It concerned Israel Beer, Ben-Gurion's adviser, who had been accused of spying for the Soviet Union, and whom Hugo had visited whenever he came to Israel. General Gonen's testimony had given him the idea of rereading the records of the trial. They contained a note about Beer's trips to West Germany and his visits to NATO bases there. The author of the note had added a personal remark in red pencil, without drawing any conclusions from it: that anyone who went to West Berlin could easily go to East Berlin. That remark was not only judicious but important. Why was it, then, that the dossier contained no list of people and places in East Berlin that Beer might have visited?

In the middle of May 1960, for example, Beer had stayed at Mönchengladbach, in the home of Reinhard Gehlen, a veteran of the Abwehr and head of the West German intelligence services. According to the dossier, Gehlen knew about Beer's visits to East Berlin but explained them as being related to secret negotiations between Israel and the Soviet Union. He had received Beer into his home, he said, in the hope of learning something about those negotiations, which were unknown to everyone at that time. This explanation didn't seem convincing. Gehlen knew better than anyone else that contacts between Israel and the Soviet Union had never really been broken off and that Berlin wasn't the most discreet place for such relations, which were already being carried on in Bucharest, Vienna, Sofia and Paris. In that case, why had Gehlen taken Beer into his home? To answer that question, Arieh would have to discover the identities of the other people Beer had seen in West Germany. "Tell me who your friends are and I'll tell you who you are." That old Arab proverb applied very well here.

When questioned about his trips to East Berlin, which were completely contrary to the explicit recommendations of the Israeli intelligence services, Beer answered that he had gone there simply out of curiosity and a desire to see some old friends again. Among them was Dr. Hans Furchmuller. This was an innocent name to Issar Harel, head of the Mossad at the time, but Arieh knew that Furchmuller was in fact Hugo's brother-in-law, and that, according to what Furchmuller himself had told Sidney, he had introduced Hugo to Wolfgang Knopff, a member of the HVA, one of the East German intelligence services. So it seemed obvious to Arieh that General Gehlen had been interested not in Israeli-Soviet negotiations, but in the machinations of the East German intelligence services and their contacts abroad.

But what part had Furchmuller really played? Had he been only an innocent intermediary or an active agent, maybe even a high-ranking one? And what about Hugo's wife Sigrid? What if she had been the killers' real target? Who could say? Arieh realized that he had to assemble a dossier on the Furchmuller family as quickly as possible.

"Good work," Benjamin said when Arieh had told him about his discoveries.

Benjamin, one of the few to have foreseen the attack of the Arab armies, had been promoted. But in spite of that, he had kept the same office. He was still on the fourth floor and the same big khaki fan still rumbled overhead, stirring the same warm, damp air. He slowly took off his glasses — that hadn't changed much either, and Arieh realized in a flash of memory that Mordecai used to take off his glasses in the same way — and looked at the young man with curiosity.

"But do you have any news of Hidar Assadi?"

"According to Sidney's story," Arieh said, "he must have known Sigrid well. And maybe her brother —"

"I'm not talking about Assadi in relation to the Hugo affair,"

Benjamin interrupted. His voice became official: "Other acts of terrorism are being planned. It's important to know if the Soviet Union is behind them in any way. Assadi is now close to Arafat, but he hasn't set foot in Beirut for a long time. We have to know why."

◻

ROME, AUGUST 1974

Why didn't I go to see him sooner? Why didn't I at least call him or write to him? His name was in Hugo's notebook and I had been in Rome several times in the last few years. But there's no escaping the workings of fate, and so I didn't meet Father Roberto Cerutti till thirteen years after Hugo's death, on August 9, 1974.

Father Cerutti was an important man in the Vatican. He was the head of Radio Vatican, which employed three hundred people and broadcast all over the world. He was often mentioned in the press as being among the few people who had real influence on the pope. He gave me an appointment for eight in the morning, in front of the Tower of Leo XIII, which housed Radio Vatican.

For Rome, eight o'clock is very early, but the Via di Porta Angelica was already clogged with traffic. Life here began at dawn. The taxi let me off in front of the Gate of Saint Anne, which meant that I had to walk across the whole Vatican. I hurried up the slope and arrived fifteen minutes late at the Tower of Leo XIII.

Father Cerutti didn't seem to mind my lateness. He was a tall, gaunt, white-haired man with blue eyes and a face that looked as if it had been carved in wax. His gray Roman collar and the little silver cross on his lapel were the only signs that he belonged to the Church. He was a Jesuit. In accordance with the agreement concluded between the Holy See and the Society of Jesus, he had been put in charge of Radio Vatican, and his three assistant managers were all Jesuits.

He greeted me and asked me to come with him. When he had invited me to sit down in a black leather armchair in his office, whose windows overlooked the Vatican gardens, he asked me in his melodious French, "So you're Hugo Halter's cousin. . . . May his soul rest in peace." He put his elbows on his huge desk, whose solid wood top was strangely empty, and looked at me intently. "I've often wondered why you hadn't come to see me. I knew you were investigating your cousin's death. How did I know? I read about it in an Italian newspaper. An Israeli came to see me, a cultivated man named Benjamin Ben-Eliezer. Also Hidar Assadi, your Soviet cousin's husband. He's a curious, secretive man. But I suppose you know them all. They questioned me about my relations with Hugo Halter. They were also trying to find out why he was killed. Tell me, what progress have you made?"

Maybe it was the hushed atmosphere of that big, white, almost empty office; or the landscape, halfway between light and shadow, that I saw through the window; or that calm, solid man with his friendly, almost paternal attitude; or simply the fatigue of my trip, my usual anxiety, my need to communicate — whatever the reason, I felt like confiding in Father Cerutti. I talked. I told him about my father's death and his desire for ancestors; Sidney's death — which he already knew about — my questioning of Judaism and Israel, God's oppressive silence. . . . And I told him how I wondered not so much about the reasons for Hugo's death as about Hugo himself.

When he judged that I had finished he gave me a look of friendly warmth, surprising in that ascetic face, and sat back in his armchair.

"We often overestimate other people's worth; we seldom underestimate it," he said. "I think a happy medium is what's needed. You've idealized your cousin too much. You've attributed all sorts of good qualities to him, along with all your dreams. Until you grant him the right to be imperfect, weak and — why not? — sinful, you won't really understand him or discover the reason he was murdered." His voice became softer, as though veiled by memory. "I used to see him often and I sometimes looked forward to his visits. I liked his passion and his questions, and I admired his observations. He wasn't outstandingly intelligent or shrewd, but he had a rare kind of simplicity, the kind spoken of by Christ, which ought to be a natural quality but often has to be acquired through study.

"He wanted peace in the Middle East and he was convinced it couldn't be achieved without mutual understanding and peace among the three monotheistic religions — that is, among the Children of Abraham. That was why he came to see me — one day in 1959 I think it was — recommended by a mutual friend, a French Jesuit. In support of his views, he quoted a parable from the Talmud that made a strong impression on me. I'm sure you know it. After creating heaven and earth, God divided all the beauty and splendor of His creation into ten equal parts. He gave nine parts of beauty and splendor to Jerusalem and only one to the rest of the world. He also divided all the world's suffering and affliction into ten parts. He gave nine parts of suffering and affliction to Jerusalem and only one to the rest of the world.

"Hugo believed that until peace was restored in Jerusalem, first between the Christians and the Jews, then with the Muslims, the world would suffer. It was an appealing idea. I later told His Holiness about it and he agreed with it."

Father Cerutti went on talking in his warm voice. He quoted from the New and Old Testaments, and even from an Arab poet, Sheikh Mohayid-din Arabi: "My heart has become capable of taking all forms: it is a pasture for gazelles, and a monastery for Christian monks, and a temple for idols, and the pilgrim's Kaaba, and the Tables of the Torah, and the Book of the Koran."

I listened to his long monologue in silence. I admired his knowledge and the fluidity of his thought, and I wondered if he was reporting what Hugo had said or sharing his own reflections with me. I now feel that he was like everyone else: he was interested in others insofar as they agreed with him.

There was a knock on the door. A young priest brought in some dispatches. Father Cerutti looked through them and announced, "Last night Richard Nixon resigned as President of the United States. I must prepare some comments on it." He stood up. "Shall we have dinner together this evening?"

39

MOSCOW – BEIRUT

Anxieties of the Third Kind

OCTOBER 1974

It was not until two years after her parents left that Olga began really feeling the weight of their absence. She had been sorry to see them go, of course, but she hadn't believed that her separation from them would be permanent. She had the illusion that they would come back soon and she recalled the many times when they had gone away before, to attend scientific conventions within the Soviet Union: Leningrad, Baku, Tashkent, Alma-Ata. . . . But this time they had been gone much longer — two full years — and there was the enormous distance between the Soviet Union and the West to which Israel belonged.

Hidar was as much in love with her as ever; their apartment on Peace Avenue was pleasantly and attractively decorated; she was satisfied with her work; she enjoyed the receptions to which she was invited and the many privileges she gained through Hidar's position and connections. But in spite of all that, she felt that something was missing and she was never able to be completely happy. What name could she give to the nostalgia that filled her whenever she thought of those lovely family evenings, those celebrations, and those arguments? When she felt at loose ends in the evening, she would often go to the building on Kazakov Street, where her parents had lived, almost without knowing what she was doing. And she would stand there a long time, motionless, letting sweet recollections seep into her.

One day in October 1974 she left her apartment as usual. When she stepped outside her building, absorbed in images from her childhood and memories of old smells and sensations, she scarcely heard a voice call her name from close by.

"Olienka! Olienka!" the voice repeated.

Her friend Maria Petrenko-Podiapolskaya, wife of a member of the Academy of Sciences who was a friend of Aron's, took hold of her arm.

"What were you thinking of? You looked like a sleepwalker!"

"I was just . . . thinking of my parents."

"Ah, yes, how are they?" Maria asked. Then, without waiting for an answer — maybe because she knew that letters from Israel were rare, that they were delivered only at distant intervals, and that the censors were always vigilant — she continued in a more light-hearted tone, "I'm on my way to have a cup of tea with the Sakharovs. Would you like to join me?"

Arm in arm, the two women went to 48A Chkalov Street, where the famous scientist lived. Since the elevator was out of order, they walked up the six flights of stairs. They rang the doorbell and were surprised when no one came to let them in, because they could hear sounds of an altercation, and other noises, from inside. They knocked, rang the bell again and knocked again; still no one came to the door.

"Wait for me here," Maria said. "I'll go down and phone them."

A few minutes later she came back, out of breath. She had dialed the Sakharovs' number from a phone booth near the building. A second surprise: no one had answered.

By now the voices inside the apartment had fallen silent. The two women heard nothing, not a murmur, not a sound of any kind. Had they imagined those voices? Had they actually been coming from the floor above? It was very strange. . . . The Sakharovs had clearly invited Maria to tea, and agreed on the time. That silence was incomprehensible. More and more puzzled, the two women decided to try to phone again.

In the street, Maria pointed out to Olga that no one was walking back and forth in front of the building, as was usually the case. This made them more worried than ever. As bad luck would have it, the phone refused to work this time and they had to go a hundred yards farther on, to the Yaouza river, to find another booth. The Sakharovs still didn't answer. Maria decided to alert some of her friends. As a result, when they came back there were already several people, all looking deeply concerned, standing in front of the building.

They all went up the stairs in single file and Maria rang the bell again. When the door opened, it seemed miraculous. Elena Bonner appeared, then they saw Andrei Sakharov inside the apartment, splicing a telephone wire that had been cut. He told what had happened. Someone had rung the bell and he had opened the door, thinking it was Maria. Armed men had burst into the apartment and presented themselves as members of the Palestinian organization known as Black September. There were five of them. They demanded that he retract the statement he had made in favor of Israel at the beginning of the Yom Kippur War. If he refused, they said, they would kill him and his family. When Maria rang the doorbell a little later, at exactly four o'clock, they became alarmed. They silenced the Sakharovs, threatening them at gunpoint and forcing them into the back room. After waiting for Maria and Olga to go back downstairs, they left the building as discreetly as they had come in.

The whole thing was incredible, Olga thought. What a frightening combination of circumstances! And why did the police react so feebly when they were alerted by the group of friends?

Later, when she asked Hidar about it, he found her very naive — or at least he said so; the fact was that he privately considered the incident as disquieting as she did. Who was out to get Sakharov? The only effect of such a commando operation would be to discredit the Palestinian cause a month before Arafat's trip to the UN. And Hidar couldn't help seeing a secret desire to humiliate him in that action taken without notifying him, since it concerned the Middle East, which was supposed to be his special domain. It galled him to have something like that happen a few weeks before his next trip to Beirut.

It was all the more upsetting because he knew that trip was not going to be easy. The leaders of the Front hadn't appreciated the rapprochement between the Soviet Union and Al Fatah. George Habash had said bitter things about him. Wadi Hadad had sworn to get rid of him, even though he had fallen out with Habash. As for Ghassan Kanafani, who had understood the advantage of that rapprochement, he had been killed by a bomb placed in his car. The Front had accused the Israelis; the Israelis, the Jordanians; the Jordanians, Wadi Hadad. But Hidar knew it was the Jordanians who were right: implicit recognition of Israel by a man like Kanafani was intolerable, and it endangered the policy of refusal that had been established and defended by Hadad. There was still Bassam Abu Sharif. . . . Yes, but Arafat and Abu Iyad accepted him less out of love than out of self-interest; and many Al Fatah leaders still mistrusted him. Besides all that, there was the fact that Lebanon was on the verge of civil war and that the strong man of the Christian Phalangists, Michel Chehab, Leila's husband, seemed to have prepared for the worst. In spite of that confusion and all those dangers, Hidar couldn't postpone his departure. Arafat would go to New York on November 13 to take part in the UN General Assembly, and Chebrikov had told Hidar to make preparations for that trip.

This time it was Chebrikov himself who had suggested taking Olga to Beirut. He felt that her presence with Hidar five years earlier had turned out to be beneficial. Hidar was glad, of course, but at the same time he was worried about the difficulties awaiting him in Beirut, the ones he foresaw as well as the ones that were still only vague premonitions. And then there was that affair of the false Arabs coming into Andrei Sakharov's apartment. . . .

Because of all this, Hidar's mind was in disarray. Not knowing what he should or shouldn't tell Olga, he lit a cigarette. He had begun smoking only recently, without knowing exactly why. Maybe it was because of the lighter that an Algerian student at Patrice Lumumba University had given him as a gift. It was a crudely made lighter with a cotton wick, but he liked it and he bought his first pack of cigarettes to try it.

After lighting his cigarette and taking a long puff on it, he asked abruptly, "Have you seen your brother lately?"

"No," Olga answered. "Why?"

Hidar hesitated.

"I don't know. . . . I was just wondering if —"

"If Sasha was involved?"

Hidar leaned close to her and lifted the lock of blond hair that hid her right eye.

"Shall we go and get something to eat, darling?"

This time Olga was disappointed in Beirut. It was raining cats and dogs. Everything that had seemed bright and sparkling before had now become drab. Looking through the French window of her hotel room, she saw that the Ras Beirut promontory, between the harbor and the Khalde beaches, was shrouded in fog.

The next day, the rain stopped. Gusts of warm wind drove the clouds toward the sea, clearing the mountains and making them suddenly loom up — so close, so powerfully present, with their pine forests, their terraces, their villages with red tile roofs, and, far away to the north, the long, snowy, boatlike shape of Mount Sannin. Olga now regained her good humor. Refusing Hidar's offer to have a guide show her around the environs while he was busy at Al Fatah headquarters, she went out to take a walk by herself. Toward noon, feeling a little tired, she reached Beshara al-Khoury Street, at the edge of a pine forest.

She was about to end her walk and hail a taxi when she saw someone she thought she recognized come out of a house with an impressive marble façade. It was a black-haired woman wearing a light-gray coat drawn in snugly at the waist. She walked away; Olga walked after her. She quickened her pace; so did Olga, and caught up with her a short time later. Yes, of course! Seeing her from close up as she stood beside a little Morris and feverishly rummaged through her purse for the key to it, she recognized her very well.

"Do you remember me?" she asked in English. "I'm Olga, the Russian cousin of your friend Sidney Halter."

Leila stepped back and pursed her lips in a strange way while her face took on a look of surprise that was perhaps mingled with a little fear. Olga stepped back too. She was about to go on her way when Leila, seeming to change her mind, ordered, "Get in."

Then, after starting the car, she said, "Yes, yes. . . . It's amazing. I recognize you too. . . . I have to go somewhere, but we can talk while I drive there." The car entered a broad street full of heavy traffic and the noise of blaring horns. "Yes, I remember you. It was five years ago. Your friend . . . but you've probably married him by now, haven't you?"

"Yes."

Leila stopped the car.

"Can you wait here for five minutes?"

"Of course."

When Leila had left, Olga looked around her. The car was parked across the street from a church, a pink and white building with a sign: Notre-Dame-des-Anges. In front of it, two beggars were holding out their hands.

"Are you waiting for Mrs. Chehab?" asked a man in a tan suit who materialized out of nowhere, making her jump as if she'd been stuck by a pin.

"Yes," she answered hesitantly. "Yes, I'm waiting for Leila Chehab."

"You're a friend of hers?"

"Not really. I'm a tourist. We met five years ago, by chance."

"Ah, good," the man said as if that vague explanation were enough for him. "Here she comes."

Leila seemed annoyed to see him.

"Hello, Bashir," she said grudgingly. "You can leave now."

She started her little Morris and drove off between two big Mercedes.

"Where are you staying?" she asked Olga.

"At the St. George."

"I'll take you there."

They drove in silence. Only when they were in front of the hotel did Leila turn toward Olga for the first time. Her big, dark eyes, with glints of violet, were full of tears.

"Forgive me. I can't see you again. My husband has me followed everywhere. He's very powerful."

"But . . ." Olga began.

Leila silenced her with a little gesture.

"Goodbye."

Then, as Olga was about to leave her, Leila said these last words, almost in a whisper: "I loved him. I really loved him."

That unexpected meeting, that ride in Leila's car, those silences and mysteries, and finally that avowal, left Olga with a painful sensation. Without really knowing why, she was certain she had just seen someone in danger. She wanted to talk about it with Hidar but he hadn't yet come back to the hotel. She hesitated a moment between her room and the terrace overlooking the sea; then, seeing that the sky was still clear, she opted for the terrace.

She had been sitting there less than a minute when a short, chubby man unceremoniously sat down facing her.

"My name is Michel Chehab. I'm Leila's husband."

"Yes," Olga said, taken aback and inexplicably terrified.

Chehab had a bloated face, a bulbous nose and colorless eyes.

"You're Mrs. Assadi, aren't you?"

"Yes, I am."

"Would you like a drink?"

"Just tea, please."

He called the waiter, then waited till he had gone away and asked, "You knew Sidney Halter, didn't you?"

"Yes, but only slightly. He was a relative of mine."

"Did you know he was my wife's lover?"

The bluntness of the question nearly stunned her.

"Well, I . . ." she stammered. "I . . . yes, I mean . . . no . . ."

"But you saw them together, didn't you?"

"They knew each other. Yes, that's what I mean: I knew they knew each other."

Chehab was silent again while the waiter served the drinks he had ordered, then he asked, "Do you know that your husband is responsible for your relative's death?"

Olga was staggered and incredulous. She looked with defiance and hatred at that fat bastard as he began describing in great detail the part that Hidar had played in planning the hijacking of planes to Zarqa in 1970.

"You're mistaken," she said in an unsteady voice.

"I'm never mistaken," he replied with a self-satisfied smile. He lit a cigarette. "And now, do you know that your husband was also my wife's lover?"

At this, Olga leaped up.

"You're lying! I don't know why I'm listening to your drivel. You're a foul, vicious man, Mr. Chehab."

She left the terrace while the waiters and the other customers watched her with amusement.

When Hidar came back to the hotel at about five in the afternoon, he found her lying on the bed, pretending to be interested in reading the Bible. But this time it was obvious that faith had deserted her.

"Forgive me, darling," he said, "it was a long meeting. And it wasn't easy, believe me." He took off his jacket and sat down beside her on the bed. "I don't have only friends in Beirut."

"I've noticed that," Olga said gruffly.

Hidar's matte face tensed.

"Did you meet someone today?"

"Yes," she answered in a tone that she tried to make as neutral as possible. "I met your mistress."

PARIS, MAY 1977

The Jesuit Roberto Cerutti eventually became my friend. Whenever I went to Rome, I called him and we tried to see each other. Did he tell me anything new about Hugo? It's hard to say. But one thing was clear, and strange: his affection for Hugo was based less on any good qualities he may have recognized in him than on his faults and weaknesses. He regarded him as "unstable, easily influenced, capable of disloyalty and treachery," but felt that he was always well aware of the difference between right and wrong. He was attracted by Hugo's anxiety and remorse, his determination to make up for his misdeeds and struggle against his faults through his desperate, touching quest for a little more justice, brotherhood and understanding among people.

Did Father Cerutti have any suspicions? Yes, he did. But for some reason he never questioned Hugo. Hugo might very well have been working for an intelligence service. Or maybe for two. Or why not three? He was dominated by his wife but he had certainly known many other women. His ideas were sound, however, and his struggle was sincere. His death may have been caused not by his treachery, but by his sincerity.

There was a curious relationship between those two men: Roberto Cerutti, the Jesuit, and Hugo Halter, the Jew from the ghetto. I tried in vain to understand it, to get a better grasp of it. Did Father Cerutti see Hugo as his brother, a Jew united with him by the Christian faith, or did he see himself as a Christian whose faith separated him from Hugo? Did Hugo's Jewishness play a part in their friendship? I later learned that in early 1960 they had organized a Judeo-Christian conference that Father Cerutti never mentioned to me. Several churchmen and rabbis took part in it. And it seems that they even planned a trip to Jerusalem, which never took place. I was also told about other plans they had made together, though I never discovered exactly what they were. To my question about them, Father Cerutti answered with a quotation: "'Blessed be the Lord God of Israel; for he hath visited and redeemed his people, and hath raised up an horn of salvation for us in the house of his servant David.' You think that's from the Torah, don't you? Well, it's not: it's Saint Luke 1:68–69."

That evening, after dinner, Father Cerutti went back to the studios of Radio Vatican and I went with him. And together we learned of the most important turnaround in the history of the State of Israel: the Labour Party, in power since 1947, had lost the elections to Likud. Menachem Begin, the former head of the Irgun, had become prime minister — Menachem Begin, of whom David Ben-Gurion had said, "If he ever comes to power, he will lead the country to its ruin."

From then on, the pace of events quickened. A few days later, in Paris, I received a call from Mohammed Hassan al-Toukhami, who gave me an urgent invitation from President Sadat. The next day I was in Cairo. Filled with emotion and convinced that this meeting would be decisive, I went with Mohammed Hassan al-Toukhami to the Egyptian president's house between the Sheraton Hotel and the Pyramids. Anwar Sadat was to give a speech before the Assembly the next day. "An important speech," he told me with a smile that narrowed his kindly eyes — the eyes of a peasant who, as he liked to recall, had grown up on the banks of the Nile.

"In politics," he said after a servant in a blue djellabah had put down the coffee tray on the table, "you jump on a galloping horse and let the others catch up with you if they can. Well, I'm going to ride a rocket, not a horse, and you'll see all those wheezing old politicians running after me, begging me to let them catch their breath!" And, after a short silence accompanied by a playful smile: "I wanted you to be here on this occasion. You'll be surprised."

At the time, I didn't understand what he meant. But the next day I listened to his speech on television, as he had wanted me to do, and the words he had used — horse, rocket, surprise — suddenly became very clear:

"I am ready to go to the end of the earth to save the life of one of my sons. I am ready to go to the devil. I am ready to go to the end of the world. . . . I am even ready to go to Israel."

The Assembly broke into applause. I applauded too. Was the dream going to come true? Hugo's dream, mine . . .

Two days later I went back to Paris full of confidence. And it was in Paris that I learned of Begin's answer: "We Israelis hold out our hands to you. . . . Let us make peace." Excitement, euphoria, happiness — but also a faint regret: there on my television screen, at the Lod airport, superimposed on the faces of Begin, Dayan, Meir, Peres, Rabin, Sadat and Mohammed Hassan al-Toukhami, all standing in front of the Egyptian president's white jetliner, were the familiar faces of Hugo, Sidney, Mordecai and my father, who would never appear again, except in the pages of my book.

I don't know what feeling of urgency made me go to my mother's apartment one morning much earlier than we had agreed. The night before, she had been pale and her hands had trembled strangely. A doctor had ordered some tests and I was going to take her to the laboratory.

I rang the doorbell without getting an answer, rang again, knocked. Nothing. Then came a faint, faraway sigh that I wasn't even sure I had distinctly heard. I leaned down, looked through the keyhole and saw my mother on the floor, trying to get to the door. I knocked again, frantic with fear. I knocked unthinkingly, for no other reason than to tell her I was there, that she mustn't worry, that I was close to her. She moaned more and more loudly, tried to call out, maybe even to answer me, to reassure me. But she couldn't raise herself high enough to reach the doorknob. Some Turkish workmen came to help. We tried together to break open the door but in vain.

Panic and terror were rising inside me, along with an ignoble, unbearable feeling of helplessness. A neighbor suggested calling the firemen. They came in five minutes, went in through the window, put my mother on her bed and opened the door for us.

Death was there. I recognized it immediately. It had the odor of my childhood, during the bombing of Warsaw. And it was exactly the same as the odor I had smelled a few years earlier, in the room where my father lay. My mother was no longer moving and she had almost stopped moaning. She had fallen into a kind of coma. I had her taken to a hospital, where she was diagnosed as having internal bleeding and cirrhosis probably caused by jaundice that had been poorly treated, or completely untreated, during the war.

Three months; three months of anguish, three months of hope. And at the end of those three months, death at last. I was now an orphan. There was no longer anyone, any barrier, between me and death. I was like a reservist who had suddenly found himself in the front lines. Everyone has either had that feeling or will have it some-day. My case, however, was more complex. In losing my mother, I had lost the last link in the family chain, the last witness to a world that no longer existed and a language that was dying: Yiddish, my mother tongue. I was doubly an orphan: I had lost my parents and my memory.

My inheritance: a few personal souvenirs; an album of photographs yellowed by time; some poems by my mother; a reproduction of the first page of the Bible published by my ancestors five centuries ago in Sonchino, Italy; the box of documents gathered by my father; and Hugo's notebook. It was a great deal and it was little: just enough to let me either forget or begin the difficult reconquest of memory. I chose the latter and threw myself into that arduous enterprise again. It was the beginning of six years of work, research, doubt, and joy at the sight of those thousands of signs cropping up on paper: *The Book of Abraham*. And then those four other years spent tracking down the Lerners, Arieh and Judith, the Halters in the United States, Olga, Doña Regina and Anna Maria — my fellow humans, my cousins, the heroes of *The Children of Abraham*.

40

BUENOS AIRES

Anna Maria: Back to Basics

FEBRUARY 1978

Perón was dead. A military junta had taken power. Repression in Argentina had become more violent, more brutal. And the leaders of the Montoneros, pursued by the police and the army, were reduced to constantly changing their headquarters and residences. They were sometimes in the province of Entre Ríos, sometimes in the Andes near the Bolivian border, sometimes in another place, farther away, behaving more discreetly and secretively; and yet the killers of the AAA, the Argentinian Anticommunist Alliance, were always on their trail.

Like her comrades, Anna Maria had become extremely cautious: she now had red hair and wore loose Creole dresses and sometimes glasses that made her face almost unrecognizable.

One warm, humid morning in February 1978 she and Mario were in La Plata, about fifty miles from Buenos Aires, delivering a package of leaflets to Father Mendoza, a noble-hearted young priest who was opposed to the junta. The nearness of Buenos Aires gave her a sudden desire to see the city again, to stroll along Corrientes Avenue, to smell the musty odor of the Río de la Plata and, above all, to hear Doña Regina's harsh accent again, at least once.

Knowing he couldn't dissuade her, Mario decided to go with her. They took a bus. For an hour they sat in one of those big, rusty, dented, multicolored coaches, decorated all over with painted festoons, scrolls and other embellishments, which were so heedless of traffic laws that the army was reluctant to try to control them.

They got off the bus three blocks from San Martín Avenue. It was noon. The sun was high and hot. In that part of the avenue, where there was almost no traffic, people lived with their windows open most of the time. And from the building next to Doña Regina's came Suzanna Rinaldi's voice:

> *Come,*
> *Sit beside me.*
> *People are suffocating*
> *In this madness, my brother.*
> *Must we be silent?*

"Is this it?" Mario asked in a conspiratorial tone.

"Mm!" Anna Maria said, putting her finger to her lips, as if the slightest sound might endanger them.

Yes, it was there. The building hadn't changed. As always, the door of the apartment was unlocked. Three years had passed, yet everything was the same. Except, perhaps, for that silence, that diffuse sadness, and that unwonted semidarkness in the living room, where she saw someone lying on the sofa as soon as she came in.

"Grandmother," she said softly.

Her grandmother opened her eyes, closed them as if she were going back to sleep, opened them again and looked at the intruders with an expression that was both incredulous and simple-minded. Then she abruptly stood up and said without surprise, as if they had seen each other only the day before, "Ah, it's you, Anna Maria."

Without asking any questions, she hugged her, shook hands with Mario and began setting the table.

"It's you, Anna Maria," she repeated. "I've been keeping myself busy. I do a little housework every day, and I get food ready in case one of you should drop in for lunch. This morning I made gefilte fish. You still like gefilte fish, don't you? I was expecting you. I've been expecting you so long. . . ."

"And how is Don Israel?"

"Don Israel? I'm not expecting *him* anymore."

"What do you mean?"

"You don't know? Your grandfather is dead, my child. Oh, yes, he's quite dead."

When she had finished putting plates, silverware and a serving dish on the table, they all sat down at it. She looked at the two young people with her round eyes shining strangely in the shadows.

"He was in bed for nearly two years," she went on in a weary voice. "He kept dying without ever being able to die. Two years, my child. Do you know how long that can be? You remember how Don Israel was, don't you? Always moving, cheerful, nervous, never able to sit still. He gave me all kinds of trouble but I liked him. Oh, if you could have seen him in his bed! Completely quiet, completely paralyzed! Not a word, not a gesture, nothing. Only his eyes still seemed alive. During those two years I had to wipe him, wash him, feed him, put in his suppositories. You can't know. . . . For two years I read the newspaper to him, and for two years I didn't know if he even heard me. This was *Don Israel!* Do you realize? . . . Sometimes it seemed to me that he was begging me to help him die. But how could I have done that?

"Did you know old Dr. Longer? He was very nice. At first he came often. Not for Don Israel — there was nothing more to do for him — but to keep me company awhile. I'd make tea with lemon for him, and cookies, your favorite kind. We'd talk about this and that, and then, when he was leaving, he'd shake his head and say, 'You have a lot of courage, Doña Regina.'

"Once, when I was asleep on a chair — during that whole time I slept there, on that chair — I woke up with a start. I felt as if Don Israel were calling me, as if he were asking me for something. I put all the sleeping pills I had into an envelope and pounded them into powder with a hammer. I mixed the powder with sugar and water, but when I went to him with the glass, he was asleep. I didn't have the courage to wake him up to help him die. And so . . . two horrible years!

"One morning, as soon as I opened my eyes, I knew. I felt liberated. It's true: he'd died while I was asleep and I felt liberated. Now I'm alone and it's sad. Before, I liked being alone now and then. But now, being alone is all I have. No plans for the future, nothing in the present, and I've even started losing the past, losing my memories.

"You know, I've found a wedding picture of Martín, your father. I'll get it for you. You haven't seen him in a long time, have you? He worries about you. He's changed a lot, you'll see. He looks more and more like my father, your great-grandfather Abraham, the printer. I still remember the smell of ink he used to bring into the house. He wrote to me during the first week of the occupation of Warsaw. I answered with a long letter and I also sent him a package. The letter came back three years later, but not the package. You want to see the envelope? Look: the name and address on it are correct — Abraham Halter, 51 Nowolipje Street, Warsaw, Poland — and they marked it 'Unknown'! That's the last souvenir I have of my father. Unknown! Did you like the gefilte fish? Did your friend like it too? Good. Shall I bring the tea and cookies now?"

When she came back from the kitchen she continued, "And your parents . . . I have to tell you about your parents. Whatever you do, don't go to see them. It would be dangerous for you, and them too. The soldiers are everywhere. Do you know they just abducted two French nuns? Actually, I don't know why I'm talking about that. We all have our little bundle of misery, and the older we get, the bigger it grows. Maybe that's why old people walk bent over. You know, any death is terrible. If only we could get ready for it, the way we get ready for a trip. But it's always a surprise. It never comes when you expect it. Who could have known that Don Israel, lively as he was, would lie there rotting for two years? I'm old, I'm all alone, and when I die no one will mourn for me very long — but I don't feel like dying. My brother Salomon is dead, cousin Sidney was killed, and so was cousin Hugo. Cousin Mordecai died in a war — you know, Mordecai, the kibbutznik, Arieh's father. I'm the last to remember him." And, after another silence: "It was nice of you to come and see me. Now it's time for you to go. And even if you don't remember, you must live."

This time she really fell silent, like a record that had played itself out.

As she left San Martín Avenue, Anna Maria couldn't hold back her sorrow or her tears.

*   *   *

A week later there was a special meeting in a dilapidated house that had belonged to a "disappeared" priest and stood in the midst of wretched huts where unemployed workers and their families lived. A big bare room with disemboweled easy chairs and an elaborate chandelier from the nineteen twenties, dominated by an enormous statue of Christ that Andean Indians had carved with axes. In the yellow light of the chandelier, it could be seen that the crackled walls had been recently whitewashed.

About sixty people were already there when Anna Maria and Mario arrived. Among them were Julio's two bodyguards, Manuel and Halcon, standing on duty in front of the door. They were middle-aged men built like gorillas, specialists in military action. They would later tell how they had procured pistols for shooting darts loaded with poison that could be used to kill torturers quietly. Seeing and hearing them was enough to show that the organization was no longer what it had been, that all the joyous fervor of the early years had been lost as clandestinity, radicalism and professionalism took over.

Julio began by explaining the reason for that special meeting. He spoke with the haste of a preacher who had been given only a limited time for his sermon. "In a few months," he said, "the World Cup soccer matches will begin. Media people from all over the world will come to Buenos Aires, and, as you know, Argentinians love soccer. We may as well take time out then, because no one will follow us on the path of violence. So we're going to propose a truce and show that the Montoneros also love soccer."

"I never thought I'd hear anything like that," Roberto whispered in Anna Maria's ear. "The revolution is being knocked out of bounds by a soccer ball!"

Juanita, whose cheeks had been hollowed by time and were still as pale as ever, pointed out that a boycott had been started abroad by friends of Argentinian democracy and that maybe nothing should be done to counteract their demonstration of approval.

Julio made an impatient gesture.

"I know, yes. Anna Maria's cousin — he and his friends in Paris had that half-baked idea. I won't go along with it. We don't agree on anything. Remember what he wrote: that we've become little warlords." There was scornful laughter among his listeners.

"He's for words and against action. Some of our comrades here in this room know what words can cost nowadays, in this country." He looked at them all, one by one. "Then everyone is in favor of the truce?"

Besides the leaders, there was a large number of basic militants — the ones Anna Maria didn't know — who couldn't afford the luxury of discussing or thinking. The motion was therefore approved.

Julio went on talking for at least an hour but Anna Maria didn't listen. That meeting seemed useless to her. She knew that the real decisions had been made long before and that the leaders gathered here were only supposed to ratify them, without debate or dispute. She asked Mario what time it was. Nearly midnight. Seeing an empty chair on Julio's left, she sat down in it and decided to follow the rest of the meeting from there. *What strange people they were,* she thought. *What a crew!* There were all kinds in that room: the original leaders, such as Julio, Mario, Roberto and Juanita; a nucleus of young conspirators who belonged to the next generation and had been given on-the-job training in guerrilla warfare; a few old Perónists; intellectuals obsessed with justice; trade unionists; a few derelicts; and some leaders from Cuba.

Anna Maria was wondering about the mysterious cement that was able to bind such dissimilar people together when the door opened. She stood up to see better: it was Carlos, the powerful and feared general secretary of the organization, who had just come back from Mexico. With his tall, slightly stooped body, his slow movements, his metallic voice, his distant way of greeting and his brief orders, he instantly transformed the friendly atmosphere of the room. He spoke of the World Cup and Julio's proposal for a truce. He also spoke of "our Palestinian comrades," "our common ideal," "the weapons they send us" and "everything that the movement owes to them." Routine, the same old refrain, just what it took to lull Anna Maria, who was exhausted after traveling six hundred miles by bus to come to the meeting. She was beginning to doze off when she heard two names that were familiar to her: Nehemia Rozenblum and Michael Sander. Why was Carlos talking about the president of the Argentinian Delegation of Jewish Associations and that nice rabbi who headed the Latin-American Rabbinical Seminary of Buenos Aires?

"What are they talking about?" she asked a plump young woman sitting on the arm of her chair.

"Two unknown men who have to be eliminated so that the logistics of the revolutionary cell can function again."

The young woman answered mechanically, like a robot, without thinking or showing any emotion. Anna Maria knew that language. She had used it all too often herself. But now, for some reason, she just couldn't accept it. Was it because the words "two unknown men" reminded her of the word "unknown" with which the Nazis had referred to her great-grandfather Abraham, and which had been running through her mind ever since her visit to Doña Regina? Was it because of that strange statue of Christ as seen by the Andean Indians? In any case, for the first time in a meeting of that kind, she felt rebellion rising inside her and had a violent urge to protest.

"Wait! Wait!" she exclaimed. All heads turned toward her. "If I've understood correctly, we're going to offer the army a truce and declare war on the Jews!"

Carlos bowed his head slightly and spread his feet, like a boxer who had just taken a punch and was about to counterattack.

"I thought," he said, "that, with us, the general interest came before our tribal attachments."

"Tribal attachments?" Anna Maria said, her face turning livid. She took a step toward Carlos. "You're crazy, completely crazy! Do you think it's tribal attachments that make me say that killing Jews because they're Jews is an anti-Semitic act?"

Carlos drew himself erect. He too was obviously making a strenuous effort to stay calm.

"I think you'd better not say anything more," he told her gently. Then he went on more loudly, stressing every word, "We must help the Palestinians. We owe it to them. No question about it. If they ask us to execute two men who are working for the Yankees, we'll do it. We'd do it even if the men were Muslims." And, addressing the others in the room: "The decision is made. Now we have to make the final arrangements: choosing guns that haven't been used before and can't be traced by the police, finding two cars, and so on."

"Bravo!" Anna Maria said, coming still closer to him. "Yes, bravo!" She raised her right fist. "Long live Marx, and Lenin, and Stalin, and Che!" She saw vast surprise in the others' faces. "You think I'm crazy, don't you? The Palestinians ask us to kill Jews — we'll do it. Tomorrow the Soviets will ask us to kill Chinese — we'll do it. Day after tomorrow the Chinese will ask us to kill Vietnamese — we'll do that too." Her voice became a little hoarse. "And we won't stop there, you'll see! We'll help the Khmer Rouge to slaughter their people, we'll help the Syrians to wipe out Al Fatah, we'll help the PLO to kill our friends in the Popular Front, we'll —"

"Enough!" Carlos interrupted.

"Please," Mario begged her, "please stop."

Their words only made her more furious than ever. Standing with her face almost touching Carlos's, she said to him in a voice filled with sheer hatred, "And when all that's been done, comrade, there will still be Anna Maria. No, come to think of it, I know you well enough to realize that you may very well start with me. It's true, comrade: you're going to liquidate me too! Three Jews are always better than two, don't you think?"

Dawn had come. It was wrapped in fog, but it was there. Anna Maria, Mario and Roberto were driving toward Buenos Aires at high speed.

"You shouldn't have . . . ," Mario said. "You knew that speaking up that way would only provoke Carlos and make him even more determined to stick to his decision. And now . . ." He turned on the windshield wipers as though to drive away the morning dew, or maybe a gloomy idea, and continued in a lower voice, "Now you're in danger."

Anna Maria made no reply.

"Mario's right, damn it!" Roberto exclaimed. He turned his round, kindly-looking face toward her. "Don't you realize it?"

She still didn't answer. It was as though, after having talked so much, she had no words left to defend herself or try to save herself. Only when they had reached Buenos Aires did she say in a neutral tone, "Please let me off at my grandmother's house."

41

BUENOS AIRES

Anna Maria: Back to Basics (Conclusion)

FEBRUARY 1978

Doña Regina wasn't asleep when Anna Maria arrived. It even seemed that she hadn't been to bed, that she had been waiting up for her granddaughter. And in the early morning light the marks of her latest ordeals could be seen even more clearly in her dark, wrinkled face. The past had left her eyes with an expression that was both aggressive and kind, harsh and amused, beneath a fringe of totally white hair.

"You've come at the right time," she said, as if she really had been expecting her. "I've made tea and cookies. After you've eaten some of them, you can go to sleep — in Miguel's room, over Don Israel's shoe shop, you remember?" She seemed to give voice to an inner monologue: "I've kept everything the way it was, I haven't changed anything. As long as we can . . . as long as they leave us alone . . ."

"Who's 'they'?"

"People . . . death."

It was true that Miguel's room hadn't changed. A table, two wooden chairs, a bed covered with a heavy checkered quilt and, on the wall, a reproduction of Van Gogh's *Sunflowers* held by four thumbtacks that the dampness was beginning to rust. Anna Maria lay down on the bed. She smelled a faint odor of dust. Overcome by fatigue, she fell asleep.

She couldn't tell how long she had slept, but when she woke up it was dark. She went down to the dining room. As soon as Doña Regina saw her, she hurried back into the kitchen.

"Poor girl, you must be hungry. While I'm warming dinner for you, you can look at the pictures I've laid out on the table for you. The man with the white beard is my father, Abraham. Next to him are pictures of Salomon, Hugo and Mordecai. The litte boy is Sidney. His father sent me that picture more than thirty years ago, from Winnipeg. Look at the big sepia one, too, and you'll see at least fifty people: the Halters who were deported. Not one of them survived. That's how it is — it's not easy to be Jewish."

And still without asking any questions, without even wondering about the why or the how of that visit, she served Anna Maria's dinner and continued her monologue.

When she had finished eating, Anna Maria asked for paper and a pen and went back to her room. She turned on the shadeless lamp standing on the table and, with the edge of her hand, wiped off some of the dust that had accumulated through the years. Then she began writing a long letter without stopping to think or make any changes, and as she wrote it she realized that it had already been in her head, waiting to be put down on paper, for a long time. It was addressed to the editor of the newspaper *Clarín*. It was naive and sometimes chaotic, as her mind was that night. Here are the main parts of it:

> A letter from a "terrorist" to a popular newspaper is somewhat unusual, but unfortunately we are not living in a usual time. The rule of law has been replaced with a medieval battlefield. Each master has his own troops, prison, torturers and justice. How do you think young people who dream of a democratic society, as I do, can survive here? By keeping quiet, going into exile, or picking up a pistol. You will find my pistol, a nine-millimeter TO-Kagypt, in the package that will contain this letter. I imagine that you do not receive such packages very often, but an unusual society calls for unusual methods.

I will be accused of all sorts of crimes. Don't believe any of it. The only crime I acknowledge is having kept a gun without a permit. As for the execution of the torturer Miguel Pelado, he deserved that punishment. The number of innocent people he tortured, or killed in horribly painful ways, places him in the category of criminals against humanity. Eichmann was judged by a state. Pelado, unfortunately, had to be judged by a few young avengers.

I can assure you I never felt at all proud of owning a pistol. I felt ashamed of it, in fact. Unamuno, Emerson and Joyce are, if not closer to me, at least dearer. But can one take refuge in books when some of our finest men and women are being abducted, and when their bodies are later found in the Río de la Plata? If I had been old enough to fight in one of the European countries occupied by the Nazis, I would have joined the Resistance. Being old enough to fight in a country occupied by its own interior fascism, I could have had no respect for myself if I had not joined in the deadly struggle against that fascism.

But what has led me to write to you now is my determination to save two lives. I have not written to the police because I do not trust a police force whose work consists less in protecting citizens than in silencing them or making them disappear. I know that once this letter is published it will place me in danger, from my former friends as well as the police. But my former friends have failed to live up to the ideal of justice and I now feel that I have little in common with them. I want nothing to do with a politics of murder. I hate the idea of a strategy based on killing. To me at least, that strategy has just made its first real wrong turn, which will make it fall into anti-Semitism, pure and simple.

As the granddaughter of a woman who took refuge in Argentina to escape from Polish anti-Semitism, and as the great-granddaughter of Abraham Halter, a Warsaw printer who, on the first day of the revolt in the ghetto, leaped onto a German tank, holding a hand grenade, in an effort to oppose triumphant barbarism with the simple force of his refusal, I cannot decently permit the murder of two representatives of the Jewish community merely because they are Jewish.

The two men marked for murder are Nehemia Rozenblum, president of the Argentinian Delegation of Jewish Associations, and Rabbi Michael Sander, head of the Latin-American Rabbinical Seminary of Buenos Aires. They are to be killed very soon. Preparations for it are far advanced. Everything must be done, everything humanly possible, to prevent that plan from being carried out. I know that I have condemned myself by writing this, and that my former friends will regard me as a traitor. There is nothing I can do about it. I am not betraying anyone, since I am remaining faithful to what is most sacred in me; it is their insanity against my memory. I have not had to search very long to discover where my choice, my loyalty and my truth are.

To avoid misunderstanding, I will say that I am still young and have a powerful desire to live. But I have always placed the notion of justice above everything else. I have dreamed of justice for all and all for justice. I cannot renounce that dream. And whatever the price that must be paid for it, I am willing to pay it.

Writing all that had exhausted her. She had had to weigh each word, listen to each syllable in her most secret depths, and consider all the risks she was running, the path she had taken and the foreseeable outcome of what she was doing. Overwhelmed with nausea and fatigue, she put her forearms on the table, rested her head on them and fell asleep. When she awoke, she reread the letter. She felt it was neither clear nor persuasive enough, but she didn't have the strength to rewrite it. She packaged it up with the pistol and mailed it.

Published two days later in *Clarín,* it created a sensation, not only in Argentina but all over the world. Its first effect was to make the police, the army and the killers of the Argentinian Anticommunist Alliance begin looking for its author. They questioned and harassed her parents, Doña Regina and several of her friends. But with the World Cup only a few months away, they didn't dare provoke public opinion too openly. They were unable to find Anna Maria.

A month later, Mario came to see Doña Regina and asked if she had heard from Anna Maria. Mistrustfully, the old lady answered that she hadn't.

"If she should call you," he said with embarrassment, "discourage her from coming here. Tell her not to visit any of her comrades, either. They'd turn her in. They've all been ordered . . ." He self-consciously pushed back the hair hanging down over his eyes and said hesitantly, lowering his voice, "Tell her also that . . . that her letter was beautiful. And tell her . . . tell her —"

"I will," Doña Regina interrupted. "I'll tell her. Don't worry — she'll understand."

42

ISRAEL

A Wedding on the Kibbutz

JULY 1979

Summer was especially hot that year. The torrid south wind known as the *khamsin* blew steadily. The children of the kibbutz ran barefoot on lawns that were dried out even though they were constantly watered by sprinklers. The adults, working in the fields, fishponds, cowsheds and workshops, impatiently waited for the sun to go down and a breath of cool air to come down from Mount Hermon.

At the end of June, another terrorist attack at Qiryat Shemona had increased the tension along the nearby border, and the press had discussed the possibility of military action against the terrorists based in Lebanon, but the people of Kibbutz Dafneh were interested mainly in the coming wedding of Mordecai's son and a young Yemenite Jewish woman. Their marriage was the staple topic of conversation in the dining hall, under the big ceiling fan that churned the hot air permeated with cooking odors. Could a marriage between an Ashkenazi and a Yemenite last? Would Arieh invite his former girlfriend, Shoshana, the nurse, to the wedding? Was that beautiful Judith known to have had any other love affairs? And so on.

In memory of one of its founders who had died in the Yom Kippur War, the general assembly of the kibbutz had decided to have an outstanding celebration on the day of the wedding: Sunday, July 15. Usually there were several weddings at once, on the same day, but an exception would be made for Arieh. Hundreds of invitations were sent to other kibbutzim in the region, relatives and friends in town, leaders of the kibbutz movement, relatives abroad, and the Arabs in Ghajar, the neighboring village. Yossi, the ladies' hairdresser in Qiryat Shemona, was even asked to come to the kibbutz, for once, on Saturday morning.

The agitation was so great that Shlomo, the mechanic, who was in charge of cultural activities, dances and lectures, was over-whelmed in spite of his boundless energy. He had to have the piano tuned because the children had pounded it unmercifully; get back the accordion that had been lent for a celebration of Moshav Shear Ishuv; put up a platform on the lawn in front of the House of Culture; brief Haika, called Pavlova because of her past as a dancer; help Jacob Oren, the general secretary, to prepare speeches that wouldn't be too pompous. Then there were all those rooms that had to be made ready for the guests who would be staying on the kibbutz: Judith, of course, as well as her father and several cousins; Richard, who, like many deeply religious American Jews, had moved to Israel and gone to live on a settlement near Hebron; Martín, who was com-ing from Buenos Aires; and many others.

The hero of the celebration arrived on Friday afternoon. Even though his mother had told him about it in advance, on the phone, it was hard for him to believe that all that bustle and commotion was for him.

The kibbutz burst into activity as soon as the sun rose on Sunday morning. Doors slammed, children swarmed over the lawns, musical instruments and amplifiers were tested. Except for the smaller-than-normal team needed for the cowshed, and the larger one in charge of security, everyone was getting ready for the wedding. Arieh tried to make himself useful. He asked to be allowed to help set up the tables and the buffet, he went to the platform where Shlomo was reigning over a dozen amateur decorators, but no one wanted him anywhere. "The groom must save his strength for the bride," he was told. Carrying a case of orange juice from the truck to the kitchen was all he was able to do.

Rabbi Natanson came from Qiryat Shemona. In spite of the heat, the old man wore a black felt hat. He questioned Arieh a long time about his Jewish knowledge and, with a short blue pencil, wrote his father's first name and the first name of Judith's father in a worn notebook. He made sure he had properly prepared the wedding rings, carefully reread the marriage contract and wrote down the names of the two witnesses, still in his notebook. Exhausted by all that effort, he asked for a place where he could rest before the ceremony. Arieh led him to his parents' house.

In the doorway, the rabbi turned his pale face toward Arieh, looked at him with his watery eyes and asked in a quavering voice, "You've never been to a synagogue, have you?" And before Arieh could answer he went on, "Of course there's no synagogue here on the kibbutz, is there? Are you all unbelievers here? It's good that you want to be married according to the tradition of our forefathers Abraham, Jacob and Isaac. It shows that the ashes of neglect haven't yet smothered the Jewish spark in you." And, suddenly reassuring: "You will be blessed. Yes, you will, because the Almighty has celebrated marriages ever since He created the world."

Shortly after seven o'clock in the evening, the guests began arriving. There were soon a thousand of them. The men wore white shirts and black or blue trousers, the women wore attractive, brightly colored dresses. They all pointed out the eminent people who had come: General Dayan, who had known Mordecai during the War of Independence; Shimon Peres, general secretary of the Labour Party, who probably considered Kibbutz Dafneh to be within his political domain; and several high-ranking military officers.

Just before Arieh gave Judith the wedding ring, Rabbi Natanson prayed aloud, "Blessed be You, O Lord, who sanctify Israel, Your people, through the wedding canopy and the consecration of marriage." Several people in the crowd showed signs of deep emotion and Sarah burst into tears. But gaiety returned with the entertainment that followed, and especially with the funny sketches that made even Benjamin Ben-Eliezer smile.

When the eminent guests had left, Shlomo began playing records on the public address system and the dining hall was turned into a dance hall. The "immediate" family gathered around a table loaded with food and drink so that, finally at ease, they could comment on the marvelous day.

"So now you're married," Aron Lerner said to Arieh as he sat down. He raised his glass in a toast to the newlyweds. "My dear Arieh and Judith, may you live in a world without war!" Then he began reciting:

> *Will it come, will it come,*
> *The last of those endless years*
> *That constantly bring back to me*
> *The sorrows and furies of war?*

Seeing his mother's face frozen by a painful memory, Arieh stopped him:

"Let's get off the subject of war and peace and find out what's happening in the land of the tango."

He turned to his Argentinian cousin, who was still showing the strain of his long trip but mumbled a few incomprehensible words in a mixture of Spanish and Yiddish. Then he turned to Richard, who had wrapped himself in hostile silence all through the ceremony. After suddenly taking off his long black coat and broad fur-trimmed hat, which had caused a sensation on that secular kibbutz, Richard felt his skullcap to make sure it was still in place and began speaking in a Yiddish that his Argentinian cousin only half understood. Richard, Arieh knew, spoke Yiddish because he, like many of the Lubavichers, believed that Hebrew, the sacred language, should be used only for prayer.

"You don't make peace with Amalek, you fight him." He leaned over the table, quickly uncurled his long earlocks, put them behind his ears and recited with a singsong intonation, "'Remember what Amalek did unto thee by the way, when ye were come forth out of Egypt. . . . Therefore it shall be, when the Lord thy God hath given thee rest from all thine enemies round about in the land which the Lord thy God giveth thee for an inheritance to possess it, that thou shalt blot out the remembrance of Amalek from under heaven; thou shalt not forget it.'" He looked around him, raised his forefinger and repeated, "'Thou shalt not forget it.'"

Sarah made an impatient gesture.

"We'll talk about that later," she said, smiling.

"No, not later," Richard insisted. "The professor spoke of peace. I'd like to know with whom we're to have that peace, and on what territory. The Almighty . . ."

"Let's leave the Almighty alone," Aron proposed.

Eager to create a diversion, Judith asked in her most urbane tone, "Have you heard from Olga?"

Aron put his glass down on the table, looked at her and answered, "Yes, Olga has given birth to a son."

"*Mazel tov!*" Arieh exclaimed.

"Thank you. I got a letter from her about two weeks ago. She said that Hidar, her husband, had been traveling. He'd gone to the Middle East again, but this time to Baghdad. Olga hopes she can go with him on his next visit to Beirut."

"You never told me about that letter!" Arieh said.

Richard raised his hand to demand attention.

"That's what we've come to!" he cried. "Jews are going to the land of Amalek!"

"Hidar isn't Jewish," Judith pointed out.

"No, but Olga is!"

The long, intoxicating wail of a tango came from the loudspeakers. The couples on the dance floor put their arms around each other. Judith stood up with the somewhat timid smile of a pretty woman not absolutely sure of her beauty. Her white dress rustled as she walked around the table in all the glory of her dark shoulders and black hair, before the admiring gazes of the men who had lined up along the wall to watch the dancers. She stopped in front of Arieh and invited him to dance.

"You shouldn't have done that," he told her reproachfully when he had taken her in his arms. "I'm afraid to leave them alone together."

"They won't kill each other," Judith said, and added, laughing, "They're all Jews."

"Haven't you ever heard of the Jewish War?" Arieh was silent for a moment. "Cousin Martín seems upset, don't you think?"

"Maybe he's jealous. You were his daughter's lover, weren't you?"

Judith pressed up against him but he gently pushed her away.

"I can't help being worried. They traveled so far to come to our wedding — we shouldn't let them tear each other to pieces."

"It's *our* wedding," she protested.

But she reluctantly followed him as he led her back toward the table.

Just then Benjamin Ben-Eliezer, who had accompanied General Dayan to the Rosh Pina airport, came back. Ordinarily pale, his face was now ruddy.

"Is that you, Martín?" he said to the Argentinian cousin. "You're exactly as Arieh described you. How is your daughter, Anna Maria?"

Martín heaved a heavy sigh.

"You must have read her letter in the newspapers . . ."

"Yes, the Israeli papers published parts of it. Where is she now?"

"I have no idea," Martín said with a sad shrug. "I haven't seen her for a long time. Violence, torture — I hope it will all be over soon."

The table creaked when Richard leaned his weight on it with one hand and pointed at Martín with the other.

"Don't you think your daughter the terrorist has something to do with all that violence?"

"What do you mean?" Martín asked, frowning.

"It's simple," Richard answered. "As Rabbi Hillel said, 'Because you drowned others, you were drowned, and those who drowned you will also be drowned.'"

Martín raised his head with a strange look in his eyes.

"Are you comparing Anna Maria to the torturers of the military junta? The victims to the killers? It's as if you compared the fighters in the Warsaw ghetto to the Nazi murderers!"

Richard took one of his earlocks between his plump fingers and quoted again, "Rabbi Azhabya, son of Mahalalel, said, 'Reflect and you will avoid sin.'"

Martín was irritated more by the tone of these words than by their meaning. His face hardened and he was obviously trying to think of an appropriate answer when Richard continued, still with his singsong intonation:

"You think I'm comparing? You're the one who's comparing. What I'm saying is that there's a difference between resistance fighters and terrorists like your daughter, and that those terrorists are accomplices of the people who murdered my father!"

His last sentence fell like a bomb. Benjamin coughed. Aron pointed out that it was getting late and Sarah said that all good things had to come to an end. Arieh nodded to Judith and they were about to go and tell the guests that the celebration was over when Martín suddenly stood up and told the others to remain seated.

"So that's how it is! You're accusing my daughter of your father's death!"

Richard also stood up. His hat fell to the floor; he picked it up, flicked the dust off it and put it on. It made him seem more imposing.

"I'm not accusing your daughter. What right would I have to accuse her? As Rabbi Yoseh said, 'Never consent to judge alone, for only the Almighty can rightfully judge alone.' I'm only saying that those who help the Palestinian terrorists are responsible for my father's death."

But Martín wasn't listening.

"My daughter just saved the lives of two people, two Jews!" he said. He made an angry gesture. "I don't like religious people. They have no common sense!"

Richard put on his coat and took a threatening step toward Martín. Sarah came between them.

"For the love of the Almighty!" she pleaded.

Just then the dance music stopped and was replaced by *Hatikvah*, the Israeli national anthem. Everyone stood up. The crowd sang:

> *As long as deep in the heart*
> *The soul of a Jew yearns,*
> *And toward the East*
> *An eye looks to Zion . . .*

Aron joined in.

> *Our hope is not yet lost,*
> *The hope of two thousand years:*
> *To be a free people in our land,*
> *The land of Zion and Jerusalem.*

So did Arieh, then Martín, then Richard.

> *Our hope is not yet lost,*
> *The hope of two thousand years . . .*

When the anthem was over, Jacob Oren stood up on a chair and raised his glass.

"I drink this last toast to life! Long life to the bride and groom, long life to the whole people of Israel!"

"Amen," Richard murmured.

"Amen," Martín repeated.

Arieh and Judith's wedding had put me into a good mood. I was especially glad of the chance it gave me to see some of my relatives again. How proud my father would have been to see us gathered there! Yet I had been apprehensive about that family reunion. A single tree can bear both healthy and withered fruit. I was in the terribly risky situation of a creator who was afraid his characters might escape from him and disappoint him. But no, it turned out that my relatives were just like the image I had formed of them. They were in the image of the whole Jewish people. Even the clash between Martín and Richard fitted perfectly into the saga I had been trying to produce for years. All the tendencies of Judaism confronted each other in my family, all its branches were there. And that reassured me.

Concurrently with all that, the cause of peace was making progress. Sadat and Begin had just signed a treaty in Washington. Shouldn't I go back to Beirut and urge the Palestinians to follow their example? I recalled Sidney and Hidar, Olga and Hugo, I thought of Mordecai and Arieh at an outside café table near the Basel Hotel in Tel Aviv, and then the wedding. . . . For all of them, and also in memory of Kanafani, I had to try.

Struggling: a temptation and a nostalgia for men of my generation. Too young to have fought in the war against the Nazis, too old to have had a carefree childhood, like my friends in the following generation. Just the right age for a guilty conscience, misgivings, a fervent quest for righteous causes, love, brotherhood. And those anxieties and dreams that I have tried to exorcise by regaining my family memory and seeking a solution to the Arab-Israeli conflict. Two adventures so close, so strangely contiguous and concurrent. I have failed in the second one. I am still pursuing the first one. Rabbi Tarphon said in his *Treatise on Principles,* which cousin Richard liked to quote, "You are not obligated to finish the work, but you are not free to dissociate yourself from it."

43
BEIRUT

Before the Siege

DECEMBER 1981

There was the funeral of Wadi Hadad. Several hundred thousand
people showed their grief in an imposing ceremony on May 28,
1978, in Baghdad. And it was Arafat himself who insisted that Hidar
go with Abu Iyad to the ceremony. An image of unity and reconcil-
iation. The Palestinian masses wouldn't have understood that discord and conflict didn't lay down their arms before death. Hadad
was dead: all his friends should pay homage to him together, and
the unanimity that had been lacking in his life and in combat should
be achieved here, through tears, pathos, sorrowful faces and the reci-
tation of passages from the Koran.

Soon afterward there was a dramatic, emotionally charged
scene between Hidar and Olga: solemnly sworn statements, promises, justifications, warnings. Hidar was highly skilled at turning
such scenes to his advantage, and this time he gave a masterful performance. He described the reasons for the airplane hijackings in
1970, the part he played in the operation and the circumstances in
which Sidney died. Above all, he gave his version of the Leila affair
and did the proper thing by humbly asking forgiveness for that passing, inconsequential weakness. He and Olga then swore steadfast
love to each other. They wouldn't have admitted it to themselves,

but their marital crisis, followed by their discussion of the points at issue between them, had the unexpected effect of strengthening the bonds between them. They talked, they wept, they even conceived a son, who was born eight months later, on April 3, 1979. They named him Marwan, after Hidar's father.

Hidar's political situation? Since he was having a run of good luck, he benefited from the promotion of Chebrikov, Andropov's protégé, who, as soon as he was given the task of supervising contacts with revolutionary movements all over the world, chose Hidar as his assistant. Hidar had never had much liking for office life, with its daily meetings and weekly reports, and now he didn't like having to confer with Olga's brother Sasha, who headed the information service of the Committee for Solidarity with the Peoples of Africa and Asia. And he couldn't help seeing in Sasha a certain natural duplicity, based on a mixture of obsequiousness and arrogance, which he deeply abhorred and tended to think of as Jewish. But aside from those reservations he was happy, and he welcomed this chance to stop living as a nomad.

Early in December 1981, however, he began feeling the first attacks of an ailment that was too Russian for him not to be familiar with it: homesickness. This was the time of year when Moscow was rainy and dreary. Some of the snow that had fallen in late November still remained in the gutters in the form of dirty little piles that kept shrinking whenever it rained, but still polluted the soul. And Hidar began telling himself that he painfully missed the sunlight, tastes, colors, sounds, movement, smells and images of the faraway Middle East.

On December 7 he was summoned to KGB headquarters at 2 Dzerzhinsky Street. This wasn't the first time he had gone there, but it was the first time he had done it alone, without his friend Chebrikov. He walked into the old rococo building that had housed an insurance company in the time of Czar Nicholas II. An officer in uniform accompanied him to the sixth and last floor, where, as he well knew, the department in charge of foreign operations had its offices. As he went up in the elevator, he saw one modestly armed guard standing casually on each floor and, as always, he was surprised by that low level of protection. Long, deserted halls. Mysterious wooden doors. Dim lighting, conducive to all sorts of plotting.

He had been there less than two minutes when one of the doors opened and he saw a bald man with little red eyes protected by glasses with very small lenses. The man greeted him wordlessly and went back into his immense office, which was dominated by two portraits with gold backgrounds: Lenin and Brezhnev. Then, with a gesture intended to be benevolent, he invited his visitor to sit down on the only chair in front of him.

"I'm glad to meet you," he said, exhibiting a row of little teeth yellowed by tobacco.

In a grating voice that made Hidar think of an unoiled machine, he summarized the latest news reported from Israel by a "mole" who had been working within Israeli army intelligence for many years. It concerned Colonel Benjamin Ben-Eliezer's trips to Juniye, in Lebanon, where he had met with Christian leaders. The report also mentioned a visit by Christian leaders to Jerusalem, in a delegation composed of old Camille Chamoun, his son Dany, Bashir Gemayel, head of the Phalangists, and Emile Farah, his right-hand man. They all came to Jerusalem on November 27, in a helicopter that landed at night on the roof of the Knesset, the Israeli parliament.

Hidar already knew all this from Chebrikov, but he had just learned the source of the information, and he was delighted and amused by the unexpected discovery that a Soviet spy was working in the shadow of Benjamin Ben-Eliezer, his old adversary, who for so many years had been relentlessly trying to thwart his efforts in the Middle East.

The red-eyed man's voice grated again:

"On January 12, 1982, General Sharon, the Israeli defense minister, will go to Beirut, where, with Bashir Gemayel, he intends to draw up plans for an invasion of Lebanon."

Why was he reporting all this? Because Hidar's new assignment was to confer with the Palestinian leaders and work out a counterstrategy, and, more important, to promote a reintroduction of the Soviet Union into the region in exchange for diplomatic aid and deliveries of weapons. He could count on help from a certain number of local agents, and also from the Syrian intelligence services. It was a delicate mission, the man warned him. It could be entrusted only to someone extremely reliable, and that was why they had naturally thought of him.

*　　*　　*

On December 10, 1981, at 3:40 in the afternoon, Hidar arrived in Beirut, at the nearly deserted Khalde airport. An old Chevrolet was parked at the end of the runway. Bassam Abu Sharif was waiting for him.

"Did you come to get me alone, without protection?" Hidar asked, embracing him.

"Nothing more can happen to me," Bassam answered with a bitter laugh, pointing to his disfigured face and observing Hidar's slightly horrified expression. "It's not pretty, is it? That's what happens when a package bomb explodes in your hands. It's the same as it was with Kanafani: our friends accuse the Israelis, who accuse the Jordanians, who accuse Abu Nidal. Who knows what the truth is? All I know for now is that I have to get used to my new face."

The two men got into the car. The driver, a young fedayee in combat uniform, started off at top speed without looking back. And the Chevrolet quickly arrived in a Beirut of sound and fury that bore little resemblance to the pure jewel of the Middle East, the city where Hidar and Olga had blissfully breathed in the smells of fritters, spices and happiness. Everywhere he looked, he saw ruins, fields plowed by artillery shells, destruction, desolation. And he was startled by a distant rumble of artillery fire.

"It's like this all the time," Bassam said, putting a friendly hand on Hidar's knee. "It comes from the vicinity of the museum on Damascus Street, where the Shiite militia is trying to drive back the Lebanese army."

The car headed for the Corniche, but as soon as it passed the stadium it veered into Mar Elias Street. This had once been a busy neighborhood, full of life. Now it seemed forsaken and ravaged. Everywhere Hidar looked, he saw gutted houses and bullet-riddled trucks and cars with flat tires, abandoned next to the curb. After several minutes of negotiating an obstacle course among wrecks and ruins, the Chevrolet finally went into a courtyard and stopped. Around the courtyard was a more or less intact building whose walls and windows were protected by metal plates and ramparts made of cement blocks. Several armed men were there, and others came out of the building. One of them, evidently an officer, came forward to meet the visitors.

"You're going to meet Abu Iyad," Bassam told Hidar, "and then you'll be taken to a hotel."

"The St. George?"

Bassam looked at him with the mixture of mockery and affection that he might have shown for a child who had asked for the moon.

"The St. George? That whole neighborhood hardly exists anymore." He led him to a staircase. "You'll stay at the Hotel Alexander in East Beirut, on the Christian side. That way, tomorrow morning you can examine General Sharon's landing field near Juniye, and the building where the meeting with Bashir Gemayel is to take place."

When they reached the fourth floor, Bassam took him into a spacious but gloomy room where a typewriter was clacking. Abu Iyad was there. He greeted Hidar with outstretched arms, ritually offered him tea and exchanged comments with him on the latest episodes in the endless battle of Beirut. At nightfall, Hidar and Bassam left.

Hidar's Palestinian friends assigned two guardian angels to him. One of them was a stout Palestinian, about fifty, with a bald forehead and slightly bulging eyes. The other, some fifteen years younger, a fast-talking little man whose movements were as hurried as his speech, was apparently a Lebanese Christian. Their names were Jael al-Ardja and Joseph Hobeika, respectively. Jael al-Ardja did not seem to remember Hidar. *That's fine with me,* thought the Tunisian.

"With those two you won't be lost in Beirut," Bassam said to him.

And when they had gotten into the big, clean and well-maintained Renault that had been placed at their disposal, Joseph Hobeika said, "Don't worry, I know the road like the back of my hand. I could drive you there with my eyes closed."

PARIS, DECEMBER 1981

My aunt Regina had never called me before, so as soon as I heard her on the phone I was sure that something very serious had happened.

"What's wrong?" I asked.

"Oh!" she said in a voice muffled by distance and tears. "Anna Maria has been kidnapped."

"Anna Maria? How? When?"

"Yesterday. Everyone was after her, poor girl: her former friends, the police, the fascists. I hid her in Dr. Longer's widow's house. You remember Dr. Longer, don't you? I thought no one would think of looking for her in an old Jewish woman's house, but . . ."

"But what?"

"Yesterday morning her friend Mario came here. He didn't know where she was hiding and he was worried sick because some of his comrades had found out where she was and turned her in to the fascists. I didn't even have time to have a heart attack. I said, 'Let's go!' But not one taxi was free in the whole city. We had to take the subway. When we got to Pueyredon Avenue, where Dr. Longer's widow lives, four husky men in civilian clothes were pushing Anna Maria into a black car. She was fighting against them, poor girl! Oh, how she fought! But no one tried to help her. Here, everyone's afraid. I started screaming. Too late. Martín went to the police and they promised to investigate. But Mario said that only pressure from outside the country could save her, and that's why I'm calling you."

Doña Regina stopped talking and I heard her sobbing. What could I tell her? How could I reassure her? And what could I promise her? I was silent for a few moments, thinking as fast as I could.

"It's terrible," I finally said. "Terrible . . ."

What was terrible was Anna Maria's disappearance, of course, but also the fact that my old aunt, the only survivor of Abraham's generation, the only one to escape the wave of fascism that had broken over Europe, had now been caught by Argentinian fascism. For long seconds I stared up at the ceiling, unable to move, or make any decision, or even say anything. Having been brought up with a certain idea of good and evil, I had adopted a wild hope: that light would triumph over the darkness of evil, that the human race would keep making progress. I had believed that when Nazism was conquered it would disappear — the Nazism in whose name two soldiers had seized me one day and said to my mother, "Tell us where your husband is and your son will be given back to you." In those days I hadn't known that light would be masked by shadow forever, that Nazism was ingrained in all of us, and that life had lost its absolute value and become a medium of exchange. I now realized all that. It was becoming increasingly clear to me as I talked with old Doña Regina on the phone. The idea was repugnant to me, but it also left a chance. *If they'd wanted to kill Anna Maria,* I thought, *they'd have already done it by now.* And as soon as I had stopped talking with my aunt, I began making calls.

I did it feverishly, loading each call with the full weight of my hope and my faith. The offices of the President of France, the chairman of the Foreign Affairs Committee of the American Senate, the president of the European Parliament, politicians, ambassadors, friends who knew politicians, influential people in Latin America, friends of friends. . . . At two in the morning, exhausted, I finally stopped calling and didn't know what else I could do. Powerless? Yes, powerless. Shamefully, scandalously powerless. I felt time passing and I wanted to stop it. I felt anguish rising inside me and I wanted to scream.

At dawn, on the verge of losing my self-control, I sat down at my desk and began writing an appeal for Anna Maria's release.

It was published two days later in France, then in the United States. Had I been able to make others share my rage? Had I had enough persuasiveness, enough talent, to make them understand it? Obviously not, as I discovered on April 7, 1982, shortly after the beginning of the war in the Falkland Islands, when I received a call from my cousin Martín in Buenos Aires. He was a broken man, gasping and sobbing so much that at first it was hard for me to understand him. His daughter's body, he said, had been left in front of Doña Regina's door during the night. Doña Regina had collapsed and was in a hospital.

How can I describe what I felt when I heard that news? It was a mixture of stunned surprise, horror and disgust. Incredulity, too, a feeling that it was impossible, that such tragedies happened only to others. And then a kind of nausea at the thought of the absurd book I was writing, which suddenly seemed so light, so futile, in the face of a young woman's death.

By the next day, I had made my decision. I went to my publisher and told him I wasn't going to finish the book. He tried to make me change my mind. He told me that not sharing a human story was a betrayal of humanity. But nothing he said had any effect on me.

When I returned home, I began putting away my notes, cards and photographs in boxes. Sometimes a word, a sentence or a paragraph caught my attention and I found myself reading it with curiosity, surprise or friendship. Who was it who said, "You are not obligated to finish the work, but you are not free to dissociate yourself from it"? I felt like an automaton, foreign to myself, to my endeavor, to my memory.

A week later I was still in that state, with my throat, eyes, body and head full of tears, when I learned that Doña Regina had died.

44

BEIRUT

Before the Siege (Conclusion)

DECEMBER 1981

The sun had just risen, round and white. It was still cool but the
hotel and the street were already full of busy people and armed mili-
tiamen. Artillery was rumbling in the distance. A Maronite monk
having his coffee at a nearby table asked them what time it was.
When they told him, he became bold enough to ask them where
they were from. Hobeika's name seemed familiar to him. Hidar's
accent gave him away. So the monk introduced himself. He was a
Christian who lived in Tunis. He pointed to his empty left socket
and explained that his eye had been destroyed by a shell fragment.
He spoke of war and misery. He denounced the Palestinians and
Syrians for having buried thousands of Christians in the ruins of
Zahle.

There was no shortage of visionary, wounded and religious
people of all kinds in the Middle East, and Hidar was used to them,
but this monk, with his voice that seemed to come from another
body and his words that seemed to belong to another time, made a
strong impression on him. That was why he decided to cut short his
breakfast and begin his trip immediately.

A smell of cold ashes, from a fire that had been put out during the night at the end of Ashrafieh Street, still floated in the air. Hidar breathed in that odor from a city at war, plundered, abandoned to fire and killers. As he looked over that tumultuous crowd, so familiar and yet so distinct from himself, those agitated men, those women with pale faces impudently brightened by makeup around their eyes, it was hard for him not to feel incredibly foreign. Was there anyone with whom he could share that feeling of strangeness and distance? He encountered only one sympathetic look — from an old Jewish shopkeeper with a ridiculous little cap on his wizened skull. He was full of bitterness when he got into the car and started off.

During the trip he remained thoughtful, letting Jael al-Ardja describe the splendors of Latin America to Joseph Hobeika, who had never left Lebanon. Eleven miles from Beirut, a few hundred yards past a sign showing the way to Ghadir and Antoura, the road turned sharply to the right and Hidar saw Juniye. But Joseph, who was driving, didn't go that way. He turned left, into a little road that skirted a village. He soon came to a field with dried-out soil and stopped the car.

"This is where the helicopter will land," he said. He pointed to the roof of a building farther on, below the level of the field. "That's the Sarba convent. Below it, at the seaside, is a building that used to be a cabaret. That's where the meeting will be held."

On the way back, Jael al-Ardja seemed agitated, almost feverish. He was obviously excited and overjoyed at the thought of having the Israeli defense minister and the head of the Phalangists both at his mercy at the same time. His shameless joy irritated Hidar and gave him a sudden desire to humiliate the imbecile.

"Why did the attempt to kill Ben-Gurion fail?" he asked.

The Palestinian showed no sign of being disconcerted.

"That's a good question," he said, turning to Hidar, who was sitting in the back seat for security reasons. "I've wondered about it myself. At first I thought there was a traitor among the leaders of the Front. And, if you'll excuse my frankness, I even thought you might be the traitor. But now I think I must have stupidly betrayed myself by talking to a Jewish doctor in a plane." He shrugged fatalistically. "Yes, that must have been what happened. What's written is written."

"A Jewish doctor?" Hidar asked insistently.

"That's right. I'd forgotten that Jews are quick to draw conclusions, and that they're all Zionists. I asked that doctor if he knew Ben-Gurion. I also talked about Lima, and since the press had reported that Ben-Gurion was going to Peru, the doctor must have seen a connection and notified the Mossad. Jews are very good at figuring things out."

"You give the Jews credit for more intelligence than they have," Joseph remarked. "But the fact is you did act like an idiot."

"Maybe. But destiny put things right. The Koran says that a man carries his destiny tied to his neck. That doctor was killed at Zarqa."

Hidar started and had to make an effort to regain his calm.

"You were at Zarqa?" he asked.

"Oh, no," Jael al-Ardja answered. "I had nothing to do with that Jew's death. Destiny took care of it." He turned to Joseph. "I think you Christians have a saying, 'Go where you will, die where you must.'"

The car soon arrived in Beirut and Hidar went straight to the meeting. There were about twenty people in the same room where he had met Abu Iyad on the day of his arrival. They were seated around three tables covered with white tablecloths. Some were drinking wine, others orangeade; there were Middle Eastern salads and pita bread, and a few people were eating pastry made with almonds, pistachio nuts and honey. The two French windows were blocked with sandbags and the room was illuminated by four powerful spotlights. Hidar saw Abu Iyad, looking a little bloated; Abu Jihad, the military chief of Al Fatah; Abu Abbas with a pleased expression; Bassam Abu Sharif hiding behind dark glasses; and others he didn't know.

Hidar's leg was hurting; his orthopedic shoe was uncomfortable. He sat down near the door and stayed there a long while, looking at his comrades. What was happening to him? He felt something painful inside him, something like doubt and obscure uncertainty. This meeting reminded him of another one almost exactly like it, twelve years earlier, before the Jordan operation that had killed tens of thousands of people — including Olga's cousin. He noticed Jael al-Ardja and Abu Abbas talking with each other under a gigantic map of Palestine. He saw them laughing and taking glasses of wine.

He thought of that Sidney whose death made him suffer and feel ashamed. He thought of Hugo and the unsolved mystery of his murder. The Arabs had a saying that the muezzins didn't repeat their calls for the deaf. . . . He knew he wasn't allowed to have any doubts. The Soviets had sent him on a mission that involved carrying out a complex task, and he had to do whatever was needed to succeed. He couldn't afford to indulge in maudlin emotion or delicate sensitivity.

While he was reflecting, two fedayeen had cleared the tables. An old woman brought in twenty white cups of coffee on a black plastic tray decorated with big red flowers, and the real meeting began.

"Well?" Abu Iyad asked Hidar.

With his round cheeks, bald forehead, open-collared white shirt and gray sweater, he could have passed for an ordinary citrus-fruit buyer.

"We went to look at the place," Hidar said. "Planning to take action there is feasible, even if we don't know all the precautions taken by the Christians. However . . ." His face hardened. He turned pale and hammered out the end of his sentence: "I'm firmly opposed to it."

"That's absurd!" Jael al-Ardja exploded.

"It's not all that absurd," Hidar replied calmly. "Patience is the ruse of the man who has no ruse."

He explained his position at length. The Israelis were going to invade Lebanon in May or June. This was established by information received in Moscow from reliable sources. The purpose of the invasion would be to destroy all Palestinian bases in the country. It was therefore urgent for the Palestinians to make defensive preparations. Rather than preventing war, killing Sharon would bring it on more quickly. The deaths of two men who had met to discuss peace wouldn't stop the Israelis from launching an invasion, and would justify it in the eyes of the world. As for Gemayel, his death would set off a bloody vendetta that would plunge the country into a fratricidal war that would benefit only Israel and Syria. What Hidar proposed was to begin preparing the fedayeen for urban resistance. Moscow would supply the needed weapons. It would then be enough simply to let Israel flounder and become bogged down. If Beirut became another Stalingrad, the Christians, with or without

Bashir Gemayel, wouldn't take part in the fighting. Some of them would refrain from it out of caution, others out of fear.

These words were greeted by embarrassed silence. Hidar's listeners looked at each other, disconcerted, pained or suspicious.

"You must be joking," Abu Abbas finally said quietly.

"We're soldiers, not diplomats," Jael al-Ardja said. "If we start judging and discussing everything, nothing will be sacred anymore." He looked at Hidar intently and pounded the table with his fist. "Nothing will be sacred! Neither Palestine nor Beit Jala!"

However unwarranted this outburst may have seemed, it expressed what the others all felt.

"We have to liberate Palestine, not defend the interests of the Soviet Union, or even of Syria," Abu Abbas declared. "It's our duty. General Sharon's hands are covered with our blood."

With his drooping Cossack mustache and his ridiculous pathos, Abu Abbas was becoming quite annoying, and so Hidar preferred to address Jael al-Ardja:

"If you want to fight, you'll soon have a chance to do it." He looked around at all the others. "Do you think you're in any position to confront the Israeli army? Do you have a strategy? Weapons? If you think so, you have no use for my opinion and my help. Kill Sharon and trust in Allah!" He stood up as though to leave, then changed his mind. "Don't forget that you have neither antiaircraft missiles nor —"

He didn't finish his sentence because everyone had begun talking at once. The military chief of Al Fatah for the city of Beirut, a bearded fedayee who wore thin-framed glasses and looked more like an intellectual than a warrior, stood up, stretched out his arms like a preacher in front of his congregation and asked Hidar please to sit down.

"I respect your opinion," he said, "but I'd like . . ." The others began listening attentively. "We'd like you to describe your strategy and tell us more clearly what help the Soviet Union will give us if there's a siege of Beirut."

The meeting lasted far into the night. When it was over, Bassam told Hidar it would be dangerous to cross the city at such a late hour and suggested that he sleep on a mattress in the next room. Hidar accepted, but for the moment he wanted to get some fresh air. He went down into the courtyard. It was full of sandbags, and armed men were keeping watch over it. He took a few steps to stretch his legs. To the left was darkness; to the right, the ground was wet from rain and gleaming in the moonlight. He was about to go back upstairs when he felt someone touch him on the shoulder. He looked around and recognized Jael al-Ardja.

"I know I'm regarded as a dirty bastard," Jael said quietly, "and I don't care. I only want to know people I like, and when I like someone I'm loyal to him. Yes, I have a few friends, and I'm willing to include you among them. I don't give a damn about the others. Almost everyone is harmful, especially women." He made a contemptuous gesture and touched Hidar's shoulder again. "Take my word for it: if you want to go on living, you shouldn't do everything you're told to do, in Moscow or anywhere else. But you don't understand me . . ."

"Yes, I do understand you," Hidar said, a little embarrassed.

He felt a kind of vague anxiety and was immediately ashamed of it.

Jael moved his face close to Hidar's and concluded, "No, you don't understand. What the camel thinks is not what's in the camel driver's head. I like you because you're intelligent and I'm sure you've been able to keep some of the naïveté of your childhood. But that naïveté is what may destroy you. Long ago I knew someone like you. He too was childlike and naive. And it was terrible: one fine day I was asked to liquidate him. Who asked me? Let's say it was your bosses. Yes, your superiors, your friends. It happened on the road to Jerusalem. But he wasn't my friend. He was a Jew."

PARIS, MAY 1984

More than twenty years after Hugo's death, I still felt as if I were walking in his footsteps. As soon as I had finished the chapter on Beirut before the siege, I received a letter from Bassam Abu Sharif inviting me to Tunis, where the Palestinians had set up their headquarters after their evacuation from Lebanon. I will summarize the events that led up to this.

On June 6, 1982, in retaliation for the assassination of the Israeli diplomat Yaacov Bar Simon Tov in London, the Israeli army invaded Lebanon, as Hidar had foreseen.

On August 23 of that same year, Bashir Gemayel became the thirteenth president of Lebanon. Only two days later, a multinational intervention force composed of French, American, Italian and British troops was deployed in Beirut, which had been under siege by the Israeli army for two months. This force was to help in transferring Arafat and his troops to Tunis. On September 14, Bashir Gemayel was killed by the Syrian bomb that blew up the Phalangists' headquarters at Ashrafieh.

On September 17, a group of Phalangists led by Elie Hobeika, Joseph's brother, carried out a massacre in the Palestinian refugee camps of Sabra and Shatila. A fact-finding commission was immediately formed in Israel. It published its report on February 7, 1983, confirming that the massacre had been committed by Phalangists, but accusing Ariel Sharon, the Israeli defense minister, of having misjudged the possibility of reprisals against the population of the refugee camps when he let the Phalangists go into them. Sharon resigned. General Yehoshua Saguy, chief of military intelligence, was removed from his command: the report that Benjamin Ben-Eliezer had drawn up with Arieh's help, on the strategy worked out by Hidar Assadi and approved by the Palestinians, and their predictions about massacres that the Israelis would be unable to prevent, hadn't even been examined, much less taken into account. And on April 3, 1984, finally, Karen Brutens, the Soviet government's special envoy, was officially and deferentially received by Shafik Wazzan, the Lebanese prime minister.

I arrived in Tunis early in the morning of May 4, 1984. The airport there was totally different from those of Cairo and Beirut. It was an intimate, family airport that reminded me of small-town airports in Wisconsin. Only the smell was different. Here, the dominant smell was of the jasmine bouquets, held together by string nets, that ten-year-old sellers offered to travelers.

A young Tunisian held up a cardboard sign with my name on it. His name was Salem and he had been sent by Bassam Abu Sharif. He took me to the Hotel Africa-Meridien on Bourguiba Avenue and immediately slipped away. Bassam had left a note for me, inviting me to lunch in a restaurant outside of Tunis and saying that a car would come for me. In the meantime, I had nothing to do but stroll toward what used to be called the native quarter of the city, in the midst of a crowd divided between arrogance and good humor.

Remembering Hugo's letter, I decided to play at following in his footsteps. I was sorry I hadn't thought to bring his notebook with me, or at least to copy all the Arab names in it. But I still had my memory. And my instinct, which told me that I was getting close to my goal and that simply by walking, letting myself go, I would discover something.

A car came for me at the time mentioned in Bassam's note.

Marsa, about a mile from Sidi-bou-Said, is a tourist village built on the site of Megara. I recalled the opening sentence of Flaubert's

Salammbô: "It was in Megara, a suburb of Carthage, in the gardens of Hamilcar." Bassam was waiting for me, alone at a low table laden with salads, under the portico of the Café Saf Saf, near the mosque. In the courtyard an astonishing wooden apparatus driven by a camel walking tirelessly around a well was raising water in clay pitchers attached to a wheel.

"So many years!" Bassam exclaimed in English, holding out his hand to me.

He had changed enormously. His face, having been operated on after the assassination attempt, had lost its subtlety. Glasses hid his eyes. He had gained weight. But his smile was still the same, engaging and friendly.

"So when are we going to have peace?" he asked me.

"I was hoping *you'd* tell *me.*"

A waiter brought us mint tea.

"The Israeli leaders still don't seem to have made up their minds to —"

"Let's forget about propaganda," I interrupted. "You know as well as I do that four hundred thousand Israelis came out into the street to protest against the war in Lebanon. The demonstrators alone represent ten percent of the country's population. Two million of them will demand negotiations with you if Arafat publicly announces recognition of Israel, an end to terrorist acts, and repeal of your charter, which calls for the disappearance of the Jewish state."

"Wait, wait," Bassam said, smiling. "You're going too fast."

"Too fast? All those deaths aren't enough for you? And look at yourself . . ."

"Let's not talk about me. Peace isn't going to be made just for me."

"No, but it will be made so that what happened to you won't happen to others."

"And you think the Israelis have already done everything they can to promote peace?"

"No. But I've criticized their resistance to change and lack of imagination enough to give me a right to criticize yours."

He suddenly relaxed and a familiar grin brightened his face.

"Let's be calm. I didn't ask you to come to Tunis to have an argument with me."

The fact was that, like me, he thought the Palestinians should specify their aims. He understood the Israelis' apprehension, and he had written a statement that he wanted to read to me before making it public.

It was a courageous statement that offered direct negotiations to the Israelis. But it mentioned neither an end to terrorism nor repeal of the charter. I pointed that out to him.

"But since we're willing to negotiate with the Israelis, the charter doesn't count anymore!"

"Then say so! And what about terrorism? What do you have to say about it?"

"That doesn't depend on Arafat alone!"

"Then what will be the use of your statement?"

Our discussion went on for a long time. He took notes. He told me, not without reason, that a statement that would satisfy me completely couldn't be published for a long time to come. Then he said he would like me to stay in Tunis two more days to meet Arafat, who had been detained in Baghdad. I declined, saying that my book was waiting for me in Paris. He questioned me about its contents and seemed surprised to learn that I talked about him in it. He told me he had never heard Hugo's name. We spoke of Kanafani and our meeting in September 1969, in Beirut.

"That was long ago, long ago," he said thoughtfully.

"And things still haven't changed," I remarked.

"But I'm trying to make them change," he said, putting his hand on my arm.

"You're not afraid?"

He raised his hands as if he were going to rest his chin in them.

"Afraid of losing face again?"

And, pleased with his joke, he laughed.

At about five in the afternoon I arrived at Hammam Lif in a taxi. A motley crowd was spilling onto the beaches in waves. I asked a passerby, a bearded old Arab whose white caftan hid his thinness, to tell me the way to the synagogue. He offered to take me there.

The building, marked by a six-pointed star, was at the corner of Theater Street and Algiers Street. Its doors and windows were boarded over. The old Arab seemed sorry.

"There are no more Jews in Hammam Lif," he said.

"None at all?"

He thought for a moment and his face brightened. Yes, yes, after all, there might be one. A cripple. Nothing much was known about him, except that his legs were paralyzed, his name was Samuel and he lived on a blind alley off Bou Kournine Street.

We went there. My guide tapped on a closed window. A head appeared. It was Samuel. He had obviously been asleep. When he learned the reason for my visit he promised to meet us at the Café Benayed, a short distance away, near the Hotel Zefir. And he arrived there fifteen minutes later, on crutches. He told me his story — Tunis, an accident — and why he couldn't bring himself to join his family in Israel: his father, old and sick, didn't want to die anywhere but there in Hammam Lif.

"What was his name?"

"Taieb."

I was surprised at not being surprised. But hadn't I known ever since I came there that sooner or later I would become involved in Hugo's story? Samuel remembered my cousin quite well. His father could have given me more details, but I had come six months too late. . . . Samuel did recall, however, that Hugo had had Arab friends. A doctor named Jemil al-Okby, for example. And old Marwan Assadi, who was very active in Neo-Destour, Bourguiba's party. His family had been scattered. His son Hidar came back now and then to visit his grave. Hugo had also come back after the war and he had always sent best wishes for the Jewish New Year from New York. Samuel was sad to learn about his death. But death no longer affected him very deeply: he had lived with it too long. He quoted from Ecclesiastes: "What profit hath a man of all his labour which he taketh under the sun? One generation passeth away, and another generation cometh: but the earth abideth for ever."

He stood up. I had interrupted his nap. He was going back to bed. But just as he was about to hobble away on his crutches, his face became animated and showed every sign of astonishment.

"Look," he whispered, "there he is — old Assadi's son!"

I also stood up. And I could hardly believe my eyes when I saw Hidar crossing the street, obviously having seen me too.

"What are you doing here?" he asked without trying to hide his surprise. Then, in the cynical tone of someone too shrewd to let the wool be pulled over his eyes: "Hugo, right?" His hawklike face had darkened, his hair was almost white and I found him handsomer than when I had seen him in Beirut. "You Jews are a strange people: you never stop probing your past."

"And you? Aren't you here because of the past?"

"Yes. I've come to pay tribute to my father's memory. But I don't question the dead. What he did, or might have done, doesn't interest me." He saw Samuel and greeted him a little disdainfully, then turned back to me. "Are you staying in Hammam Lif?"

"No, I'm going back to Tunis."

"Do you have a car?"

"No."

He threw up his arms in an indefinite gesture that could have been either welcoming or fatalistic.

"Then come," he said, "I'll take you."

45

NEW YORK — MOSCOW — TEL AVIV

The Achille Lauro

OCTOBER 1985

Jerry Cohen had felt guilty ever since Sidney died. He told himself he had had nothing to do with that trip to Frankfurt, that the TWA plane hijacked by the Palestinians hadn't even been going to Beirut, and that terrorism was part of fate, which kept turning up no matter where you went — but in spite of all that, he couldn't help feeling at least partly responsible for Sidney's death.

Was that why he saw Marjory and Richard so often? And was it the reason he had settled down, trading his dissolute life for a charming Dorothy twenty years younger than himself? She was like a marvelous mirror in which he could wipe away his wrinkles and gray hair. With narrower hips and livelier eyes, she could have been very beautiful. But he was happy with her and was seriously thinking of marrying her.

It was early in May 1985. New York smelled of springtime. Leaving the hospital, Jerry crossed Third Avenue, then Lexington, and turned left when he reached Park. Despite the burning pain of the sciatica that had been tormenting him in the hip for some time, he had a strong urge to walk. It was a warm afternoon but a cool sea breeze pleasantly caressed his face. In New York, May was made for walking! On Fifty-ninth Street he headed for Central Park. Across the street from the Plaza Hotel, two folk singers were strumming their guitars, surrounded by curious onlookers. Central Park South was full of idly strolling people and his practiced nostrils even picked up the smell of horse manure: the Central Park carriages were busy with tourists.

On his way down Fifth Avenue he stopped to look at the display window of the Doubleday bookstore, noted that another Judith Krantz novel had come out and wondered if he was going to hail a taxi. Yes or no? He finally decided not to. He needed to think. Dorothy had told him the day before that she was pregnant, and he had always liked to walk while he thought.

Near Rockefeller Center he stopped again, this time in front of the Italian tourism center. He liked Italy. Florence, Rome, Naples, the wall paintings of Pompeii . . . why not take Dorothy on a cruise before the child was born? He opened the door and went in. One of the brochures on a display rack described cruises around the Mediterranean. He looked it over and decided on an itinerary: Genoa, Naples, Alexandria, Port Said, Ashdod, Piraeus. . . . Naples and Israel would be ideal, just what he was looking for. He asked about prices, departure dates and other details. The idea appealed to him so much that as he was leaving he wondered if he shouldn't think about taking Marjory and her daughter Marilyn on that cruise too. Dorothy liked them so much!

This time he did take a cab. The driver, undoubtedly a Russian Jew, was listening to a radio program in Yiddish. Jerry looked over the brochure again. Maybe they would get on the ship at Naples, take time to visit Pompeii, then go on to Ashdod and discover Israel. To his great shame, Jerry Cohen had never visited the Jewish state.

By the time he got home, he had made up his mind to do it. They would leave on October 5 and the baby would be born after they came back. A chance to get his sea legs and delve into the Jewish soul — what could be better?

When Dorothy heard the news she threw her arms around his neck.

"What's the name of the ship, Jerry?" she asked after dinner.
"The *Achille Lauro*."

"The *Achille Lauro*?" asked Viktor Alexandrovich Chebrikov.

It was October 3, 1985. Hidar Assadi had called to ask to see him as soon as possible, and had gone straight from the airport to his office on Kropotkin Street.

"Why that particular ship?" Chebrikov continued.

Hidar shrugged. His face was tanned by the Tunisian sun. It was stuffy in the office, whose bay window was still hidden by a curtain. He unbuttoned his collar.

"It was only by chance," he answered. "For a long time Abu Abbas had been looking for a way to get some fedayeen into Israel — not into the border villages, but into the middle of the country. Jael al-Ardja was in charge of making preparations for the operation. He decided that the simplest way would be to have the fedayeen mingle with the hundreds of tourists who cruise the Mediterranean and visit the Holy Land. Arafat was against it, and so was I, maybe not for the same reasons, but it doesn't matter. Anyway, the *Achille Lauro* plan was replaced by an operation at Larnaca in which three Israeli agents died on September 25. You know what happened next: the Israelis claimed it wasn't ordinary tourists who were involved and two days ago, in retaliation, they bombed PLO headquarters in Tunis."

Chebrikov lit a cigarette.

"Would you like one?"

"No, thanks, I've stopped smoking."

"All right, go on, I'm listening."

"As you can well understand, Viktor Alexandrovich, after the Israeli bombing our Palestinian friends were all stirred up. They were eager for action and the *Achille Lauro* plan was revived. The men recruited by Abu Abbas are still ready and a cabin has been reserved for them on the ship."

"But you still haven't told me your opinion."

"To tell you the truth, I'm afraid. I'm afraid of slip-ups. Jael al-Ardja isn't lucky. As for Abu Abbas, he's completely irresponsible and I don't trust his judgment in choosing the men."

Chebrikov stubbed out his half-smoked cigarette in a solid silver ashtray and looked up at Hidar.

"I hope you realize that the death of innocent tourists will be disastrous for the image of the Palestinian leadership."

Hidar nodded. Chebrikov nervously took another cigarette.

"Can the operation still be canceled?"

"Impossible. Everyone's in favor of it. The ship leaves in two days and the men are already in place."

Chebrikov frowned. He looked for matches, found them, lit the cigarette and immediately put it out.

"I see only one solution," he said, and he saw Hidar stiffen. "You will be on the *Achille Lauro*. That way you can keep a close watch on the men."

"But . . . but what about the ticket, and . . . and all the other details?"

"No problem. I'll get in touch with our agent in Genoa."

"In Genoa, you say?"

Benjamin Ben-Eliezer spasmodically blinked his eyes. He was perplexed by what Arieh had just told him: several Palestinian terrorists had come to Genoa. According to unconfirmed reports, weapons taken from Tunis to Genoa in a red Renault had arrived on the ferry *Habbib*. Since there were no Israeli targets in Genoa, the Palestinians were aiming at something else. What was it?

"I see only one scenario," said Arieh. "I've had someone check on all the ships docked in Genoa, to find out where they've come from and where they're going. Only one of them is scheduled to stop in Israel: an Italian cruise ship, the *Achille Lauro*."

"Have you looked over the passenger list?"

"For the moment, I have nothing on any of the passengers who will get on the ship at Genoa. But a cabin has been reserved for four men whose identities don't seem credible to me. And do you know who bought their tickets? Ahel Oz, the military chief of the Palestine Liberation Front, which is affiliated with Arafat's *headquarters!*"

Benjamin whistled softly.

"What a mistake!" Then, after a silence: "At least the situation is clear, thanks to Ahel Oz. The Palestinians want to respond to the Tunis bombing by a terrorist attack in Ashdod. I just hope there won't be any Israelis on the ship. We'll pick up those four gentlemen as soon as they get to Israel."

344

He called Myriam on the interphone and asked her to come in. Seeing Arieh, Myriam couldn't help teasing him.

"I hear Judith is pregnant again — are you really determined to fulfill the promise that the Lord made to Abraham?" She laughed, pleased with her joke, and then, seeing Benjamin's stern look, she handed him a telex. "Here, this is hot off the wire."

Benjamin read it and gave it to Arieh without comment. It said that the KGB commander in Genoa, a man named Renzo Antonioni, had succeeded, after making strenuous efforts, in getting a single cabin on the *Achille Lauro,* which had announced that no more accommodations were available.

Benjamin and Arieh looked at each other in surprise.

"What does that mean?" Benjamin asked, taking back the telex.

"It means that a lot of people are interested in that old ship. Renzo Antonio, or whatever his name is, certainly didn't get that cabin for himself: his face is too well known. I'll try to get a picture of the new passenger. All passengers have to provide photographs of themselves when they sign the contract with the shipping company."

"Work fast. The ship is leaving tomorrow."

"I'll have it by tomorrow morning," answered Arieh, who was already in the hall.

He was back at eight o'clock the next morning. Benjamin avidly scrutinized the photocopy on the desk in front of him.

"Impossible!" he exclaimed.

He glanced at Arieh, then looked back at the picture with the same mixture of surprise and determination he had shown fifteen years earlier when he learned of Sidney's abduction.

"Something's going on, no doubt about it," he said. "If I'm not mistaken, this is Hidar Assadi!"

"And that's not all," Arieh said, triumphantly holding up several typed pages. "I also have a list of the passengers who will get on the *Achille Lauro* at Naples."

"What about it?"

"There's a group of Americans, including — brace yourself! — Marjory Halter, Sidney's widow, and her daughter Marilyn!"

"Damn!" Benjamin grumbled. "Always sticking their noses into everything. Always there when . . ." He stopped short. "Does Assadi know them?"

"I don't think so. But he knows their names."

"And does Marjory know him?"

"No, and she doesn't even know his name."

"All right. . . . Is that all? Or do you have some more good news for me?"

"There's also a young Israeli couple, two teachers who unexpectedly got on board this morning at Genoa. They decided at the last moment to go back to Israel by ship."

"Are they real Israelis?" Benjamin asked with a skeptical smile.

"Yes, I checked on them."

"You'll have to warn them."

"Too late. By now, the ship is already getting under way. But I've made arrangements . . ."

Benjamin frowned and gave him a questioning look.

"I've reserved a cabin, from Naples," Arieh went on, "in the name of Angus Murdoch, and in an hour I'll have a British passport." He noted Benjamin's astonished expression. "Angus Wilson and Iris Murdoch — I admire them both. I've thought of everything: Marjory and Marilyn have never seen me, and even if they've seen a photo of me somewhere, the way I'll look when I go on board they'll never recognize me."

He took a black, bushy mustache from his pocket, stuck it on his upper lip and put on a pair of metal-framed glasses.

"There, do *you* recognize me?" he asked. He took off his disguise. "Hidar Assadi has never seen me, though he knows who I am. I'm leaving early this afternoon. I'll keep you posted on what's happening. Last night I studied the dossier a long time. I already know the layout of the ship by heart. The captain is Gerardo de Rosa, an old Neapolitan. If things go wrong, I think he'll help me. But my plan is based on the hope of making contact with Assadi when we're at sea. I don't trust Marjory and Marilyn: they'd be overjoyed to meet me and they'd start talking about my life, and theirs, and so on. As for the terrorists, if they find out who I am they may panic and try to kill me. But Assadi is my best ally. You've always known about him! The fact that he's decided to go on the ship in person means that he wants to forestall mistakes and avoid irreparable acts. He knows they'd ruin the Palestinians' image."

Benjamin had been listening with his glasses off and his eyes half closed, without interrupting or asking any questions. Did he really share Arieh's view of the situation? Had he let himself be carried along by the younger man's enthusiasm? In any case, he saw no other solution. He opened a desk drawer, took out a sheet of paper and wrote a name and phone number on it.

"Let me give you some advice," he said. "When you're on the ship, spend your first day observing. Don't be in a hurry." He handed him the sheet of paper. "Learn this name and number by heart. Since you're British, this man will be your business partner. The two of you have a little data-processing firm, called DataService, in Oxford. Call him twice a day, within fifteen minutes of eight in the morning and seven in the evening." He stood up. "And now, have a good trip — and good luck."

46

ACHILLE LAURO

The Cruise

"Dorothy, I really don't know how I'm going to dress for the captain's party tonight. I canceled my appointment with the hairdresser. I just couldn't face it. . . . Anyway, I'm sure it won't kill me to show a tiny fraction of an inch of gray hair, for once. When you get old enough to have gray hair, don't make the foolish mistake of dyeing it. It's a real pain in the neck, believe me."

Marjory looked briefly through the porthole. She was happy. Happy with the cruise, happy at having left New York, happy that Jerry Cohen and Dorothy had thought to distract her and make her forget the emptiness of her everyday life, at least for the anniversary of Sidney's death. And the other people on the ship seemed happy too. It was as if they had been purified of all their miseries, worries and pettiness. They plunged into trivial games and frivolous pleasures as if that shipboard life, cut off from the rest of the world, were going to last forever. The traditional welcoming party given by the captain had occupied everyone's thoughts and conversation since the departure from Naples two days earlier.

"No, I wasn't daydreaming," Marjory answered Dorothy, who had jolted her back to reality on the other end of the phone line. "I was looking at the sea. Are you going to wear your green dress? Why not wear your silver one? Ah, here's Marilyn. I'll let you go now."

She hung up and gripped her daughter's wrist.

"Where were you this time?"

Marilyn grimaced.

"Let go, you're hurting me!"

Marjory let go of her, but frowned and asked again, more gently, "Where were you? I was looking for you everywhere." No answer. "Take off your Walkman and stop acting like a teenager!"

At twenty-four, Sidney's daughter was refreshingly vivacious and rather pretty, though a trifle chubby. Her curly red hair attracted attention. Her laugh had a likable quality. She enjoyed flirting with the males on board without allowing any to spend enough time with her to become serious; she would brazenly flit from one to another, or jilt them all and go off to writhe to the music on the dance floor of the Arazzi ballroom. Her behavior sometimes drove her mother to despair. "How can you expect to do well in grad school," Marjory had once said to her, "when you smoke up a storm and keep your ears glued to a Walkman?" Yet Marilyn still had an engaging personality. She did everything, good or bad, with such energy and high good humor that it was impossible to be angry with her for very long.

"You promised me you'd study," Margory said with weary reproachfulness, "and you haven't even opened a book for the last two days. If your father were still alive —"

"We wouldn't have gone on this cruise!" Marilyn interrupted, laughing. But, seeing her mother's face go tense, she said, "Don't get mad. I'll study tomorrow."

"Tomorrow we'll be in Alexandria!"

"Then the day after tomorrow."

And, with another burst of infectious laughter, Marilyn disappeared into the passageway that led to the Lido deck and the swimming pool.

There were more than seventy Americans on the *Achille Lauro*, most of them from New Jersey. Among them were several young people and a good-natured disabled man in a wheelchair. But Marilyn preferred to be with a young Israeli couple who were going to leave the ship at Ashdod, and especially with the Italians aboard, who were more cheerful and carefree than her compatriots. Despite her desire to play the field, she had a weakness for one of them: Giovanni Badini, the chief engineer, who was perhaps twice her age. Not seeing him at the pool, she was about to go up to the next deck when Jerry Cohen, stretched out in a deck chair, stopped her.

"You shouldn't be running after a man. Let him run after you."

Marilyn made a face.

"I wish you'd stop being such a pain!" Annoyed with herself for her reaction, she sat down on an arm of the deck chair next to Jerry's. "I'm surprised you haven't asked me if I'm in love with him."

"Why? Does your mother ask you that?"

"Oh, my mother . . ."

"What's so terrible about your mother?"

"Nothing."

"Don't forget that it's hard on her being alone now . . ."

"And don't forget that you're not my father, Jerry!" She stood up and said as she was about to walk away, "So long. See you at the party. My Italian will be there. Would you like me to introduce him to you?"

At seven-thirty, men and women in their best clothes were standing in a long line in the Scarabeo salon, as if they were waiting to get into a Broadway theater with a hit show. But here the whole show consisted of shaking hands with the captain. Stewards brought champagne. Conversations sprang up.

"Jerry still isn't here," Marjory remarked to Marilyn.

"It's because of Dorothy. She's always late."

Marjory looked her best that evening. She wore a long, low-cut black dress with a broad belt.

"You're making a big splash," her daughter said with a stifled laugh. "All the men are looking at you. We'll see which one of them is the bravest. Here comes the first one."

A man of average height had just left his bar stool and was coming toward Marjory, drink in hand.

"You're American?" he asked in English with a strong Middle Eastern accent. And, without waiting for an answer, he introduced himself: "My name is Antonio Ramirez. I'm Peruvian. I couldn't help noticing you and I wanted to tell you that you're —"

"Very beautiful?" Marilyn concluded for him.

"Is this your younger sister?" he asked gallantly.

"No, she's my daughter," Marjory answered with an embarrassed smile.

Antonio Ramirez's lively, slightly bulging eyes opened wide in pretended astonishment.

"Incredible! Amazing!" He leaned closer to her. "May I know your name?"

"Yes, of course. It's Marjory."

"What a lovely name!"

The line was slowly moving forward. Jerry and Dorothy finally arrived. Ramirez excused himself, expressed the hope of seeing Marjory again very soon and discreetly went to the end of the line.

"Who's that?" Dorothy asked.

"One of Mama's admirers," Marilyn said.

"You see the man in the wheelchair shaking hands with the captain?" Jerry said. "That's Leon Klinghoffer. His wife is one of my patients."

"Really?" Marjory exclaimed out of politeness.

As the line continued to move forward, Marilyn became more tense: "her" Italian, Giovanni Badini, who could have been a stand-in for Robert De Niro, was standing beside the captain in his white uniform and seemed to be paying no attention to her.

In the Arazzi ballroom an English orchestra and a Polish singer were performing an Argentinian tango while couples glided across the dance floor. Marilyn was still sulking. She looked around the room with her most disdainful expression, then suddenly exclaimed, "Look! See that man over there, under the balcony? Doesn't he look a lot like the snapshot of cousin Arieh?"

Marjory turned her eyes in the direction pointed out by Marilyn.

"Yes, he does," she said. "Except, if I remember the photo rightly, Arieh doesn't wear glasses and doesn't have a mustache. But those four men standing next to him . . . ."

"What about them?"

"It seems to me . . . there's something a little sinister about them."

"Don't be silly! There's nothing wrong with them. One of them, in fact — the one with curly hair — is rather handsome."

Sensing that the conversation was about to take an unpleasant turn, Jerry stood up and buttoned his jacket.

"This is a place for dancing, not arguing."

He held out his hand to Marjory. As he was leading her toward the dance floor, his eyes met the ironic gaze of a man with a hawklike face and almost white frizzy hair, sitting alone near the orchestra.

47

ACHILLE LAURO

The Cruise (Conclusion)

AT SEA, OCTOBER 1985

On October 7, the day after the captain's party, Marjory was awakened at dawn by voices in the passageway and a strong rocking of the ship. She got up, groped a little and drew back the curtain. In spite of the morning mist, she saw the lights of Alexandria close by, the outline of the city against the sky, and the docks. And she heard the cries in Arabic that suddenly came into the cabin.

"We're in Egypt," she said.

"Let me sleep," Marilyn moaned. "What a stupid idea to arrive in *any* country at six in the morning!" But she got up anyway, and pulled down the tattered T-shirt that she wore as a nightgown. "How are you feeling, Mama?"

"I have a horrible headache."

"Then take some aspirin," Marilyn suggested. She yawned. "You must have danced too much with your Peruvian last night."

Marjory shrugged.

"I only danced with him twice. He seems like a nice man."

A loudspeaker drowned out the noises of the waterfront: "After breakfast, passengers wishing to go ashore will please go to the information office. Those who have not yet bought excursion tickets for Cairo and the Pyramids must do so immediately."

"I don't think I'll go," Marjory said. "I don't feel up to it."

"You're going to miss the Pyramids?"

"I can live without them. But you go — you don't need me."

"I don't know yet what I'm going to do. It depends on Giovanni."

"What do you see in that man, anyway?"

"He's a lot better than your Señor Ramirez!"

"Don't talk to me that way! The big difference is that I don't go to bed with Ramirez!"

As soon as she had said this, Marjory regretted having lost her temper. She remembered a passage from Proverbs Sidney used to quote: "He that is slow to anger is better than the mighty." But she couldn't help it: Marilyn could be so infuriating sometimes! And besides, this headache was killing her.

Luckily Marilyn came toward her, sat down at the foot of the bed and said, with the exquisite delicacy she sometimes showed, "I'm sorry, Mama. . . . I think I'll stay too. The Pyramids will never look as good as they do in Cecil B. DeMille's *The Ten Commandments*."

And she burst out laughing, completely awake at last.

Most of the passengers had debarked at Alexandria and the *Achille Lauro* had put to sea again. It was now moving along the Egyptian coast in the direction of Port Said. It seemed almost empty: of its seven hundred and forty passengers, only about a hundred and fifty were left. There was a strange feeling in the air, like the sadness at the end of a vacation. And when Marjory went for a walk on the Lido deck, she was disappointed not to find Antonio Ramirez there. After wandering awhile in that nearly deserted space and exchanging a few words of small talk with Leon Klinghoffer, she went back to her cabin.

She stayed there till twelve-thirty, when she went to the dining room. The headwaiter seated the few remaining passengers all together at the back of the big room. During lunch, Marjory and Marilyn sat with three Austrians and an American couple. The conversation was insignificant and falsely lighthearted. Still that emptiness, that touch of melancholy. . . . The loudspeaker was softly playing an aria from *La Traviata*. All at once, totally unexpected and incongruous, there was a cry, followed by a moan and another cry, then, strangest of all, several shots that made all heads turn. Two men were standing at the entrance to the room, holding submachine guns and watching the passengers. Without a word, they walked in and stood up on an empty table.

The first one, a young man with curly hair and a tense face, had two grenades attached to his belt. He waved his gun and shouted, "Stand up, all of you! Go to the middle of the room! Quickly! Sit down on the floor and put your hands behind your head!"

He fired a burst at the ceiling, as though to show that this was a serious matter. That was when Marjory recognized two of the four young men she had thought to be Arabs, at the captain's party.

Each of the two terrorists now went to a different table, one behind the sitting passengers, the other in front.

"They're crazy!" Marilyn murmured, sitting beside her mother. Then, with a little stifled laugh, "They won't kill us, Mama!"

The first terrorist began shouting again: "We're Palestinian fighters! The captain is in safe custody. We've put explosives in the engine room. Any of you who try to interfere with our plans will be shot immediately."

As if to give substance to his threat, there was another burst of submachine-gun fire, this one from the upper deck. Then the captain's voice replaced La Traviata in the loudspeaker.

"This is Captain Gerardo de Rosa. You must keep calm. The ship has been taken over by Palestinian terrorists. They have promised not to harm the passengers if their demands are met. They want the release of fifty prisoners in Israel, including Samir Kantari."

A crackling sound, a shot. The captain said nothing more. The passengers in the dining room heard the engines slow down. The vibration of the floor increased. A third terrorist came in and announced that the ship had changed course and was now heading for the Syrian port of Tartus.

The group was ordered to go to the ballroom. Soon a hundred and fifty terrified, incredulous men and women were clustered together like a herd of cattle on the floor where they had danced so gaily only the night before. Marjory's headache had come back. She thought once again of Sidney and the suffering he had endured in

Zarqa. She pressed her head between her hands, as if she could squeeze the pain out of it. Then, disheartened, she put her arms around Marilyn and sobbed on her shoulder.

At the end of the afternoon a terrorist brought a box of sandwiches. Evening passed and night came. Far from lessening, the feeling of waiting, incomprehension and horror intensified. The passengers were frightened and bewildered. Here a sob was heard, there a moan. Only Leon Klinghoffer, silent in his wheelchair, stared at the terrorist sitting on the stairs with two grenades beside him.

"I'm scared," Marilyn said.

"Put your head on my lap and try to sleep," Marjory told her, stroking her red hair.

At dawn one of the terrorists came with a list of passengers and read it aloud. Eleven Americans, six Britons, two Austrians.

"Follow me. Everyone on deck."

The order was punctuated by shots fired through the portholes. A middle-aged Austrian woman stood up, leaning on a cane, and had a little fit of hysterics. Another passenger began screaming. But it took only a few minutes for all nineteen of them to go up on deck.

The captain's voice was heard again: "This is Captain Gerardo de Rosa. We're now off the Syrian port of Tartus. The terrorists are negotiating by radio with the authorities."

"At least we know the captain is still alive," Marilyn said.

"Have you noticed," Marjory whispered, "that the people they've brought up here are all Jewish?"

"Except for the Austrians."

"They must have thought they were Jewish because of their names."

The terrorist fired into the air and shouted, "Quiet!"

The sun was high overhead now. The terrorist, who was hot too, allowed the little group to move a short distance to find shade. Just then two armed patrol boats came alongside the ship. Marjory saw a man raise a megaphone. He said something in Arabic and one of the terrorists answered him. The one guarding the nineteen passengers, obviously wanting to impress them, translated what had been said: the Palestinians were demanding the release of fifty-two of their comrades in the camp at Nahariya, in Israel, as well as a Red Cross boat bringing the American, British, Italian and German ambassadors accredited to Damascus, and if their demands were not met they would blow up the ship. He didn't translate the Syrians' reply, but when the terrorist on the bridge spoke again, the guard translated curtly, "We're giving an ultimatum. They have till three o'clock."

A cloud passed. Fine, warm rain wet the deck. The guard herded the group toward the bow of the ship. Marjory pressed Marilyn tightly against her. She was no longer able to put any order into her thoughts or memories. An explosion made her start: one of the Syrian patrol boats had fired a warning shot. Then she heard the sound of engines: the *Achille Lauro* was heading back out to sea. The guard spoke a few brief Arabic sentences into his walkie-talkie, listened to an answer and took the little group to the ballroom, where sandwiches and drinks were waiting for them. Marjory became aware that Leon Klinghoffer wasn't there. She went over to his wife.

"Yes, I'm worried about him," Mrs. Klinghoffer said, very pale. "With the help of a cabin boy, the terrorists took him up on deck, and —"

"Quiet!" ordered the man with the curly hair, who was obviously becoming more and more nervous.

They heard a few more shots from one of the decks above them. They all held their breath and looked at each other. They knew, they *sensed,* that this was something very serious, that the tragedy that had been in abeyance for hours and hours had finally happened.

"Where's my husband?" cried Leon Klinghoffer's wife.

"He's in the infirmary," the guard told her. "But if the Israelis don't give in, you'll all be blown up with the ship."

No one, of course, believed that Klinghoffer was in the infirmary. Tormented by fear and overwhelmed with fatigue, the passengers huddled closer together until they formed a single body. They stayed that way till evening, when the ship stopped offshore from the port of Larnaca, in Cyprus.

More negotiations. Another failure. After two or three hours the ship headed for Port Said, where it arrived at dawn. The negotiating began again. It was long and laborious, and probably confused also. But the passengers no longer paid any attention to it. None of them believed in it.

Toward noon Captain de Rosa's voice said, "Everything is all right on board. Everyone is safe and sound."

The two terrorists who had been watching the little group raised two fingers in the shape of a V and walked out of the ballroom, leaving the passengers unguarded. They all had one name in mind: Leon Klinghoffer.

PARIS, OCTOBER 1987

At the time when, like everyone else, I was following the story of the *Achille Lauro* hijacking in the media, I had no idea that Marjory, Sidney's widow, and her daughter Marilyn were on the ship. Strange as it may seem, I didn't find out till a year and a half later, when I came to New York for the publication of *The Book of Abraham* and met them both.

As I listened to their disorderly account, interrupted now and then by personal judgments that were sometimes contradictory, I recalled Benjamin Ben-Eliezer's predictions. The *Achille Lauro* hijacking illustrates better than anything else how terror has become banal. What could be more frivolous than a cruise, the ideal setting for forgetting the worries and aggressions of everyday life? Hidar Assadi's "media terrorism" had come so far in such a short time! And how far it was from the "exploit" of Zarqa! With the *Achille Lauro*, terrorism had become irretrievably sordid. It was that shift, as much as the presence on board of my American relatives, that made me want to carry out my own investigation.

Luck smiled on me: the company that owned the *Achille Lauro*, having learned from a newspaper report that a book I was writing included an account of the hijacking, invited me to come aboard. So on October 8, 1987, I found myself with Captain Gerardo de Rosa on the deck of the famous ship in the harbor of Naples. Nothing had changed: the excursion schedule, the crew and the captain were still the same. But among the several hundred passengers eager for one last ray of sunlight or curious to see new landscapes, I was the only one interested in the hijacking, even though it wasn't exactly ancient history at that time.

"On October eighth, at about three o'clock in the afternoon," the captain told me, "I was on the bridge when I heard two shots. It was completely unexpected. Till then, the terrorists had only fired their submachine guns in the air, to frighten us. I was going to hurry down to see what had happened, but Mahmud, the terrorist assigned to guard me, wouldn't let me go. A little while later, Molky, one of his accomplices, came running up, holding a passport. It was Klinghoffer's."

"What did he say to you?"

"He said, 'American kaputt!'"

It was strange, I thought, that out of all languages, expressions and words, that young Palestinian, born long after the war, had chosen that German word to announce the death of a Jew. "Kaputt!" I had heard it shouted for the first time by Nazis in the Warsaw ghetto. The death of that old, paralyzed Jew, and the image of a child with his hands raised before Nazi rifles in the ghetto, were superimposed in my mind and became a single event.

"When we reached Port Said," the captain continued, "Abu Abbas said to me in the presence of several newspaper reporters, 'Our comrades had to take control of the ship, although our original plan was directed against the Israeli enemy. We will later make public the reasons that prevented them from leaving the ship at Ashdod and forced them to take control of it.' That was a lie, of course, a blatant lie, because there was a fifth man in that bloody affair. He was stocky, in his fifties, partly bald, with slightly bulging eyes and a bushy black mustache — that can all be seen in a picture that the ship's photographer happened to take of him. There was a strange name on his passport: Pedros Floros. He was unquestionably a professional, one of those specialists in international terrorism who are called on to plan big operations. I'm sure he was really the one in charge of the hijacking."

The captain showed me the photograph and, from what

Marjory had told me, I thought I recognized the man who had courted her, the one who had introduced himself as a Peruvian named Antonio Ramirez. It suddenly occurred to me that he might be Jael al-Ardja, the man who had talked with Sidney on the flight back from Beirut and who, according to Benjamin Ben-Eliezer, had been in charge of the plot to kill David Ben-Gurion.

I questioned the captain further and, with my heart pounding, learned that while the four terrorists had shared one cabin without a porthole, cabin V82, Pedros Floros had had a luxurious cabin on one of the upper decks. And, as the investigation showed, he had made the same trip a month earlier, to familiarize himself with the ship. On the night of the traditional party when the other passengers had lined up to meet the captain, Pedros Floros, instead of introducing himself, had put a string of thin amber beads in the captain's hand and murmured, "Allah!"

More and more strange, I told myself. Why had he done that? To warn the captain of a danger? If so, why hadn't he done it more clearly? Was he afraid? Of whom? Those were questions the captain raised. For my part, I believed that Jael al-Ardja, alias Pedros Floros or Antonio Ramirez, having already failed in one of his undertakings, was quite simply superstitious and wanted to ward off bad luck. It was possible that the presence of the young Israeli couple with whom Marilyn had become friendly made him decide unexpectedly to leave the ship at Alexandria, but in my opinion it was unlikely, because it would have been unprofessional. It was also possible that there had been a sixth person, a *deus ex machina* unknown to the media.

But here is the most curious part of it. In September, a few days before the cruise began, Gerardo de Rosa received a gift in the mail: a piece of gold jewelry representing two birds, one above the other. With it was a card bearing these Arabic words written in Latin letters: *Kaidar alayk salam*. The words *alayk salam* were clear: they meant "Go in peace." But what about *Kaidar*? Neither the Egyptians in Cairo nor the Israelis in Tel Aviv could explain it to me.

After six days at sea, the *Achille Lauro* finally stopped at Haifa. The loudspeakers broadcast the famous aria from *La Traviata*.

"The same song we were playing when the four terrorists came into the dining room," said Captain Gerardo de Rosa.

*   *   *

Back in Israel, when I told Arieh all this, he smiled with a slightly smug expression that annoyed me a little. Then he took me to lunch in a little restaurant on Dizengoff Street, one of the few in the country that still served matzo-ball soup and gefilte fish. It was a beautiful day and we sat at an outside table. The only part of my story that seemed to surprise him was the gift that Captain de Rosa received in the mail. As for the word *Kaidar,* he had his own explanation: it was a faulty transcription of the name Hidar.

"So he was the sixth person?" I asked.

Arieh's only answer was a wink.

"There must also have been an Israeli agent on the ship," I went on, "someone Hidar knew."

"Oh?" Arieh said cryptically.

"Yes. It's like a jigsaw puzzle: as long as you haven't put the pieces together, you don't know what the picture is, but when all the pieces are in place the picture is perfectly clear. Unlike Captain de Rosa, I believe what Abu Abbas said. The terrorists' objective really was Ashdod, and that's why Jael al-Ardja was on the ship. He was the one — the captain is right on this point — who was supposed to plan and supervise the operation. But I think Hidar must have been there because the Soviets wanted to prevent the Palestinians from doing something irreversible. A massacre of civilians at that time would have irreparably damaged Arafat's image. In a way, the Israeli agent was Hidar's ally. Their goals were the same. But neither of them could have foreseen the unforeseeable: that is, as always, human madness. Jael al-Ardja followed Hidar's advice and disappeared in Alexandria without telling the other terrorists. Hidar followed him, and he himself was pursued by the Israeli agent. And then they all made a mistake: the four terrorists, abandoned to their fate and having no precise plan for their operation in Ashdod, didn't give up, and invented another operation to replace the first one."

Arieh smiled sadly.

"There's a Chinese saying: 'The archer is the model for the sage, for when he misses the bull's-eye he blames only himself.'"

"What do you mean?"

"I've always liked action novels: Jack London, Hemingway, Malraux. I recently read *For Whom the Bell Tolls.* . . . If you just write about a ship making a cruise in the Mediterranean, you won't interest anyone. But if you make one of the passengers a young woman in search of adventure, and have the ship hijacked by terrorists, and have a murder committed on it, and have a secret agent intervene to prevent a massacre, and have him run away, pursued by another agent — then your ship will jump out of your book, like a rabbit jumping out of a magician's hat."

As I listened to him, I realized that he had changed: he was more mature, more cultivated, and his mind was sharper.

He seemed to have read my thoughts.

"I've surprised you, haven't I?" he said. "That's because we don't know each other."

He asked for the check and we walked along Dizengoff Street. It was nearly empty, and partly closed to traffic. Today was Shabbat. The sky was blue, the air was transparent and the people on the sidewalks all seemed to be absorbed in the pleasure of aimless strolling.

I don't like idle cities, without rhythm or movement. Streets are made for traffic. Buildings are made for people to live or work in. A city isn't made for strolling, for pure leisure. To stave off my feeling of uneasiness, I asked Arieh about his mother and his wife. Judith was pregnant again. As for Richard, he was still living in the West Bank settlement near Hebron. Then, as we were approaching the Habimah national theater, Arieh casually told me that he had finished his report on Hugo's death.

This was exciting news to me but I pretended to take it as calmly as he had told it. When I asked him for a copy of the report, he refused, smiling. Then he changed his mind and said he could let me read it in his office.

"What about Hidar?" I asked. "Do you know what he's doing?"

Arieh looked at me gravely and ran his hand through his curly hair.

"He's in danger. I wish I could help him, but I don't see how."

Sensing that he wouldn't tell me anything more, I dropped the subject.

48

TEL AVIV

Hugo: Arieh's Report

Subject: Hugo David Halter. Born November 27, 1915, in Berlin.
Died March 29, 1961, assassinated on the road between Tel Aviv and
Jerusalem. No one claimed responsibility for the assassination.

Hugo Halter was born into an orthodox Jewish family of printers. No major problems in his childhood. He went to a Jewish school
and learned his father's trade at an early age. When he was a young
worker of eighteen, Hitler's coming to power made him begin fre-
quenting socialist circles. His mother died in 1935. During Kristall-
nacht, November 8, 1938, his father's print shop was ransacked. The
police found anti-Nazi leaflets in it. His father and his brother were
arrested and sent to Dachau. Hugo managed to escape.

In January 1939, after a long series of vicissitudes, he arrived
in Warsaw. His uncle Abraham Halter helped him to leave for America. On February 19, 1939, he boarded the passenger ship *Stefan
Bathory*. In New York the American Jewish Joint Distribution
Committee received him and found lodgings for him. A friend of
Abraham's named Kastoff got him a job as a makeup man for the
Yiddish newspaper *Forward*. One day at work he met a mail clerk
named Sarah Roth, a Hungarian refugee. They became lovers and
lived together intermittently. She became pregnant.

1939–1940. During this period, Hugo Halter tried by every means at his disposal to alert public opinion to the danger that threatened European Jewry. On August 18, 1940, Sarah Roth died in childbirth. The child, a son named Abraham, was taken in by the Lubavichers. Four years later, the child was run over and killed by a car in Brooklyn, when Hugo was fighting in the war in Europe.

On September 20, 1941, Hugo met two prominent Zionist leaders, Rabbi Stephen Wise and Nahum Goldmann. He worked out a plan to assassinate Fritz Kuhn, head of the pro-Nazi German-American Bund, but changed his mind at the last moment. He sent several letters to the *New York Times,* which did not publish them.

On December 20, 1941, two weeks after Pearl Harbor, Hugo was one of the first volunteers to enlist in the army. On November 8, 1942, he was sent to Casablanca, in Morocco. When General Omar Bradley, commander of the Second Corps, landed in Tunisia, he needed a German interpreter. Hugo was given the position. He came to Tunis in February 1943, discovered the Arab world and became a friend of Marwan Assadi, one of the leaders of the Neo-Destour party. (He later encountered Marwan Assadi's son, Hidar, in Berlin.) On May 10, 1943, he took part in the liberation of Hammam Lif.

In July 1944 he was sent to Palermo, then to Naples. On August 18 he landed at Saint-Raphaël, France, with General Dahlquist's 36th Division. He became Marshal Montgomery's liaison officer in the Ardennes. In January 1945 he was sent to General Jean de Lattre de Tassigny's French forces near Strasbourg, and on February 12, 1945, he was wounded on the Rhine.

Up to that point, there are few mysteries in his life; it corresponds fairly closely to the accounts he gave of it himself. But from then on he transposed, shaped and rearranged everything according to his way of seeing the world and his duties.

After his death, the police found his personal belongings in the Hotel Dan in Tel Aviv and sent them to Mordecai Halter, my father. Among them were a few books, including a book of prayers in Hebrew and English. My father sent everything to Paris, except for the books, which he kept for reasons unknown to me. One day when I was looking through some extracts from the *Treatise on Principles* in the book of prayers, I found this passage by Rabbi Eliezer, son of

Azariah: "Without law, no civilization; without civilization, no law. Without wisdom, no piety; without piety, no wisdom. Without knowledge, no reasoning; without reasoning, no knowledge. Without bread, no studies; without studies, no bread." I have quoted this passage underlined by Hugo because I feel that it sheds light on his life in many ways.

All evidence indicates that at the time when he was wounded, Hugo was a Zionist. He believed that a Jewish state would be created in Palestine after the war. He believed in coexistence between Jews and Arabs. He reproached the West, and especially the United States, for having gone to war too late, thus sacrificing European Jewry.

His wound affected him deeply. According to Dr. Samuel Rappoport, who treated him for nearly a year in Miami, at a convalescence center for American officers wounded in Europe, Hugo felt guilty for having failed to preserve the family memory because he allowed the documents entrusted to him by Abraham to be covered with his own blood. He also felt guilty for not having been able to personally take part in the capture and destruction of Berlin, as he had dreamed of doing.

At the convalescence center, he seems to have set some goals for himself. He felt it was a survivor's duty to preserve the memory of the Holocaust and to reconstruct his people's memory. Those two tasks led him — quite naturally, according to him — to participate in the creation of a state that would contribute to the triumph of peace in the world.

Dr. Rappoport also speaks of the almost hysterical gratitude that Hugo felt toward the Furchmullers, who had saved his life. This, still according to Dr. Rappoport, made him excessively dependent on Sigrid Furchmuller, who later became his wife.

After he met that young German woman, Hugo's life became more complicated. His meeting with her did not correspond to the account he gave of it. As he was fleeing from an outpost of the German army near Strasbourg, he came upon Sigrid, but she was not alone: her brother Hans was with her. They did not treat his wounds on the spot, as he later claimed, but took him to Kiel, where the German army was in full retreat. Sigrid did not need Hugo to exonerate her, but her father, a general in the Wehrmacht, needed favorable testimony in order to escape prosecution. He later became an assistant to General Gehlen, the powerful head of West German intelligence — but, before that, his name had to be cleared.

Hugo said that after the war he resumed working for the Yiddish newspaper *Forward* in New York. He stayed there only six months, however, because Sigrid did not like New York and went back to Kiel, and he rejoined her there at Christmas, 1945. In the environs of Kiel he found one of the camps for "displaced persons" that the Allies had set up for survivors of the death camps, and there he met Moshe Sneh, an emissary from Mossad Alya Beth, an organization for clandestine emigration attached to the Mossad. Sneh had come to Germany to supervise the clandestine departure of Jews for Palestine.

Almost three years later, on May 20, 1948, six days after the proclamation of the State of Israel, Hugo went to Prague with Sneh to negotiate a weapons sale. But the Czechs delayed sending the weapons to Israel. Meanwhile the situation in Israel was deteriorating. The Arab armies were invading the young Jewish state. It was then, I think, that Sigrid may have suggested to Hugo that he try to deal directly with the Soviet Union. Her brother Hans arranged a meeting for that purpose and it took place in Berlin on May 27, 1948. I have proof that on that day, at nine o'clock in the morning, Hugo met Vladimir Volossatov, a representative of Soviet intelligence, for breakfast at the Café Kranzler on the Kurfürstendamm. Volossatov promised to clear the weapons for shipment — on certain conditions.

Here I have no proof, but I gather that Hugo promised to collaborate with the Soviets without knowing where it would lead him. He knew that his wife and her brother were already collaborating with them. At that time, what mattered most to him was saving the Jews who had survived the Nazi inferno, and preserving the State of Israel. The fact that the transaction took place in Berlin, his native city, was probably also important. With regard to Germany, his position was clear: "Forgive without ever forgetting."

In any case, the weapons were shipped and Hugo became a Soviet mole. He was a very special mole, a kind of double agent whose second employer was none other than himself. But a mole just the same. He believed that with the means that the Soviets placed at his disposal, he could promote peace, in his way. He was convinced, in fact, that he could bring the Soviets to support an operation that might ultimately go beyond their control. Was this naïveté on his part? No, it was cold, cynical calculation. He had a goal, and he cared little about the price that would have to be paid to reach it. During the first world peace conference in June 1948, for example, he persuaded the KGB leaders that working to bring about a dialogue between the Arabs and the Israelis would be greatly to the advantage of the Soviet Union.

In Frankfurt, on December 12, 1953, at 3:30 in the afternoon, he had his first meeting with Israel Beer, David Ben-Gurion's personal adviser in the Israeli defense ministry. And it was this same Hans Furchmuller who — contrary to what he told Sidney Halter in Frankfurt — recommended them to each other. Hugo and Beer became friends. Hugo was convinced that Beer shared his determination to make Israel's future secure. Beer encouraged him to pursue his contacts and even advised him to go to Cairo to meet Sami Sharif, a close associate of Nasser.

In Frankfurt, on December 12, 1953, at 3:30 in the afternoon, he had his first meeting with Israel Beer, David Ben-Gurion's personal adviser in the Israeli defense ministry. And it was this same Hans Furchmuller who — contrary to what he told Sidney Halter in Frankfurt — recommended them to each other. Hugo and Beer became friends. Hugo was convinced that Beer shared his determination to make Israel's future secure. Beer encouraged him to pursue his contacts and even advised him to go to Cairo to meet Sami Sharif, a close associate of Nasser.

I had reached this point in the report when Arieh interrupted my reading.

"I forgot to tell you one fantastic story!" he said with all his youthful enthusiasm.

"Yes?"

"Do you remember Zvika Amihay, the Bulgarian? I told you about him: Benjamin Ben-Eliezer had him give me the dossiers on

Hugo and Hidar Assadi. I also mentioned his strange behavior, which I reported to Benjamin. He became suspicious and ordered an investigation. Well, listen to this: Zvika, it turned out, was working for the Russians! Can you believe it? A mole in Israeli army intelligence!"

49

TEL AVIV

Hugo: Arieh's Report (Conclusion)

The Suez Campaign began on October 29, 1956. Preparations for it remained secret till the last moment, but Israeli intelligence is convinced that the Soviets were informed of it, even though they did not feel it necessary to warn Nasser. Why not? Because Egypt's difficulties were rather gratifying to them and could only make the country even more dependent on their aid.

A year later, on September 25, 1957, Hugo Halter was again in Berlin. Then, in the United States, at a demonstration against racist violence in Little Rock, Arkansas, he met Hidar, son of his old friend Marwan Assadi, who had come to the United States to attend a convention. According to documents in our possession, that meeting was not fortuitous. An Arab who was close to the Palestinian organizations, Hidar soon became a valuable man in Hugo's peace strategy. A little irritated at being kept under surveillance by the Furchmuller family, Hugo was glad to escape their scrutiny by means of his new ally. At that time he did not know that the Soviets were still keeping watch on him.

He began traveling alone. In Tel Aviv, at six o'clock in the afternoon of December 10, 1957, he met David Ben-Gurion. Then, with

Hidar Assadi, he made several trips to Beirut and became acquainted with Ghassan Kanafani. For some reason, all the secret agents I have met give the impression of being glib talkers who are highly intelligent but exceedingly vain. Hugo was not an exception to that rule. As the Bible says, "Pride goeth before destruction, and an haughty spirit before a fall."

Be that as it may, he succeeded in arranging two Arab-Israeli meetings: one in Florence on June 12–13, 1959, thanks to the help of Giorgio La Pira, the mayor of the city; the other in Bologna on April 14, 1960, under the auspices of Guido Fanti, the Communist mayor. I am convinced that while he was working to achieve his main goal, he was also working to reconstruct the history of our family. It was a debt he had contracted, he said, to uncle Abraham. I was able to find traces of his presence in Soncino, in the Italian province of Cremona; in Lublin, Poland; in Amsterdam; and even in Istanbul. During that period he spent a considerable amount of time with Father Roberto Cerutti, a Jesuit and the head of Radio Vatican, who had great influence with the pope. He invented schemes, organized Judeo-Christian conferences and tried to create an ecumenical committee for Jerusalem. It is not impossible that he received money from the Vatican, but I could not prove it.

In the middle of May 1960 he rejoined Sigrid, who was visiting her father in Mönchengladbach, West Germany. From that time on, his behavior seems to have ceased being logical. He left Germany for Beirut, where he met Hidar Assadi. Our agents in Lebanon saw him in La Grotte aux Pigeons several times. Then he went to Moscow, where he met several high KGB officials and leaders of the Committee for Solidarity with the Peoples of Africa and Asia. From Moscow he went to Paris, but did not see his cousin Salomon there; on the same day he arrived, he took an Air France plane to New York. I think I can now trace all his movements from his visit in Mönchengladbach until his death on the road between Tel Aviv and Jerusalem in March 1961.

On May 12, 1960, then, he was in Mönchengladbach at the invitation of his father-in-law, Wolfgang Furchmuller, who worked for the West German secret services, as Hugo knew. What he did not know was that he would see Israel Beer strolling in the garden of the secret services with Wolfgang Furchmuller's superior, General

Reinhard Gehlen. He told Sigrid about it and she was surprised that, being close to Israel Beer, he did not know about Beer's commitment to the Soviet Union. She asked Hugo to keep all that secret. Officially, Wolfgang Furchmuller knew nothing about the activities of Sigrid and her brother, and General Gehlen knew nothing about Beer's activities. I can now state that West German intelligence was clearly aware of Beer's machinations as well as his constant contacts with Hans Furchmuller and, through him, with the HVA, an East German intelligence service. But that did not bother him at all. By following the trail of the Furchmuller family, General Gehlen obtained all information almost at the same time as the Soviets.

For Hugo Halter, however, it was a shock. He now realized that the course of action he had undertaken, thinking it was under his control, was in fact actually beyond his control. Instead of using the Soviets, he had been letting them maneuver him for years. What were his feelings at that moment? I can say only that he then began traveling a great deal. Too much. I have found proof of a trip to Moscow, two trips to the United States, to which he had not returned in two years, then a trip to Tunis and another one to the United States. That feverish traveling is explained, in my judgment, by his wish to free himself from the spider's web in which he had become entangled.

In Moscow on June 22, 1960, at three in the afternoon, he met with Vladimir Volossatov, from whom he hoped to receive advice. Volossatov spoke of large expenses incurred by his organization and said that receipts for them, signed by Hugo, were in his possession. Hugo was panic-stricken. He naively told himself that if he could manage to pay back the money for the conferences and travel financed by his troublesome friends, he would regain his freedom.

He discussed this with Hidar Assadi when he saw him in Tunis on September 3, 1960, at the Hotel Africa on Bourguiba Avenue. What advice did Assadi give him? I do not know. What I do know is that, trapped by his desire for peace, Hugo went to New York in early October. He visited Shimon Weber, editor of the Yiddish newspaper *Forward,* at his home in Brooklyn. Weber, whom I have had occasion to question, said that Hugo seemed worried and wanted to resume working in the newspaper's print shop. During this period he was often seen meditating, without phylacteries or a prayer shawl, in the synagogue at the corner of Lexington Avenue and Fifty-fifth Street.

On October 11 he went to the branch of the Manufacturers Hanover bank at 407 Broadway, where he had kept an account, and asked for a loan of three hundred thousand dollars. John MacKinsey, who was in charge of his account, died soon afterward, so I could not question him, but I know that on October 12, the day after his visit to the bank, Hugo saw his cousin Sidney and asked him to cosign the loan.

It was then, I believe, that he decided to break open the whole affair. He bought an airline ticket for Tel Aviv via Paris and called General Gonen, whom he had met years before in David Ben-Gurion's house, and had seen again in early 1960. In Paris he planned to see his cousins Salomon and Perl and their son Marek. When he went to the Hôtel Madison on the Boulevard Saint-Germain in Paris, where he had reserved a room, he must have been greatly surprised to find his wife Sigrid, who had probably been alerted by Vladimir Volossatov. She was with him when he visited Salomon Halter, and later, when he went to Israel.

According to General Gonen, Hugo postponed meeting him three times. In my opinion, there is only one explanation for that: he tried, unsuccessfully, to escape from Sigrid's vigilance. Meanwhile the Soviets were trying to find a way to prevent him from revealing everything to the Mossad, thus exposing Israel Beer, one of their best agents in the Middle East. They obviously found no better solution than simply to liquidate him. In all likelihood it was Viktor Chebrikov who decided to have him killed. Hidar Assadi was opposed to it. During a meeting in Moscow on January 27, 1961, he tried to defend his viewpoint and his friend's life. He failed. The death sentence was confirmed. And it was Assadi who, by a diabolical twist of fate, was ordered to inform Wadi Hadad of the decision and the details of how it was to be carried out.

On March 4, 1961, Assadi met Hadad in Beirut, at the headquarters of the PLO. According to evidence that I have been able to gather, it seems that he made a final attempt at sabotage. Knowing that Hugo had an appointment with General Gonen and two Mossad agents for Thursday, March 30, in Jerusalem, he convinced Hadad that the appointment was for Wednesday, March 29. What Assadi could not have foreseen was that relations between Hugo and his wife would become so filled with mistrust that, to give himself time in Jerusalem to escape from Sigrid's unflagging vigilance, the best plan he could come up with was to set off one day ahead of his appointment, on March 29. They left by way of the road on which Hadad's killers were waiting for him. In any case, the die was cast; no matter what subterfuges Assadi might have used, it was no longer possible for him to avert what had become Hugo's destiny.

The bitter irony of the whole affair was that Israel Beer had been unmasked by Issar Harel, head of the Mossad, a day earlier. His arrest, kept secret at first was not announced until just before the Passover Seder, on March 30, 1961, at 2:30 A.M. But my father's cousin was already dead, and he obviously died for nothing.

That is all the information I have been able to gather on the death of Hugo Halter.

Report written on October 7, 1987

PARIS, SEPTEMBER 1988

Arieh's report on Hugo's death still left me perplexed. Although it cleared up certain things that I had wondered about, it gave me no answer to the enigma of Hugo himself and my strange, persistent relation to him. I had chosen him as the vehicle of the family memory. I had transformed him into a witness to the hope and failure of the generation of survivors. I had made him the very symbol of all those people who, because they are the last vestiges of a world that no longer exists, have no right to think, feel or act as if that destruction had not taken place. Was I wrong? Had I invested him with a demand and a dream that actually belonged to me? Maybe. Yes, maybe — but so goes life. So went our lives. When an author and his characters live through the same situations a few years apart, and when such a troubling kinship, bridging the gap of time and generations, is created between them, how can he not accept that identification and make the most of it?

This story is finished. All those voices, of Abraham, Mordecai, Sidney, Anna Maria, all those ghosts I have tried to revive and incarnate in these pages, are going to fall silent again. And so, by burning the Scroll of Abraham, then killing Hugo — that is, by destroying those two relays of a two-thousand-year-old memory — I have abruptly found myself alone again, confronted with the consternation of oblivion.

Sometime after the end of that adventure, when the faces of all those heroes and semiheroes were beginning to fade in my memory, I received a strange phone call.

"*Te recordas de mi?*" asked a voice with a heavy Argentinian accent.

"No, I don't remember you," I answered. "Who are you?"

The caller hesitated a moment. I thought he was going to hang up, but then he said, as though regretfully, "This is Julio Feldman."

Julio Feldman! Just hearing that name made me start. It had been six years since Anna Maria was betrayed and killed, and this ghost, on the other end of the line . . .

"I'm in Paris," he went on. "My poems are going to be published in French. I'd like to see you."

We met on the second floor of the Café de Cluny, where I had met Vladimir Volossatov for the last time a few years earlier. Julio had changed. His hair, his mustache, even his skin, had turned white. Everything about him was pale and weary. He really did look like a kind of ghost.

"I'm glad to see you again," he said. "Yes, really glad."

And he talked for a long time, endlessly, in a muffled, almost inaudible voice. I learned that his daughter had been tortured and was in a Buenos Aires hospital, that his older son had been killed, that his younger one had disappeared, and that his wife, overwhelmed by all that grief, was in a psychiatric hospital in a suburb of Rome.

"It's the fault of the Argentinian fascists," he said with hatred blazing in his eyes, "but it's partly ours too. We'd become little bosses, with no perspective on the real situation, no understanding of it. We were capable of sending a whole generation to its death. Instead of fighting fascism, we nourished it."

I said nothing. What could I have said? And Julio continued, in the same faraway voice:

"I broke off with the Montoneros, for good. It was hard, believe me. So hard! The movement had become my family. When I'd left it, I was nowhere, in a void. Can anyone live without roots, without knowing where he came from, where he's going, what his hopes are?

When I got to Rome, I wrote to my mother. You remember her, don't you? She's now in a Jewish nursing home in Buenos Aires. Anyway, I don't know why, but in my letter to her I asked her to tell me the story of her life. Here's her answer. I just received it." He took an envelope from his pocket and took out several sheets of blue paper covered with irregular handwriting. "I'd like to read it to you, or at least parts of it. Do you mind?"

In faulty Spanish, the old lady told about her childhood in a little Jewish village in Lithuania. She described her grandfather, the rabbi. She said that whenever the community was threatened by a war or a pogrom, he brought the whole family together and took out a parchment scroll on which the names of all the heads of the family since the seventeenth century had been written, along with the dates of their birth and death. And he would read the list aloud — names and dates, names and dates — like a prayer. "It was more than a prayer to us," she wrote, "it was proof of our survival and our indestructibility."

Julio went on reading, but I was listening only distractedly. Without knowing it, he had just given me the key I had been looking for so long in vain. Julio Feldman had been a rabid fanatic, a man who wanted to wipe away the past, a Montonero terrorist, one of the most firmly determined to destroy his own memory, not to say his own consciousness — and the fact that he was reading me that letter amounted to a fantastic confession.

In my family, too, there had been a family book, and my grandfather used to talk about it. It was the scroll that was destroyed in 1943, in the Warsaw ghetto, except for a few parts of it that Hugo preserved until he was wounded in 1945, near Strasbourg. And it was Hugo who, in my mind, had been called upon to be the standard-bearer of our tattered memory. *Hugo, or The Memory.* To me, Hugo was emblematic of Jewish existence and destiny.

Now Hugo is dead, like so many members of his generation. There are still Gloria and Martín, my Argentinian cousins, growing old in Buenos Aires. And Marjory, Sidney's widow, growing old in New York. Marilyn is living with a famous lawyer and runs an art gallery. Richard has married the daughter of a descendant of the rabbi of Gur. He already has four children and teaches in a yeshiva in Qiryat Arba, near Hebron. Arieh's mother, Sarah, is still at Kibbutz

Dafneh. Arieh himself has been promoted to colonel and lives with Judith and their three children in Zahala, near Tel Aviv. Aron Lerner is still in Jerusalem and recently published an essay in Hebrew: *Ptolemy Philadelphus and the Bible*. His wife Rachel died two years ago. Sasha still lives in Moscow and has gone through several palace revolutions in the Kremlin without too much damage. As Arieh predicted, Hidar Assadi was killed, by two Palestinian extremists, in a Lisbon hotel. After endless bureaucratic annoyances and a press campaign in the United States and France, Olga was able to emigrate to Israel with her two children. As for me, I have celebrated my first half-century. The longer I live, the more my world is reduced to those piles of boxes filled with documents, letters and photographs that I inherited from my father.

Not long ago, just before Yom Kippur of the year 5749 after the creation of the world by the Almighty, blessed be He, I went to the cemetery, as I do every year, to honor the memory of my father and mother. It was Sunday. There were many people in the cemetery, which was unusual. I was walking hesitantly on paving stones covered with a thick layer of autumn leaves when, up ahead, I noticed a man in overalls cleaning my parents' grave.

"Ah, here you are!" he exclaimed when he saw me coming toward him. "I'm glad to know you. I've been sweeping this grave for years, and this is the first time I've met you."

I looked at him, surprised by his scolding tone and touched by his concern.

"I'm a poor Jew, one Jew among millions," he went on, "but I clean graves and you write books. Books are graves. Graves are books. Basically, you and I do the same kind of work. It's a pity that I come back every year — and that you've left your *Book of Abraham* unfinished."

He didn't give me his name and I didn't have the presence of mind to ask him for it. For a few moments I watched him walking away on the path. Then I moved closer to the grave and said a prayer. Like my father, like my grandfather, like my great-grandfather, and so on back through all the generations.